Thomas Jefferson: Scientist

Thomas Jefferson: Scientist

·

Edwin T. Martin

Henry Schuman   New York

THE JEFFERSON PORTRAIT ON THE JACKET

*The portrait was painted by Mather Brown and hangs
in the National Gallery of Art.
Permission to use it was secured through the kindness
of the Honorable Charles Francis Adams.*

Contents

Illustrations

Preface

Thomas Jefferson had a great personal love for science. He regarded science as one of the surest means of advancing social progress and human happiness. There is no period in his life, even through the most pressing trials of private affairs or of public office, when one does not find him occupied with some scientific or technological problem, or pondering over some practical application of scientific knowledge.

Jefferson had a remarkably receptive mind. He was ready to accept any new truths based upon sufficient fact or experiment, and aid in the discovery of new scientific knowledge even where it might contradict his own beliefs. In his wish to dispel the clouds of obscurantism and the mists of error, he assisted any and all individuals and learned societies interested in science and its applications. He made a patriotic use of his scientific knowledge to give the outside world a truer understanding of actual conditions in his native country, while seeking, untiringly, to bring scientific learning to his own countrymen. And one hears his persistent demand that the benefits of science be made available to the common man so that his lot might be progressively bettered.

Jefferson's scientific knowledge was not always exhaustive. His facts were not always right, nor his conclusions always correct. He could not keep sufficiently abreast of the more rapid developments in certain scientific fields in the late eighteenth and early nineteenth centuries. There were times when he perhaps over-stressed immediate, utilitarian values. And certain of his preconceptions obscured his grasp of scientific truth.

Yet, for a man who labored for his state and country so long and faithfully as a public servant, Jefferson's outlook and scientific attainments were truly remarkable. His interests ranged over such fields as meteorology, paleontology, ethnology, archaeology, astronomy, chemistry, agriculture, geology, exploration, botany, medicine, and inventions. His errors were shared by many leading thinkers of his time. But some of the scientific objectives and data which he brought so forcefully to the attention of his contemporaries and some of his suggestions regarding them contributed to the progress of science in his day.

Furthermore, the mere fact that a figure of such worldwide political reputation interested himself in science helped to raise its status in America. And, considered internationally, Jefferson's activities greatly enhanced the reputation of the United States as a young country rich in opportunities for scientific investigation and capable of producing men of culture and learning devoted to this end.

Thomas Jefferson: Scientist

1

Characteristics and Attitudes

•

A dominant aspect of Jefferson's mind was an insatiable desire to learn and to know. Like the man of the Renaissance, his interests were universal. His intellectual travels took him over virtually the entire world of knowledge. Though chiefly motivated by considerations of utility he appreciated statistics, techniques, principles, and cultural or aesthetic experiences as values in themselves. The mere process of learning and the simple possession of pure knowledge gave him intense personal pleasure. It is not always possible to distinguish in him the desire for the useful from the desire simply to know. Both were there, and between them, they brought him into possession of one of the best-informed and most broadly cultured minds of his day in America.

Jefferson was ever torn between the call to public service for his country and a deep longing for a private life devoted to his family and to such pursuits as travel, literature, art, music, architecture, gardening, agriculture, science, and inventions. "Nature intended me for the tranquil pur-

suits of science, by rendering them my supreme delight,"
he wrote his friend Du Pont de Nemours, when retiring
from the Presidency in 1809. Only the "enormities of the
times," he continued, had forced him to give these up and
commit himself to the "boisterous ocean of political passions." Now that it was over, he felt like "a prisoner, released from his chains."

This conflicting devotion to science and to public service marked Jefferson's entire career. In 1778, during the
hectic years of the Revolution, he wrote to a foreign correspondent that, though his energies were largely employed "in the councils of America"—he was then serving
as Governor of Virginia—he yet found time to indulge his
"fondness" for scientific studies. Before going abroad in
1784, to represent his young country at the court of Louis
XVI, he wrote to Lafayette that he had also been im-
pelled to cross the Atlantic by the desire to see countries
"whose improvements in science, in arts, and in civilization" he had admired from a distance. While serving as
Washington's Secretary of State he wrote to another friend,
in 1791, that politics was his "duty" but natural history his
"passion." A month later in a letter to Thomas Mann
Randolph he described himself as longing to be free from
this office and its "detestable" drain upon his time and
energies and to take up the study of the Hessian fly and
other scientific "pursuits of this kind."

In 1797 he arrived in Philadelphia where he had previously spent the years 1790–1793. He came not only as
Vice-President, but also as a scientist. His baggage included
the bones of a prehistoric animal, about which he intended
to inform the American Philosophical Society, then the
nation's leading scientific organization, of which he had
just been elected President. Before leaving Monticello, he
had already written to his scientist friend, Dr. Benjamin
Rush, rejoicing in the anticipated pleasurable "philosophical evenings" he intended to spend in the company of his

scientific friends. He chose John Francis's hotel for his lodgings because of its nearness to both the Statehouse and the halls of the Philosophical Society.[1]

He found Philadelphia torn asunder by the political animosities of the Republicans and Federalists. His letters home showed him "more and more disgusted with the jealousies, the hatred, and the rancorous and malignant passions" he observed about him. People in Philadelphia were "like salamanders," he said in 1798: they appeared "to consider fire as their element." He yearned for private life with his beloved family and, when he could, he enjoyed "philosophical" days and evenings spent among men of science and learning. In a letter to his daughter Martha in 1800 he wrote, "My absence from you teaches me how essential your society is to my happiness. Politics are such a torment that I would advise everyone I love not to mix with them. I have changed my circle here according to my wish, abandoning the rich and declining their dinners and parties, and associating entirely with the class of science, of whom there is a valuable society here." [2]

Then our nation's capital was moved from Philadelphia to the banks of the Potomac. There followed the exciting days of February, 1801, while the new and still crude little city of Washington was electrified by rumors of revolution and bloodshed as Congress pondered whether Burr or Jefferson should become the third President of the United States. Through this critical time Jefferson continued his scientific interests. From his boarding house near the capitol he wrote to Dr. Caspar Wistar of Philadelphia about certain fossils recently discovered in New York which he was trying to purchase for the American Philosophical Society. According to information he had lately received in letters from Chancellor Robert R. Livingston of New York, Dr. Wistar might be able to select specimens from such parts of the animal as the teeth, tusks, vertebrae, a jaw fragment, the sternum, scapula, tibia, and that part of the head containing the socket of the tusk.

Nor were such interests wholly eclipsed by the demands of public duty when Jefferson later moved into the unfinished President's mansion and took over the helm of state for the next eight years. The writings of his friend, Mrs. Samuel Harrison Smith, wife of the founder of the *National Intelligencer,* leading Jeffersonian newspaper in Washington, offer interesting glimpses of Jefferson carrying on solitary botanizing expeditions along the Potomac or among the surrounding hills and woods. Not "a plant from the lowliest weed to the loftiest tree escaped his notice," she records. Getting off his horse, "he would climb rocks, or wade through swamps to obtain any plant he discovered or desired and seldom returned from these excursions without a variety of specimens."

Greatly interested in introducing useful foreign plants and vegetables to America, Jefferson himself distributed among the market gardeners of Washington many of the seeds he received from abroad. While riding about alone on his horse, he would drop in on acquaintances and leave such seeds as he could interest them in planting.[3]

In his Washington residence we see him not only with his beloved flowers, plants, books, and pet mockingbird, but also with carpenter's tools, garden implements, maps, globes, charts, a drafting board, and scientific instruments.[4] We see him at his desk engaged in continuous scientific correspondence. To the scientists of Philadelphia he dispatched minerals, skins, animals, and birds which he had received from the Lewis and Clark Expedition. He distributed models of the moldboard for a plow, which he had invented. On display in the Presidential mansion, for the inspection of Congressmen, was the model of a dry dock he had designed. He enthusiastically promoted a device, the polygraph, which made facsimile copies, as one wrote. Serving his own personal convenience led him to the designing of new furniture. He was a tireless collector of meteorological data. He was a leader in the introduction, in America, of vaccination against smallpox. He filled the unfinished East Room of his residence, which Abigail Adams had used for hanging out wash, with a huge fossil collection he had gotten from the Big Bone Lick. On his lawn passersby might, at one time, have seen young grizzly bears brought by Meriwether Lewis from the far West. His political enemies jeered at Jefferson's "bear-garden." [5]

Friends and foes testify to President Jefferson's love of science. The dramatist William Dunlap, who spent the winter of 1805–1806 in Washington, recorded that he had heard the first croaking of frogs on February 19. But Jefferson informed him that he had heard them "10 Days ago, & noted down the circumstance." Samuel Latham Mitchill of New York—physician, scientist, member of the House, and later Senator, a man who, for his vast and varied store of learning, was termed by Jefferson the "Congressional Dictionary"—noticed three particular books on the mantel of Jefferson's parlor, one January morning in 1802. They were a volume of Tacitus, with the Latin text on one page and a Spanish translation on the other, an "elegant" copy of Plato, and the *Encyclopédie,* a periodical publishing the latest expressions of French thought on government, sociology, religion, philosophy, inventions, and science. President Jefferson talked to Dr. Mitchill on cowpox "with the intelligence of a physician." To his wife Dr. Mitchill wrote that Thomas Jefferson was "more deeply versed in human nature and human learning than almost the whole tribe of his opponents and revilers." Following a dinner at the Presidential mansion in 1804, Senator, later President, John Quincy Adams recorded in his memoirs that, among other things, Mr. Jefferson had shown his guests "a Natural History of Parrots, in French, with colored plates very beautifully executed." [6]

These dinners at the Presidential table appear to have

been delightful affairs. They were informal, with no protocol and no toasts. But there was a plentiful supply of fine food, prepared by Jefferson's French chef, and the best of imported wines. "You drink as you please, and converse at your ease," Mitchill wrote to his wife. He was impressed by Jefferson's "ice-cream . . . produced in the forms of balls of the *frozen* material inclosed in covers of *warm pastry*, exhibiting a curious contrast, as if the *ice* had just been taken from the *oven*." Conversation flowed freely. Sometimes matters of state business were discussed; sometimes the President entertained with tall stories and amusing anecdotes of his old friend Ben Franklin; or the subjects might be immigration, literature, architecture, the domestic manners of the Parisians, the qualities of different wines, the educational value of learning foreign languages, a comparison of Epicureanism and other ancient philosophies, the good and evil effects of horse racing, etc.[7]

Very often the subject was science. Discussion turned upon recent inventions, medical knowledge and practice, the scientific value of exploration, Jefferson's meteorological observations in France, the potentialities of upland rice as a food crop, experiments on the nature of light. When Humboldt and his party visited Washington in 1804, on their return from their explorations in Latin America, Jefferson and Humboldt were often together. The painter and naturalist Charles Willson Peale, a close friend of Jefferson's, accompanied the group from Philadelphia to the capital. He records "a very elegant dinner at the President's," during which "not a single toast was given or called for, or politics touched on, but subjects of natural history, and improvements of the conveniences of life." [8]

Jefferson's company, one evening in early November, 1807, according to John Quincy Adams, one of the guests, consisted "chiefly of members of Congress." After some talk of wine and philosophy, Samuel L. Mitchill "mentioned Mr. Fulton's steamboat as an invention of great importance. To which Mr. Jefferson, assenting, added, 'and I think his torpedoes a valuable invention too.' He then enlarged upon the certainty of their effect, and adverted to some of the obvious objections against them, which he contended were not conclusive. Dr. Mitchill's [*sic*] conversation was very various, of chemistry, of geography, and of natural philosophy; of oils, grasses, beasts, birds, petrifactions, and incrustrations; Pike and Humboldt, Lewis and Barlow, and a long train of et cetera—for the Doctor knows a little of every thing, and is communicative of what he knows—which makes me delight in his company. Mr. Jefferson said that he had always been extremely fond of agriculture, and knew nothing about it, but the person who united with other science the greatest agricultural knowledge of any man he knew was Mr. Madison. He was the best farmer in the world."

Senator Adams, son of Jefferson's Federalist opponent, John Adams, was no great admirer of Republican Jefferson. But the evening had been so delightful that he was moved to summarize it as "On the whole . . . one of the *agreeable* dinners I have had at Mr. Jefferson's." [9]

Thus both Jefferson's friends and enemies testify to the truth of his assertion that science was one of his "supreme delights."

Jefferson's writings are a gold mine of information about the scientific interests of the late eighteenth and early nineteenth centuries. Jefferson often referred to himself as a "zealous amateur," asserting a sincere love for science but making no pretense to the specialization of the scientist. His estimate of himself is essentially correct. However, much of Jefferson's knowledge is detailed and full; he was never a mere intellectual philanderer.

Agriculture was to Jefferson "a science of the very first order." He wrote on agriculture as a way of life both for the individual and for our nation as a whole. The specific subjects he touched on are staggering. They include agricultural education, the advantages of agricultural societies, the necessity for a more scientific approach to agricultural problems, agricultural research and experimentation, the application of technological progress to farming implements and machinery, mills and milling problems, home manufactures as adjuncts to an agricultural economy, the value and use of agricultural correspondence, journals, and books, general farm management, the proper employment and treatment of slaves, the role of overseers, diversified farming, soil erosion, conservation and soil building, the use of gypsum, green-dressings versus fallows, manuring, Lord Kames's proposal for an essence of dung, crop rotation, contour plowing and deep plowing, harvesting methods, the introduction of new strains of farm stock and improvement of the old, the introduction of new vegetables, fruits, and plants of all kinds and improvement of standard varieties, new sources of oils and wines, the possibilities of native silk production, live hedges, the study and control of insect pests, pest-resistant crops, veterinary medicine, the common and the more scientific use of the word *paccan* (our pecan), a discussion as to whether the turkey and honeybee are native to America.[10]

Jefferson's fascinated interest in agriculture is reflected in a letter to Lafayette in 1787, while touring through rural France. "I am never satisfied with rambling through the fields and farms," he wrote, "examining the culture and cultivators, with a degree of curiosity which makes some take me to be a fool, and others to be much wiser than I am."

Other interests include the phenomenon of the rainbow (Jefferson fearing that the recent theory announced in Paris has disproved the previous explanation of de Dominis, Descartes, and Newton), causes of the velocity of river currents, chemical advances, the problem of distilling fresh water from sea water, and exploration of the American West.

He was also interested in archaeological excavations, the application of mathematical principles to architecture, and city planning. The origin of the Indian race in America intrigued him and he proposed to settle this issue by the application of linguistic principles. He discussed new methods of determining the heights of mountains (by mathematical means or by use of the barometer) , measuring atmospheric moisture by use of the hygrometer, analyzing the prevailing winds of America, recording temperatures, and adding to climatological knowledge by such observations as the flowering of trees and a tabulation of the annual rainfall. From such matters he turned to optical investigations, the "application of the double refraction of the Iceland Spath to the measure of small angles," problems in magnification, the observation of eclipses, the moon's motion, the determination of latitude and longitude, the use of the sextant, the value of rustless metal for the specula of telescopes, problems in surveying, coinage, weights and measures, methods of overcoming friction, the employment of acids in engraving on glass, the bleaching of paper and linen, the advantages of varnish as a lining for biscuit barrels, the preservation of bridge pilings by saturation in fish oil, the use of *essence de l'Orient* for artificial pearls, new discoveries in gunpowder, the probable cause of Mediterranean tides.

Jefferson's interest in new inventions and technical improvements will be given fuller treatment in a later chapter, but we may here observe briefly some reflections of it in his writings. We find him discussing things like plows, farm machinery and conveyances, cisterns, the orrery, the polygraph, the pedometer, the odometer, a "geometrical wheelbarrow" (discussed, as an incidental, in a letter from Paris to Tom Paine, July 11, 1789, dealing with the critical political situation in France), a "hydrostatic waistcoat" (a forerunner of the modern Mae West), air pumps, compasses, the use of wooden and ivory diagrams in geometrical demonstrations, canal locks, balloons, the great future possibilities—particularly for America—in the application of steam power to machinery.

Jefferson was not content with hearing about a new invention or technique; he had to see it for himself. News of a boat in Paris propelled by a screw revolving in air brought Jefferson forth for a demonstration. He thought it would work with less loss of power in water. He felt sure, he added patriotically, that "a countryman of ours, Mr. Bushnell of Connecticut," had anteceded this Frenchman in the use of screw propulsion. Hearing of a new method of making muskets with standardized parts, Jefferson hastened to look into this promising idea. The workman presented him with the separate parts of fifty locks and allowed him to "put several together" himself. Immediately seeing the possibilities of this principle for mass production he wrote to John Jay that it might be "interesting to Congress."

Announcement of a new instrument "for determining the true time of the musical movements, largo, adagio, etc.," immediately caught Ambassador Jefferson's eye. The article about it in the *Encyclopédie* was not enough for Jefferson. He went to see the inventor, Monsieur Renaudin, who showed him his first model and subsequent improvements. On a trip to London, Jefferson visited a grist mill powered by steam. When Boulton, its inventor, was in Paris, Jefferson had long talks with him about what we now call "horsepower."

That broad field of science known as "natural history" (then an even more inclusive term than today) led him to the study of prehistoric animals, the possibility of volition in vegetables, the use of electricity in stimulating plant growth, wild sheep and horses, the flora, fauna, and mineralogy of the West, a flower in Connecticut reported to live on air (he wrote asking the President of Yale for information), birds native to Virginia, methods of preserving dead birds, problems of geology, the extinction of species, and systems of classification in botany. To his daughter Martha he wrote: "There is not a sprig of grass that shoots uninteresting to me."

Jefferson could be scientifically objective about this sprig of grass. His interest in nature's laws, his observation of her creatures, could be cool, unemotional, statistical, and utilitarian. To be so was a fundamental trait of his mind and personality. His travels were partly motivated by such personal ends as health, diversion from business, "amusement," but, perhaps predominantly, "instruction"—the gathering together of any and every scrap of knowledge which might some day be put to practical employment by himself or his fellow Americans, whose concern for the "useful" he shared to a high degree. The point is made in his letter to James Madison, describing himself as "an enthusiast on the subject of the arts"—and adding defensively that this was an enthusiasm of which he was "not ashamed" since it had its patriotic, utilitarian side—to "improve the taste" of his countrymen, "to increase their reputation, to reconcile to them the respect of the world, and procure them its praise."

Or there is the case of the imaginary dialogue between his Head and his Heart which he wrote in Paris and sent to the attractive Mrs. Maria Cosway, the woman in whom he appears to have become most deeply interested after the death of his wife. In this little fantasy, Heart accuses Head of putting it to sleep with its constant interest in such cold and practical things as "diagrams and crochets"—to which Head replies that this interest arises from a desire to observe and note down whatever is useful for America, perhaps a market to be built at Richmond, a bridge to be thrown across the Schuylkill River at Philadelphia.

Along with this practical, dispassionate side of Jefferson's nature, there is evidence in his writings of a sensitive, emotional quality, the reality of which must be taken into account if one is to understand Jefferson the man and Jefferson the scientist. Though he gave an impression to many as a man who was aloof, who lacked personal warmth, others found him companionable, congenial, emotional, compassionate, and good-humored. Readers of his letters will find support in them for both these appraisals. One encounters a surprising reserve where an expression of personal feeling might have been expected. Yet at other moments there is a strong note of passion, a depth of poignancy, a brief, spontaneous expression of exhilaration, a welling up of aesthetic responsiveness, a striking ascendancy of Heart over Head.

Jefferson could describe a Rhine landscape or a gallery of paintings at Dusseldorf as "sublime," praise a scene along the Rhone for its "romantic, picturesque and pleasing air," convey to a sensitive reader some of the "stupor of mind" he felt over the death of his wife and some of the "tenderest love" he held for his daughters, note that the "glow of one warm thought" was worth "more than money," express to a correspondent the "tender and sublime emotions of the mind" which raced through him as he read James Macpherson's romantic *Ossian,* "kindle" with anticipation over the classical grandeurs he expected to encounter in Rome, extol music as the "favorite passion of my soul," or rhapsodize over the architectural beauty of the *Maison Quarree* in Nimes, gazing "whole hours . . . like a lover at his mistress." In one of his earlier letters after his arrival in Paris, he wrote: "Were I to proceed to tell you how much I enjoy their architecture, sculpture, painting, music, I should want words. It is in these arts they shine. The last of them, particularly, is an enjoyment, the deprivation of which with us, cannot be calculated. I am almost ready to say, it is the only thing which from my heart I envy them, and which, in spite of all the authority of the Decalogue, I do covet."

The same warm responsiveness is accorded to nature, despite his utilitarian views. He might use the location of Monticello to observe astronomical phenomena or to help him solve the optical problem of "looming"; but that wonderful, that sublime view from atop his little mountain pleased his heart. Jefferson's head and notebooks might be more crammed with precise, scientific, meteorological data than those of any other American in his day, but he could also become enthusiastic to a friend over the enjoyments of a "delicious" springtime at Monticello, whose "soft . . . temperature . . . , just above the want of fire, enlivened by the reanimation of birds, flowers, the fields, forests & gardens, has been truly delightful & continues to be so." [11]

Of the Natural Bridge in Virginia Jefferson left not only a factual description and a brief discussion of its geology, but this tribute: "It is impossible for the emotions arising from the sublime to be felt beyond what they are here: so beautiful an arch, so elevated, so light, and springing as it were up to heaven! The rapture of the spectator is really indescribable!" He thought it worth one's while crossing the Atlantic to gaze upon this marvel.

Though Jefferson's writings on flowers are often concerned with technical identification and nomenclature, it would be hard to find a keener response to their sensuous and aesthetic values. He sometimes conjoins these two characteristics, as when he thanks a granddaughter for a letter containing "the delicious flower of the Acacia, or rather the Mimosa Nilotica." Touring revolutionary landmarks in New York and New England in 1791, and commenting on them in a letter to Thomas Mann Randolph, he did not write as a national leader might have been expected to do. He expressed himself as "more pleased . . . with the botanical objects which continually presented themselves." There were the sugar maple, the pines, "an

azalea, very different from the nudiflora, . . . the richest
shrub I have ever seen," the honeysuckle, the paper birch,
"an aspen with a velvet leaf," a "shrub-willow with downy
catkins," and other objects of scientific, sensuous, or emotional appeal.

Jefferson discussed birds in scientific terms with the
ornithologist Alexander Wilson. But he could also speak of
his "enchantment" at hearing a nightingale in France, or,
on the contrary, his disagreeable impression of a stork seen
in Frankfort, a "miserable, dirty, ill-looking bird." He
loved mockingbirds and kept one in the President's House
in Washington. Mrs. Samuel Harrison Smith records that
he used to let it sit on his shoulder and peck food from his
lips.[12]

And there is also something more than scientific objectivity in his plans for his park at Monticello, something
more, too, than the requirements of a country gentleman's estate. This park of his, as he envisioned it in 1771
—his original intentions were not wholly fulfilled—was to
contain birds, elk, deer, squirrels, pheasants, guinea hens,
and a buffalo. The Marquis de Chastellux, who visited
Jefferson in 1782, has left us a pleasing sketch of Jefferson
feeding his twenty deer grain from his own hands.

There was something of the antiquarian, the collector,
the museum-maker in Jefferson anyhow. He loved to
gather about him striking examples, specimens, reminders
of those things which had appealed to his taste or piqued
his scientific curiosity. It caused him to place grizzly bears
upon his lawn in Washington; it roused his enthusiastic
interest in Charles Willson Peale's Philadelphia Museum
and the fine cabinet of natural history owned by the American Philosophical Society. It led him to devote his
beautiful entrance hall at Monticello to a heterogeneous
collection of *objets d'art* and curiosities.

Among them one might have seen, at various times, portraits of Columbus, Lafayette, Raleigh, or Washington,

and two scientists and a philosopher whom Jefferson considered his "trinity of the three greatest men the world had ever produced"—Bacon, Newton, and Locke. With these was a reclining figure of Cleopatra, awaiting death, with the coiling asp nearby. There were also busts of Turgot, Voltaire, and others.

To this historical exhibit was opposed a zoological exhibit, the heads and horns of the moose, the elk, various other American deer, the mountain ram, and the buffalo. Then an ethnological exhibit, some of the objects hanging from antlers, of "Indian and Mexican antiquities, articles of costume, war clubs, shields, spears, bows, quivers of arrows," peace pipes, moccasins, wampum belts, dresses, cooking utensils—according to Randall, "almost every conceivable specimen of aboriginal art." Conspicuous in this exhibit were seated statues of a male and female Indian, thought to have been unearthed in Tennessee, an Indian map of the southern basin of the Missouri River, and an Indian drawing of a bloody battle between the Pani and Osage tribes. Map and drawing were done upon dressed buffalo hides. There was also a fossil collection, including one of Jefferson's prize possessions, the head of a "mammoth." Most of these came from the Big Bone Lick of Kentucky. Then there were collections of minerals, shells, petrifactions, crystallizations, and other miscellanies. When young George Ticknor, later a Harvard light, visited Monticello in 1815, he found some of these objects "in odd union with a fine painting of the Repentance of Saint Peter."

One visitor, whose account of a trip to Monticello appeared in *Niles' Weekly Register,* January 4, 1817, "supposed there is no private gentleman in the world, in possession of so perfect and complete a scientific, useful and ornamental collection. To discuss them with his numerous visitors was one of Jefferson's pleasures in his later life.[13]

Everywhere he went, Jefferson's scientific curiosity found
something to engage it. On board the *Ceres* bound for
Paris in 1784, he made daily records of the temperature
and recorded observations of birds and marine life.[14]
Crossing the Alps into northern Italy, he tabulated plants
according to their powers of resisting cold. He also took
with him an account of Hannibal's passage of the Alps, to
see if the exact route could be determined, and concluded
that it could not, with the information then available.

Jefferson's minute diaries similarly disclose the enormous sweep of his curiosity. His student diary in Williamsburg records a sum paid to see a tiger, and a hog which
weighed more than 1,050 pounds, and a puppet show.
Early in the critical month of June, 1776, he went to see
a monkey. His Paris budget books list admission fees paid
to see a "windlass plough" (3 francs),[15] the King's library
(3 francs), a machine (6 francs), a "Concert Spirituel" (6
francs), and another machine (only 3 francs).[16] While Secretary of State he went to see "a lion 21 months old" and a
small seal. On March 10, 1797, he paid to see an elephant
(.5d) and some elk (.75d). A January, 1798, entry reads:
"pd seeing Caleb Phillips a dwarf 25d." Characteristically,
he jots down details, including Phillips' weight at birth.
Other items recorded include a painting, an alligator, a
trained pig, and "a wax figure of the King of Prussia." [17]

Jefferson could appreciate the value of general scientific
principles, but he always insisted upon empirical observation as their basis. This was a marked personality trait
for he practiced what he preached. In his passage through
life he appeared to be goaded by a compulsion to make
a meticulous record of data.

With Jefferson, to see or to hear was virtually to record.
He was constantly making notes. Like others of his day, he
began, as a young man, to keep a commonplace book in
which he covered such topics as religion, political science,
and law. Even when on horseback, during the British in-

vasion of Richmond, Jefferson made memoranda "on scraps of paper" taken from his pockets. These were to prove useful to him in disproving his enemies who tried to make him out a coward and a deserter. In France he made it a practice immediately to commit to writing what he learned of affairs of state. His notes on his trips to North Italy, Holland, and Germany probably record everything he saw. His memoranda while serving in Washington's Cabinet, particularly of his debates with Hamilton, were similarly meticulous. These "scraps, . . . ragged, rubbed, and scribbled," he later revised and allowed to be published as *The Anas.* It is "truly unfortunate," he once remarked, that so few public figures take notes, without which "history becomes fable instead of fact."

Out of his notes on parliamentary procedure grew his authoritative *Manual of Parliamentary Practice.* His habit of drawing from others and of observing for himself "any information of our country which might be of use to me in any station, public or private" made possible his world-famous *Notes on the State of Virginia.* His *Garden Book,* started in 1776 and continued almost uninterruptedly for the next fifty years, is a mine of information about him, as are his *Account Books,* also kept up almost continuously from 1767 to the year of his death. The entries reflect innumerable activities and interests. He also kept a *Weather Memorandum Book* from 1776 to 1820. For matters more exclusively agricultural he had a *Farm Book.*[18]

Ferrying across the Po River in Italy, he recorded: "We pass in eleven minutes." The Rhine crossing at Essenberg required "eight to ten minutes." At a chateau in Heidelberg he recorded a four-syllable echo. In the same city he was not satisfied with seeing its famous tun but had to ascertain its exact dimensions. "I . . . found its length external to be twenty-eight feet ten inches; its diameter at the end twenty-feet three inches; the thickness of the

staves seven and a half inches; thickness of the hoops seven
and a half inches; besides a great deal of external framing."

To his daughter Martha, Jefferson wrote, "A mind
always employed is always happy. This is the true secret,
the grand recipe, for felicity. The idle are the only wretched." [19] He himself was always up with or before the sun,
and after sometimes bathing his feet in cold water, began
a busy day. "Mr. Jefferson was the most industrious person
I ever saw in my life," said his overseer. Only twice in
twenty years did he find Jefferson sitting unoccupied in
his room, once with toothache and once with neuralgia.
"At all other times he was either reading, writing, talking,
working upon some model, or doing something else." [20]
Once when laid up with rheumatism at Poplar Forest, his
smaller home, he amused himself "with calculating the
hour lines of an horizontal dial for the latitude of this
place, which I find to be $37°22'26''$." The calculations
were made for every five minutes of time. In 1801, stranded
for three days at an overseer's house by a heavy rain, with
nothing but an almanac to read, he used the time to com-
pute how long it would take to pay the national debt.[21]

He left innumerable statistics, measurements, and calculations connected with farming, gardening, and kindred
interests—from contour plowing, through the planting of
seed with a drill, to the first date that a bud appeared or
a leaf turned green, and on down to the exact measurement of a flower. Jefferson's overseer said that he always
carried around a little pocket ruler. Near Marseilles, he
personally measured the trunks of fig trees and found
them to be "sometimes fifteen inches in diameter." Near
Nice he found fig trees "eighteen inches in diameter, and
six feet, stem." It was also at Marseilles that he had stopped
to measure a mule, "not the largest, five feet and two inches
high." At Monticello he noted that 500 "forwardest and
. . . middling peas" weighed "3^{oz}-18^{dwt}," and that "about

2,500 fill a pint," whereas of the Charlton Hotspur, 500 peas "weighed 3^{oz}-7^{dwt}," and 2,000 of them filled a pint. His strawberry plants in 1767 bore 20 berries per plant, of which 100 berries filled half a pint. In 1775 he figured that there were 900 good cottonseed to a pint; or 57,600 seed to a bushel. At four to a hill a bushel would plant 14,400 hills; planted in hills two feet apart, an acre would contain about 11,025. Hence a bushel of seed would plant 1⅓ acres.

In calculating distances, Jefferson sometimes simply measured the length of a horse's stride, counted the number of strides, and multiplied. During the construction of Monticello, he studied the operations of his workmen like a modern efficiency expert. He found that a man could fill a two-wheeled barrow in three minutes and roll it thirty yards in an additional minute and a half. This equalled four loads of the common one-wheeled barrow. Jefferson continues: "so that suppose the 4. loads put in the same time viz. 3. minutes, 4. trips will take 4 x 1½ minutes = 6' which added to 3' filling is = 9' to fill and carry the same earth which was filled & carried in the two-wheeled barrow in 4½'." Use of the two-wheeled barrow was obviously indicated.[22]

In his two terms as President, Jefferson kept a schedule of the earliest and latest appearance of thirty-seven vegetables upon the market. From his record he could count on broccoli appearing around April 7 and disappearing around April 24, artichokes between June 9 and July 16, mushrooms between August 11 and October 19, watermelons between July 7 and September 3, and squash between June 11 and October 17.[23] One might also find out from Jefferson's records when the first shad was to be bought. In 1798 this was on March 16.[24]

Jefferson also recorded the first appearance of birds and insects and the first croaking of frogs. Such records expressed not only a statistical passion but his desire to correlate climatological data and observations of bird migrations. Letters to his daughters, David Rittenhouse, and others are full of such statistics. In New York he heard the first whippoorwill on June 8, 1790, and the first swallows and martins on April 21. In 1791 the first blackbirds and robins arrived at Philadelphia on February 27, and on May 21 Jefferson saw his first martin. The whippoorwill appeared earlier at Monticello than at Philadelphia: in 1794 Jefferson heard one at his Virginia home April 2, whereas he had not heard one in Philadelphia in 1791 until May 17. Frogs croaked a bit earlier at Philadelphia in 1791 than in 1800; in 1800 Jefferson did not hear one until March 30, whereas nine years earlier he had heard one on March 9.[25] From his records Jefferson concluded that katydids would appear at Monticello between July 14 and July 20. Fireflies were recorded there on May 8.

Jefferson made delighted climatic comparisons of Monticello with other places to show its superiority. In Philadelphia, after recording the first appearance of the shad on his table and the tardy appearance of color in the weeping-willow leaf in 1798, he wrote to his daughter Martha: this "proves that we have near two months in the year of vegetable life, and of animal happiness so far as they are connected, more in our canton than here." [26]

Jefferson's account books give exactly what it cost him to visit an art gallery, to look at a lion, to eat at an inn, to hire a servant, to run a farm, to buy one of his daughters a dress, to cross a ferry, to have his laundry done. The figures are valuable not only as an economic record of his times but also as a mirror of his habits and interests. Wages and prices received his close attention. At Aix, in France, he recorded that a laborer's wages were a hundred and fifty livres a year, a woman's sixty to seventy livres, plus food. Wheat bread cost three sous a pound, cow's milk

sixteen sous a quart, sheep's milk six sous a quart, and
butter from sheep's milk twenty sous a pound. An ass cost
three louis and the best mule thirty louis. On his trip down
the Rhine from Germany he examined a millstone five
feet in diameter which cost six florins. The beauty of the
Italian Riviera near Albenga, where "water and earth con-
cur to offer what each has most precious," impressed him,
but he also noted that ortolans (buntings) sold at thirty
sous and the bishop's revenue came to forty thousand livres.

His passion for data took unexpected turns and often
were put to later use. In 1822 he informed John Adams
that in 1820 he had received 1,267 letters. Notes he had
made of the Canal of Languedoc in southern France were
later sent to George Washington for consultations over the
proposed Potomac Canal. The notes he made and the city
maps and plans he had collected of European cities—Frank-
furt-am-Main, Karlsruhe, Amsterdam, Strasbourg, Paris,
Orleans, Bordeaux, Lyons, Montpelier, Marseilles, Turin,
and Milan—were sent to the architect L'Enfant, in 1791, for
such use as they might have in the planning of Washington.
He also had his own ideas about city planning and health.

He drew diagrams of arches, noted how joists were laid,
sketched the manner of fixing a flagstaff to the mast of a
vessel, made exact diagrams of dining tables "letting down
with single or double leaves, so as to take the room of their
thickness only with a single leaf when open," made sketches
of buildings and of a Dutch wheelbarrow, and jotted down
details on bridges. In his passion for exact measurements
he calculated that he walked "4 miles 264 yards an hour"
and paced off a French mile in 1,254 steps,[27] dropped a
stone in a fountain at Nismes and recorded that it took
"thirteen seconds descending from the surface to the bottom," found that the bridge at Mayence was 1,840 feet long
and that its pontoons numbered forty-seven; that at Lyons
the "Pont d'Ainay has nine arches of forty feet from centre
to centre. The piers are of six feet"; that the Arles amphi-

theater has "sixty-four arches, each of which is, from centre to centre, twenty feet, six inches"; and that the Roman bricks of the circus of Bordeaux were nineteen to twenty inches long, eleven or twelve inches wide, and from an inch and a half to two inches thick.

To his friend William Short, Jefferson described his manner of traveling along the Canal of Languedoc in southern France: "I dismounted my carriage from its wheels, placed it on the deck of a light bark, and was thus towed on the canal instead of the post road. That I might be perfectly master of all the delays necessary, I hired a bark to myself by the day, & have made from 20 to 35 miles a day, . . . of all the methods of travelling I have ever tried this is the pleasantest. I walk the greater part of the way along the banks of the canal, level, & lined with a double row of trees which furnish shade. When fatigued I take a seat in my carriage where, as much at ease as if in my study, I read, write, or observe. my carriage being of glass all round, admits a full view of all the varying scenes thro' which I am shifted, olives, figs, mulberries, vines, corn & pasture, villages & farms." There were cloudless skies, limpid waters, and the "delicious" music of "a double row of nightingales along the banks of the canal, in full song." [28] There is some of this kind of thing also in his *Memoranda* of his trip. But here he was more careful to note such facts as that it took "one hour and thirty-three minutes" to pass through the eight locks at Bezières, that his bark was "about thirty-five feet long" and was drawn along by one horse at the rate of some two or three geographical miles an hour, that he met a raft "of about three hundred and fifty beams, forty feet long, and twelve or thirteen inches in diameter, formed into fourteen rafts, tacked together."

As a young man, Jefferson had felt deeply the death of his friend Dabney Carr, yet he had noted down the time it took to grub the plot of ground around Carr's grave and had "calculated that one laborer could do an acre in four days at that rate." [29] At eighty he returned humorously to his beloved figures in a letter to Abigail Adams: "I have ten and one-half grandchildren," he wrote, "and two and three-fourths great-grandchildren, and these fractions will ere long become units."

Jefferson amassed the wealth of his knowledge not only from direct observation but also from books and other printed sources. For these he had what he termed a "canine appetite." He became one of the best-read men of his day in America. Nobody knew better than he the cultural and scientific values which lay between the covers of a book or periodical. In later life he listed books, science, farming, family, and friends as the greatest "passions" of his life. "I cannot live without books," he wrote to John Adams, and to Abigail he spoke of "my greatest of all amusements, reading." Mere life experience, thought Jefferson, was not enough to make a full man: "I know it is often said there have been shining examples of men of great abilities in all the businesses of life, without any other science than what they had gathered from conversations and intercourse with the world. But who can say what these men would not have been, had they started in the science on the shoulders of a Demosthenes or Cicero, of a Locke or Bacon, or a Newton?"

Jefferson returned from France in 1789 with eighty-six packing cases, fifteen of which contained books. Their titles were entered in a notebook. Jefferson's interests are reflected in the number of pages in this record devoted to each subject. These are, approximately, thirty-eight pages to history, twenty-three to natural philosophy (science), twenty to religion and ethics (including international law), thirty-five to law, nineteen to politics, four to mathematics, sixteen to geography, and fifty-seven to fine arts—with a miscellany including the health of soldiers and sailors, cold bathing, games, agriculture, gardening, shorthand, cookery, and numerous technical arts. His books on chemistry included works by Chaptal, Duhamel, Fourcroy, Hales, Ingenhousz, Lavoisier, Parmentier, Rumford, Scheele, Wallerius, and Watson.[30] His was one of the finest libraries of his day in America. It became the nucleus of our Library of Congress.

Feeling more strongly, as time went on, that America should have unrestricted access to the learning of Europe, he came to the opinion that she should have very little if any import duties on books. He also sought to establish circulating libraries throughout Virginia. "I have often thought," he wrote in 1809, "that nothing would do more extensive good at small expense than the establishment of a small circulating library in every county, to consist of a few well-chosen books, to be lent to the people of the country, under such regulations as would secure their safe return in due time. These should be such as would give them a general view of other history, and a particular view of that of their own country, a tolerable knowledge of Geography, the elements of Natural Philosophy, of Agriculture and Mechanics." He wished to see that his native land produced men whose knowledge was superior because it was founded upon the culture of Demosthenes and Cicero, and the science of Bacon and of Newton.

Jefferson's prodigious industry as a young law student (he studied fifteen hours a day), as well as his idea about the breadth of book learning which should go into the making of a lawyer, is seen in a program of study he outlined for a young friend. Before beginning directly upon law itself, a "sufficient groundwork must be laid," he wrote. For this purpose "an acquaintance with the Latin and French languages is absolutely necessary. . . . Mathematics and Natural philosophy are so useful in the most familiar occurrences of life, and are so peculiarly engaging & delightful as would induce every person to wish an acquaintance with them." Mathematical reasonings and deductions he thought especially good preparation "for investigating the abstruse speculations of the law."

After this preliminary foundation—which also includes astronomy and geography—one then begins upon laws themselves, together with the kindred studies of "Physics, Ethics, Religion, Natural law, Belles lettres, Criticism, Rhetoric and Oratory." The day is to be divided into five periods of work. From dawn until eight o'clock Jefferson's young friend is to occupy himself with physical studies, ethics, religion (natural and sectarian), and natural law. Physical studies include agriculture, chemistry, anatomy, zoology, and botany. The study of law occupies the second period, from eight until twelve o'clock. Jefferson's list of authors and titles is specific and detailed and accompanied by comments. Politics are to be read during the third period, from twelve to one o'clock. During the afternoon, the fourth period, Jefferson's friend is to study all branches of history. After supper comes the study of polite literature, criticism, rhetoric, and oratory. This program of intellectual labor will, says Jefferson, give the student "an useful & satisfactory degree of knolege" in the various branches of learning recommended, while the books themselves will "form a valuable and sufficient library for a lawyer, who is at the same time a lover of science." For Jefferson breadth of learning was always to supplement technical competence.

But his interest in and respect for published material did not lead to a neglect of first-hand, direct observation, experimentation, and inquiry. It was where this was not possible that he turned to his books—and he knew where to turn. Letters written in the latter part of his life to John Adams, for example, in reply to questions on Indian traditions, religion, and origins, go into the data to be found in Lafitau, Adair, de Bry (three folio volumes in Latin), Reinold Foster, Brerewood, Bernard Romans, and Dr. Benjamin Smith Barton. At another time, discussing possible textbooks in science, Jefferson speaks of the "earlier and invaluable

works of Euler and Bezont," and of the more recent works
of "Lacroix in mathematics, of Legendre in geometry,
Lavoisier in chemistry, the elementary works of Haüy in
physics, Brot in experimental physics and physical astronomy, Dumeril in natural history, to say nothing of many
detached essays of Monge and others, and the transcendent
labors of Laplace."

When in 1814 Jefferson turned his attention to the different methods of classification used by naturalists, he discussed in some detail the theories and systems of Ray,
Klein, Brisson, Linnaeus, Blumenbach, Cuvier, Jussieu,
Buffon, Wildenow, and Persoon. To decide the grant of
patent rights to Oliver Evans for "his Elevators, Conveyers,
and Hopper-boys," Jefferson's research took him through
Shaw's travels to Egypt and the Barbary coast (where Shaw
had observed somewhat similar machines in use), Morti-
mer's work on husbandry, Ferguson's on mechanics, the
Universal History, Vitruvius, Perrault (who edited Vitruvius in Paris in 1684), Bossuet's *Histoire des mathématiques,*
Wolf's *Cour de mathématiques,* Desagulier's *Experimental
Philosophy,* the *Encyclopédie* of Diderot and D'Alembert,
De la Lande's continuation of Montuclas' *Histoire de mathématiques,* Prony's *Architecture hydraulique,* and classical
works dealing with the screw of Archimedes. In his own
Notes on Virginia, one of the really important early books
produced in America, Jefferson cites eighteen foreign
authorities and quotes and translates from four foreign languages.[31]

In lesser ways also Jefferson turned to the printed page
for scientific knowledge. To prove that the Irish potato was
not native to North America, he surveyed Zimmermann's
Geographical Zoology and Clavigero's *History of Mexico.*
He first learned of upland rice by running across an article
on it. In a technical work on roofing he came upon a principle which he later employed at Monticello.

It is little wonder that the Marquis de Chastellux, after a

visit to Monticello, wrote of his host that "no object had escaped Mr. Jefferson; it seemed as if from his youth he had placed his mind, as he had done his house, on an elevated situation, from which he might contemplate the universe."

2

Principles and Practices

•

I

Activating all these interests were a group of directing principles derived from Jefferson's philosophy of life. One was a profound belief in the freedom of the scientific mind, in its right to inquire everywhere and to arrive at independent conclusions. In fact, the scientist had not only a *right* to freedom of inquiry and independence of conclusions; it was, at the same time, a *necessity* that he exert this right at any and all times. Otherwise there could be no certainty of scientific truth and no scientific progress. In Jefferson's day, when science was regarded with a suspicious eye, it was a very important matter that a man of his standing held such a view.

"I have sworn upon the altar of God, eternal hostility against every form of tyranny over the mind of man," wrote Jefferson to Dr. Benjamin Rush in September, 1800, in his defense against the "lying pamphlets" of political opponents decrying his religious opinions. He planned the University of Virginia to be "based on the illimitable freedom of the human mind. For here we are not afraid to follow truth wherever it may lead, nor to tolerate any error so long as reason is left free to combat it." Discussing the classification systems of his day—Blumenbach's, Buffon's, Cuvier's, Linnaeus's, and others—Jefferson declared himself unafraid of "innovations recommended by reason." Such fears he imputed to "those whose interests or prejudices shrink from the advance of truth and science." He contrasted the case of Galileo who "was sent to the Inquisition for affirming that the earth was a sphere" with those of Descartes and Newton who were allowed to develop scientific and religious truths. He approved of the modern advance: "Reason and experiment have been indulged, and error has fled before them. It is error alone which needs the support of government."

Jefferson sought a religion unhampered by dogma and productive of the greatest social utility, which he defined as the quiet and happy living of a good life in a state of moral and benevolent harmony with one's fellow men. This opposition to religious sectarianism, together with his emphasis upon reason, upon the right of free inquiry, and the necessity of scientific conclusions independent of political or religious sanctions, raised a storm of opposition against him. This will be treated more fully in Chapter 9, but it may be well to glance at it here.

In his *Notes on Virginia* Jefferson had questioned the universal flood and all mankind's descent from Adam and Eve, not hesitating to challenge established religious opinion and doctrine which seemed to him contrary to reason and natural laws. He dismissed the *Apocalypse* "as merely the ravings of a maniac," would not accept the Trinity, the immaculate conception, the miraculous powers of Jesus, his resurrection and visible ascension, and his corporeal presence in the eucharist, and rejected as "fables" such things as "calves speaking, of statues sweating blood, and other things against the course of nature."

For this Jefferson was roundly damned during election campaigns. Typical was the Reverend John Mason's *Voice of Warning, to Christians, on the Ensuing Election* (1800), which called him an infidel.[1] Undismayed, Jefferson, in a letter to Moses Robinson, Senator from Vermont, charged the New England clergy with viewing "all advances in science as dangerous innovations."[2] To his scientist friend Joseph Priestley he wrote in 1801: "The barbarians really flattered themselves they should be able to bring back the times of Vandalism, when ignorance put everything into the hands of power and priestcraft. All advances in science were proscribed as innovations." And he added, perhaps a little overoptimistically, that he was glad to be able to welcome Priestley, "great apostle" of science, to a land where "science and honesty are replaced on their high ground."

I I

Jefferson, as we have seen, stressed the importance of basing conclusions on observation and experiment. This was another of his fundamental principles. He sometimes knowingly indulged in "conjectures" or derived conclusions from insufficient data, or proved unable to break through established preconceptions, when faced with controverting data. But such lapses were few. He insisted, time and again, that a hypothesis or theory be proven by experiment and careful observation before acceptance. It is "laudable to encourage investigation, but to hold back conclusions," he wrote. Through his own example and his insistence upon investigation, voiced to his correspondents, he helped to promote a respect for thorough and independent investigation in his day. Discoursing on his beloved mathematics, he wrote to Dr. Benjamin Rush: "We have no theories there, no uncertainties remain on the mind, all is demonstration and satisfaction."

In his *Notes on Virginia,* attacking the fantasies of Monsieur Buffon and others regarding America, he stated: "A patient pursuit of facts, and cautious combination and comparison of them, is the drudgery to which man is subjected by his Maker, if he wishes to obtain sure knowledge." From Paris he advised his friend Charles Thomson in 1787, concerning certain Indian remains discovered in the western parts of America: Those who collected these objects of Indian antiquity should, for the present, forego theories and stick to exact descriptions. "The moment a person forms a theory, his imagination sees, in every object, only the traits which favor that theory." Congratulating Tom Paine on the success of an iron bridge built from his plans, he wrote: "I was sure of it before from theory; yet one likes to be assured from practice also."

In a characteristic letter to his friend, the Reverend James Madison, President of William and Mary College, Jefferson took note of the experiments of Dr. Ingenhousz who had concluded that "vegetation might be promoted by occasioning streams of the electrical fluid to pass through a plant," a theory in which others had concurred. But Ingenhousz's later tests showed that electricity had no effect whatever, which drew from Jefferson the remark that it is "always better to have no ideas, than false ones; to believe nothing, than to believe what is wrong." In a letter to Rutledge in 1788, he expressed high regard for the Swiss scientist de Saussure, who was cautious in "not letting his ascent run before his evidence," and set him in favorable contrast with French scientists of that time who were so given to unverified and hasty speculation that they should be classed "with the writers of romance."

Yet Jefferson did not rule out hypotheses whose values for science he recognized. In a letter written in 1822, after remarking on his "sceptical disposition" and describing himself as "an empiric in natural philosophy, suffering my faith to go no further than my facts," he added that he was pleased

"to see the efforts of hypothetical speculation, because by
the collisions of different hypotheses, truth may be elicited
and science advanced in the end." Concerning apparently
inexplicable phenomena of nature (a fall of meteorites in
Connecticut in 1807), he held that we "certainly are not to
deny whatever we cannot account for," but we must suspend judgment, and examine all facts if we are ultimately
to arrive at valid conclusions. Jefferson could not believe
that stones had fallen from the sky, a conclusion he thought
contrary to the laws of nature. But he advised that the American Philosophical Society be consulted upon the matter. On
one thing he was sure: his correspondent would be wasting
his time to send one of these stones to Congress for examination since, though these gentlemen might be "most highly
qualified" to act in a political capacity, they could not be
"supposed most familiar with subjects of natural history."

Jefferson's readiness to introduce new agricultural machinery, productions, and methods and his own willingness
to practice what he preached about experimentation are
seen in his farming operations. He wrote Governor Milledge
of Georgia that "the scripture precept of 'prove all things &
hold fast that which is good' is peculiarly wise in objects of
agriculture." He consciously took the lead in agricultural
experimentation in his neighborhood hoping to bring about
a general "reformation" in farming methods. In Professor
Betts's estimation Jefferson's experiments with scientific seed
germination "put his knowledge of planting far in advance
of that of his neighbors." He ran a one-acre experiment in
1795 which convinced him that, contrary to common opinion, run-down land was as good at producing wheat as rye.
When an acquaintance discovered a new method of planting corn on unplowed land, Jefferson got permission to try
it out on an acre of ground. Crop rotation and contour plowing, new ideas in his day, keenly interested him.

He maintained an experimental garden and nursery at
Monticello and in other ways promoted experimentation

with new seeds and plants in Virginia. His *Garden Book, Farm Book,* memoranda, and other documents record experiments with upland rice, silk nettle, pecans and walnuts, huge cabbages (one, to Jefferson's surprise, was reported to grow seven feet high, and he considered it "worth seeing into"), giant cucumbers (cucumbers were a favorite dish of his), figs from France, vetch from England, peas from New York, fiorin grass from Europe, strawberries and corn from Italy, the silk tree, the sugar maple, apricots, seeds and plants brought back from the Lewis and Clark Expedition, capsicum from the Southwest, and countless others.

His experiments extended to his guests at Monticello. He served "various companies" salad made with benne oil instead of olive oil. Their favorable reaction made him resolve to grow benne himself. He also tried out a native wine upon his visitors, which he ranked with "the Crûmartin of Burgundy" and was gratified when his guests could not tell the difference.[3] He hoped to see American benne oil and native wines supplant foreign importations.

Improvement and simplification of agricultural implements and techniques were among the aims of an Association of Agricultural Societies that he was active in promoting.

Enthusiastic though he was in new inventions, he insisted on careful testing of each. His patient pursuit of data before establishing any final conclusions regarding the climate of America is seen in his vast accumulation of data which he himself refrained from speculating upon. It was to be used, after further observations, to validate conclusions to be drawn in the future.

Jefferson may have felt that "reason" promptly perceives truth in the matter of natural rights, religion, or morals. But in science he demanded statistical and experimental proof.

I I I

Another of Jefferson's principles was that science must be useful, must contribute to an ever-increasing total of human happiness. In a letter of 1825, not long before his death, he wrote: "I revolt against metaphysical reading . . . the business of life is with matter that. gives us tangible results. handling that, we arrive at the knoledge of the axe, the plough, the steam-boat, and every thing useful in life. but, from metaphical speculations, I have never seen one useful result." Elsewhere he spoke of his "fondest wishes for the advancement of our country in the useful sciences and arts."

Religion, literature, art, education, and science—all were to be made socially useful. Religion should be transformed into a practical and common-sense moral code productive of social harmony and happiness. For him religion boils down to the four words, "Be just and good." The production of "honest men" was "the only point society has any right to look to" in religion. Religion should be simplified. Jefferson hoped no one would "give up morals for mysteries and Jesus for Plato." He wished to see religion divorced from its creeds, symbols, rituals, mysteries, incomprehensibilities, sacerdotalisms, social and political proscriptions, obscurantist opposition to freedom of the mind and intellectual progress, emphasis upon otherworldliness, indifference to social utility and man's earthly happiness achieved by daily benevolence and moral living. "The doctrines of Jesus," he wrote to Dr. Benjamin Waterhouse in 1822, "are simple, and tend all to the happiness of man."

Jefferson pointed out that even in his beloved and beautiful Monticello "the law of convenience" came first and, except that it hurt his national pride, he was not too concerned that America had not yet produced large numbers of literati. Art, which would come in due time, could be useful in keeping the wealthy out of vice. He emphasized the moral good to be found in literature, and pointed out that "the entertainments of fiction are useful as well as pleasant." In fact, "everything is useful which contributes to fix in the principles and practices of virtue."

But though, as abundant examples have shown, Jefferson's taste in and appreciation for art and literature was not bound by utility, it dominated his thinking and colored his evaluations.

Utility also came first in most of Jefferson's ideas on education. Though he held abstractly that education should develop "the illimitable freedom of the human mind," he tended to stress more obviously utilitarian ends. He wished to found in Virginia, he said, a university "where every branch of science (that is, knowledge), deemed useful at this day, should be taught in its highest degree." To Joseph Priestley he described his proposed university as "an institution meant chiefly for use." But his concept of the useful was broad, and he "looked to education as a means of social, moral, and political uplift to society as well as an aid to personal and professional progress for individuals." [4] A complete education should produce men who were in *all* ways useful to society—useful because intelligent, cultured, well-informed, technically competent, moral (this particularly), capable of earning a living, happy, and fitted for political and social leadership. Jefferson always sought in his own life to set an example of his utilitarian demands.

In demanding utility from science, Jefferson was typical of the best minds of his day in America. The necessities of building a new nation led to an emphasis upon practical affairs and direct material utility instead of literature, art, or "pure science." "Our citizens," Jefferson wrote approvingly in 1803, "almost all follow some industrious occupation, and, therefore, have little time to devote to abstract science." He was delighted over the vast increase in useful inventions which had followed America's patent law.

Nevertheless, Jefferson could interest himself in a science or technical matter whose utility was neither direct nor obvious. This is seen in a letter to Robert Patterson in 1802: ". . . no discovery is barren; it always serves as a step to something else." His insatiable thirst for knowledge was often a sufficient stimulus alone to awaken his enthusiasm and arouse him to action. This may be seen in such things as his interest in the origin of the Indian in America and his untiring work in vertebrate paleontology. However, even his interest in the "mammoth" he managed to make useful to himself and his country, for it furnished him valuable facts for his refutation of the French scientists Buffon and Raynal (a matter which we shall notice later). And, conversely, the usefulness of his facts in this case may further have deepened his interest in paleontology.

Perception of immediate utility in a principle, discovery, or invention gave the greatest of pleasure to Jefferson. On receiving what he termed a "charming treatise on manures," he wrote to the sender that "science never appears so beautiful as when applied to the uses of human life." He considered Linnaeus praiseworthy not only for the intrinsic scientific value of his contributions but because of their direct usefulness to man. He complimented Sir John Sinclair, first president of the London Board of Agriculture, for directing his labors and science to "the utilities of human life." He reverted admiringly, again and again, to Benjamin Franklin as the model of a man who had rendered "great services in the advancement of science" and the production of "inventions useful to man."

This concern with the social usefulness of science can be seen in action, in the part Jefferson played in the introduction into America of Jenner's method of vaccination to prevent smallpox. Jefferson was critical of certain medical practices of his day, and went so far as to remark jokingly that "whenever he saw three physicians together, he looked up to discover whether there was not a turkey-buzzard in the neighborhood." [5] He particularly objected to physicians who allowed their "fanciful theory" to outrun their facts. "I have seen," he said, "the disciples of Hoffman, Boerhaave, Stahl, Cullen, Brown, succeed one another like the shifting figures of a magic lantern, & their fancies, like the dresses of the annual doll-babies from Paris, becoming, from their novelty, the vogue of the day, and yielding to the next novelty their ephemeral favor. The patient, treated on the fashionable theory, sometimes gets well in spite of the medicine." Give up "visionary theories," he counseled, and place your reliance upon well-tried medical aids, "sober facts," "clinical observation," anatomical studies, and a modicum of surgery. Thus "some diseases not yet understood may in time be transferred to the table of those known." For him medical science was obviously "the most important of all others" since, in the final analysis, health and life are dependent upon it. He considered Edward Jenner's work on smallpox a shining example of proper practices in achieving the eradication of one of mankind's worst scourges.

In a letter to Jenner in 1806, he wrote, "Medecine [sic] has never before produced any single improvement of such ability. Harvey's discovery of the circulation of the blood was a beautiful addition to our knowledge of the animal economy. but on a review of the practice of medicine before & since that epoch, I do not see any great amelioration which has been derived from that discovery. you have erased from the Calendar of human afflictions one of it's greatest. yours is the comfortable reflection that mankind can never forget that you have lived."

Jefferson played a large part in introducing Jenner's discovery into the United States. His direct intervention and, indirectly, his scientific and civic prestige greatly facilitated acceptance of this discovery. Dr. Benjamin Waterhouse of Boston, who first sought to add Jenner's vaccination to

American medical practice, met with general indifference, professional jealousies, popular fear, and direct opposition.

Among the obstacles Waterhouse had to contend with were reports that "taking the virus of cowpox from a cow [Jenner's method] and putting it into a child had the effect of slowly but surely turning the human into the animal kind"; that vaccination greatly increased the death rate of patients; that the new treatment was "too beastly and indelicate for polished society"; that it was just another piece of money-making quackery; and that immunization, at best, did not last more than a year or two. In addition the new method had to overcome both professional and public inertia, the handicaps of inexpert procedures, antiquated laws; and other obstacles.

Realizing the value of the support of a high public official, Waterhouse appealed to President Adams, who did not go beyond friendly letters. When he turned to Vice-President Thomas Jefferson, he found the ally he needed. On assuming the Presidency, a short time later, Jefferson initiated an active campaign of support for Waterhouse.

Jefferson turned over the first cowpox virus he received from Dr. Waterhouse, in 1801, to Dr. Edward Gantt in Washington, who immediately inoculated a number of people, but without success. He again turned over part of another shipment from Waterhouse to Gantt, and some he sent to Monticello, to his friend Dr. Wardlaw. Suspecting that the failures in Washington were due to the effects of air and temperature upon the cowpox matter, Jefferson devised a special method of shipping. He suggested that Waterhouse enclose a vial of the live matter in a larger bottle of water. Waterhouse attributed the success with later shipments to this simple device of Jefferson's.

On his return from Washington to Monticello in August, Jefferson began experiments upon his relatives and slaves, and encouraged his sons-in-law to do likewise. By November he was able to report on some two hundred treatments and a definite rise in public interest. Dr. Gantt's first successes in Washington came from virus Jefferson sent him from Monticello. Jefferson also shipped some to Georgetown, Richmond, Petersburg, "and several other parts of this state." From Washington, he also sent virus to Philadelphia, where it was tried with success. Jefferson further encouraged the publication and dissemination of information received from Waterhouse. When Chief Little Turtle, accompanied by a group of Indian braves, visited Jefferson in Washington, he was informed of this gift from the Great Spirit, and was persuaded, along with nine or ten other warriors, to undergo inoculation, and take back some of the virus to the tribes.

Waterhouse declared that the President had "forwarded the practice in Virginia at least a year if not two." Others also recognized his part in promoting public acceptance of this new medical procedure. In England, a paragraph in a tribute to Jenner, in 1803, began with: "This beneficial practice is patronized by JEFFERSON in the New World, & by the EMPEROR OF GERMANY, the EMPRESS DOWAGER OF RUSSIA in the old." [6]

Jefferson's concern with social utility is most directly seen in his interest in inventions, which he viewed as a useful application of scientific theory. He cited his own plow as an example of the "combination of a theory which may satisfy the learned, with a practice intelligible to the most unlettered laborer."

Replying to an inventor who had sent him the plans of a steam engine, Jefferson wrote that he had not been able to keep abreast of technological developments in this field, but liked the engine because of its "valuable properties of simplicity, cheapness and accommodation to the small and more numerous calls of life." He observed that "a smaller agent, applicable to our daily concerns, is infinitely more valuable than the greatest which can be used only for great

objects. For these interest the few alone, the former many."
He also felicitated a Frenchman for an improved means of
preserving flour, in these terms: every discovery "which
multiplies the subsistence of man, must be a matter of joy
to every friend to humanity." The utility of printing,
which had so enlarged the mind of man, was constantly emphasized by him.

Jefferson's desire to see useful inventions made available
to the public was expressed in his activities in the Patent
Office and his opinions on patent rights. As Secretary of
State he had the responsibility of administering America's
new patent law, about whose constitutionality he had some
doubts. His chief desire was to see that, though the inventor were given his full rights, no monopoly should be
established whereby technological progress should be withheld from other inventors and from the mass of Americans.
"An inventor ought to be allowed a right to the benefit of
his invention for some certain time," he wrote to the inventor Oliver Evans, but it is "equally certain it ought not to
be perpetual; for to embarrass society with monopolies for
every utensil existing, and in all the details of life, would
be more injurious to them than had the supposed inventors
never existed; because the natural understanding of its
members would have suggested the same things or others as
good." He pointed out, however, that nobody wished more
than he to see that "ingenuity should receive a liberal encouragement." He was not quite sure that the fourteen-
year period during which a patent held good was long
enough in a country so large, where the spread of ideas
and machinery was necessarily slower than in a smaller
country like England.

Jefferson examined all inventions and devices brought
before him, and where he was in doubt he called in assistance. To ascertain the value of a process for obtaining
fresh water from sea water, he had Isaacs, the discoverer,
perform an experiment before David Rittenhouse, Presi-

dent of the American Philosophical Society, Caspar Wistar, professor of chemistry in the College of Philadelphia, Dr. Hutchinson, also a professor of chemistry, and himself. As a result of this experiment Jefferson advised Congress that a patent should not be granted.[7] He considered the grant of a patent right tremendously important and during the first year of the patent law only three patents were recorded. Thirty-three were granted in 1791, eleven in 1792, and twenty in 1793—a total of only thirty-seven under Jefferson's administration of the original law. Jefferson's strict construction of this law led to a revision of it in 1793, to which he was opposed.[8]

American inventive genius began to flourish during the 1790's. Two months after the original patent law was signed, Jefferson remarked that it had "given a spring to invention beyond [his] conception." He was pleased at this practical application of American genius to the business of living, wishing "to see new inventions encouraged, and old ones brought back again into useful service." Though he felt that, legally, he did not owe Oliver Evans any patent fees for the machinery used in his mill, he made payments "as a voluntary tribute to a person whose talents are constantly employed in endeavors to be useful to mankind." [9]

Jefferson disapproved of ready grants of patents that had the effect of retarding technological progress or the use of machinery by the public, through monopolistic practices. On his own inventions he never took out a patent. He gave his plow away freely, remarking in a letter to his friend, Charles Willson Peale, that he had "never thought of monopolizing by patent any useful idea which happens to offer itself to me." Nor would he patent his dry dock, his hemp machine, or any other of his ideas. He wanted no "interloping patentee" to get hold of them. Inventions were among the most useful products of man's mind, and should be made available to all mankind.

In rating the utility of the sciences for America, Jeffer-

son drew up the following list for Joseph Priestley in 1800
(he employs the term *science* in both its specialized and
broad meaning): botany, chemistry, zoology, anatomy,
surgery, medicine, natural philosophy, agriculture, mathematics, astronomy, geography, politics, commerce, history,
ethics, law, arts, and fine arts. He observed that the list was
drawn up on the spur of the moment and might not be
complete. His writings contain numerous other references
to the utility of the different sciences.

Jefferson had a high regard for chemistry. While he was
Ambassador to France he got into conversation, one day in
1788, with the naturalist Buffon. Jefferson admired Monsieur Buffon, with whom, however, he had certain disagreements. The conversation turned on the "present ardor for
chemical inquiry." Buffon, says Jefferson, "affected to consider chemistry but as cookery, and to place the toils of the
laboratory on a footing with those of the kitchen." Where-
upon Jefferson defended chemistry as "among the most
useful of sciences, and big with future discoveries for the
utility and safety of the human race." This despite the fact
that he then considered chemistry, as he expressed it, "a
mere embryon," whose "principles are contested; experiments seem contradictory; their subjects are so minute as
to escape our senses; and their result too fallacious to satisfy
the mind."

In a letter written in 1805, Jefferson emphasized "the
importance of turning a knowledge of chemistry to household purposes. . . . The common herd of philosophers
[i.e., scientists] seem to write only for one another. The
chemists have filled volumes on the composition of a thousand substances of no sort of importance to the purposes of
life." He praised the chemist Chaptal for having explained
"the chemistry of wine making." Several years after his retirement from the Presidency, he again scored those chemists who failed to apply their science to useful ends. As a
model to the chemists he emphasized "the just esteem

which attached itself to Dr. Franklin's science, because he always endeavored to direct it to something useful in private life." He urged them to apply their science "to domestic objects, to malting, for instance, brewing, making cider, to fermentation and distillation generally, to the making of bread, butter, cheese, soap, to the incubation of eggs, etc." In 1826, Jefferson advised the Professor of Natural History at the University of Virginia to devote one-third of the year to botany and zoology and two-thirds to "Chemistry and its associates, mineralogy and Geology." He intended most of this time to be devoted to chemistry, and he remarked that even this would be inadequate.

He qualified his recommendations of geology because its conclusions were not certain and it had no obvious utility. Therefore he advised his university professor to give "the least possible time" to mineralogy and geology, particularly the latter. He had shown a keen interest in the minerals of the unexplored parts of North America and regarded mineralogy as useful (though not nearly so much so as botany) to the education of a country gentleman. "To learn, as far as observation has informed us," he wrote, "the ordinary arrangement of the different strata of minerals in the earth, to know where we find one mineral, whether another, for which we are seeking, may be expected to be in its neighborhood, is useful."

But as for that branch of geology which dealt with the formation and history of the earth—Jefferson wanted none of it. As he expressed it, "the dreams about the modes of creation, inquiries whether our globe has been formed by the agency of fire or water, how many millions of years it has cost Vulcan or Neptune [in the language of important schools of thought in his day] to produce what the fiat of the Creator would effect by a simple act of will, is too idle to be worth a single hour of any man's life." In a further expression of his inadequate knowledge of geology Jefferson wrote to his friend Volney that he had never pursued the science to any great extent "from a belief that the skin-deep scratches which we can make or find on the surface of the earth, do not repay our time with as certain and useful deductions as our pursuits in some other branches" of science. What difference does it make, he once remarked, whether the earth is six hundred or six thousand years old? Nor does it matter much to know the composition of the various strata of the earth "if they contain no coal or iron or other useful metal." [10]

For botany Jefferson had the highest regard. Botany, he said, "I rank with the most valuable sciences, whether we consider its subjects as furnishing the principal subsistence of life to man and beast, delicious varieties for our tables, refreshments from our orchards, the adornments of our flower-borders, shade and perfume of our groves, materials for our buildings, or medicaments for our bodies." He looked upon it as indispensable for a country gentleman—far more so than chemistry—not only for its immediate utility but because it enabled him to walk out into nature with a greater understanding of her productions and a greater pleasure derived from his observations. "No country gentleman should be without what amuses every step he takes into his fields."

Ever desirous for American youth to be well instructed in the descriptions of plants, especially of their properties and uses, he exerted himself to bring to America any plant which might promote her welfare. In his plans for an experimental garden at the University of Virginia, he proposed that "exotics of distinguished usefulness" be the object of experiment. He suggested "the Larch, Cedar of Libanus, Cork Oak, the Marronier, Mahogany, the Catachu or Indian rubber tree of Napul, . . . Teak tree, or Indian oak of Burman, . . . the various woods of Brazil, etc." When he was sent the seeds of the breadfruit tree for experimental planting, he termed them a "precious" gift which he would immediately try to introduce into the southern states. "One service of this kind rendered to a nation," he wrote, "is worth more to them than all the victories of the most splendid pages of their history, and becomes a source of exalted pleasure to those who have been instrumental to it."

Jefferson's comments on other branches of science show similar emphasis upon utility. His interest in astronomy was intensified by its relations to surveying, navigation, and the determination of longitude. However, he spoke more fondly of the usefulness of botany than of astronomy; he preferred plants to planets. Jefferson's curiosity about climate extended beyond its utilitarian values, but he continued to point out the value of meteorological information for health, for long-term planning of plant and animal breeding, and for the immediate, daily operation of farms and gardens.

Jefferson also recognized fully the useful role which science might play in prospecting and developing the natural resources in the American West. He was careful to see that explorers brought back accurate and full scientific data.

In Jefferson's opinion agriculture was the most useful of the sciences for America. For the individual it was valuable both as a profession and as a way of life, more apt than any other occupation to produce a happy and morally sound society. In later life Jefferson somewhat enlarged his economic horizons as conditions changed, inventions increased, and manufactures sprang up in America, but his preference for the farmer over the "twirlers of the distaff" remained. He had an instinctive fear of "the powerful fascinations of great cities." In a letter of 1817 he characterized agriculture as "the employment of our first parents in Eden, the happiest we can follow, and the most important to our country." [11] In a letter to George Wythe in 1787, describing his trip into southern France and northern Italy, he wrote: "In architecture, painting, sculpture, I

found much amusement; but more than all, in their agriculture, many objects of which might be adopted with us
to great advantage."

"Agriculture," said Jefferson in 1803, "is the first in
utility and ought to be the first in respect. . . . It is a
science of the very first order. It counts among its hand-
maids the most respectable sciences, such as Chemistry,
Natural Philosophy, Mechanics, Mathematics generally,
Natural History, Botany. In every College and University, a
professorship of agriculture, and the class of its students,
might be honored as the first. Young men closing their
academical education with this, as the crown of all other
sciences, fascinated with its solid charms, and at a time
when they are to choose an occupation, instead of crowding
the other classes, would return to the farms of their fathers,
their own, or those of others, and replenish and invigorate
a calling, now languishing under contempt and oppres-
sion." Promotion of agriculture would increase the sum of
man's industry and diminish his misery. In accepting a
gold medal from the Agricultural Society of Paris for his
invention of the moldboard, Jefferson wrote that he was
"attached to agriculture by inclination, as well as by a conviction that it is the most useful of the occupations of
man."

I V

Another of Jefferson's general principles was that more
science should be taught in America's schools, colleges, and
universities.

As far back as 1779 Jefferson had replaced the professor-
ships of divinity at William and Mary with those of law,
medicine, chemistry, and modern languages.[12] In his letter
of thanks to Harvard's president, Dr. Willard, for an honorary Doctorate of Laws, Jefferson, discussing features of
the learning he had observed in Europe, enlarged on the

possibilities of scientific investigation in America and urged its extension at Harvard: "The Botany of America is far from being exhausted, its mineralogy is untouched, and its Natural History or Zoology, totally mistaken and misrepresented. . . . It is for such institutions as that over which you preside so worthily, Sir, to do justice to our country, its productions and its genius. It is the work to which the young men, whom you are forming, should lay their hands."

To a young man contemplating a political career he recommended the study of such sciences as chemistry, botany, mathematics, natural philosophy, and natural history. He sent his own grandson, young Randolph, to Philadelphia to study because the sciences were so well taught there. His other grandson, John Wayles Eppes, was to study mathematics, natural philosophy, astronomy, chemistry, mineralogy, botany, and natural history at Columbia College (later the University of South Carolina). Such subjects as "ethics, metaphysics, logic, etc." Jefferson thought he could acquire for himself in private study.

Jefferson's University of Virginia was to be built "on a plan . . . broad and liberal and *modern*," and was designed as an institution where those sciences "useful *to us, and at this day*, should be taught in their highest degree." Jefferson proposed Bacon's *arbor scientiae* as a foundation, with the omission of such impractical branches of knowledge as "Oriental learning." The relative importance of science in Jefferson's educational scheme is seen in the following list of the eight schools, within the University of Virginia, when it was organized on April 7, 1824: Ancient Languages, Modern Languages, Mathematics, Natural Philosophy (this included several branches of science), Natural History, Anatomy and Medicine, Moral Philosophy, and Law. A student was allowed to study in one or more of these schools.[13] Jefferson hoped that certain of his larger educational plans would, when put into effect, produce

graduates skilled in the "useful arts"—such as civil government, military science, medicine, and inventions for saving
labor and increasing man's comforts. Jefferson advocated
instruction in "technical philosophy" for artisans, to enable them to acquire knowledge of those sciences necessary
to their trades and therefore useful to them for a full and
happy life.

In his efforts to increase and improve the teaching of
science in America, Jefferson hoped to import some of the
best professors in Europe, particularly those from Edinburgh and Geneva, which he called "the two eyes of Europe in matters of science." At one time he entertained
hopes, which did not materialize, of bringing over almost
the entire scientific faculty of Geneva.

Jefferson well knew that a full education was a life-time
matter. Even with the best of teaching and the best of
learning, he did not feel that a complete cultural or scientific education could be acquired in school. We "do not
expect our schools," he said, "to turn out their alumni
already enthroned on the pinnacles of their respective
sciences; but only so far advanced in each as to be able to
pursue them by themselves, and to become Newtons and
Laplaces by energies and perserverances to be continued
through life."

V

In 1810, on receiving the announcement that he had
been elected to the Royal Institute of Sciences, Literature,
and Fine Arts at Amsterdam, Jefferson replied that among
the blessings of science was its promotion of a "fraternal
relation . . . among the whole family of its votaries,
wheresoever dispersed through nations friendly or hostile."
This belief he shared with many leaders of his day. That
science promotes international harmony and peace was
particularly true, Jefferson thought, in the case of scientific

societies. "These societies," he wrote, "are always in peace, however their nations may be at war. Like the republic of letters, they form a great fraternity spreading over the whole earth, and their correspondence is never interrupted by any civilized nation."

Toward such ends Jefferson suggested that the scientific societies of the world should promote adoption of a uniform system of measures, weights, and coins. He thought the American Philosophical Society should take the leadership in such a move. He himself got into political trouble by permitting the exportation of cottonseed for experiment in France during the Embargo. In his defense he cited the fact that although France and England had been at war at the time, the Agricultural Society of Paris had sent one of its improved plows to the Duke of Bedford, a member of the Society; that George Washington had received from the same Society the seed of the perennial succory, which Arthur Young had carried over from France to England; and that he himself had been sent the seed of the Swedish turnip. Proof, Jefferson thought, that men of science are capable of living in harmony and peace throughout the world, and that the world could look for greater international understanding under their leadership.

Jefferson was not alone in such cosmopolitan thinking. Dr. Nicholas Collin, Rector of the Swedish Churches in Pennsylvania, in his "Essay on Those Enquiries in Natural Philosophy, Which at Present Are Most Beneficial to the United States of North America," read before the American Philosophical Society in 1789, declared: "Philosophers are citizens of the world; the fruits of their labours are freely distributed among all nations; what they sow is reaped by the antipodes, and blooms through future generations." Dr. Benjamin Rush even went so far as to suggest that the societies of Europe and America should form a kind of confederation, to make their influence so powerful as to restrain all rulers and thus bring about a better world. Tom Paine, in a letter to the Abbé Raynal, spoke of learning in general as "the partisan of no country, but the beneficent patroness of all." "The philosopher of one country," he continued, "sees not an enemy in the philosopher of another: he takes his seat in the temple of science, and asks not who sits beside him. This was not the condition of the barbarian world."

Less floridly expressed, this internationalism is seen in the charter of the American Philosophical Society, granted in 1780, while the Colonies were still at war with England. It reads in part:

And whereas nations truly civilized (however unhappily at variance on other accounts) will never wage war with the Arts and Sciences and the common Interests of humanity.

Be it further enacted by the authority aforesaid, That it shall and may be lawful for the said Society by their proper officers, at all times, whether in peace or war, to correspond with learned Societies, as well as individual learned men, of any nation or country, upon matters merely belonging to the business of the said Society, such as the mutual communication of their discoveries and proceedings in Philosophy and Science; the procuring books, apparatus, natural curiosities, and such other articles and intelligence as are usually exchanged between learned bodies for furthering their common pursuits; *Provided always,* That such correspondence of the said Society be at all times open to the inspection of the Supreme Executive Council of this Commonwealth.[14]

Some leaders of Jefferson's day looked at the matter from a less idealistic point of view, but they shared the belief that science would eventually substitute One World for distinctive national rivalries. Robert Fulton hoped that steam navigation, by facilitating mutual intercourse and making naval warfare impractical, would bring about international peace and world unity. Franklin similarly saw the balloon bringing an end to wars. "Five thousand Balloons, capable of raising two men each," he wrote to Jan Ingenhousz in 1784, "could not cost more than Five ships of the Line; and where is the Prince who can afford so to cover his Country with Troops for its Defense, as that Ten Thousand Men descending from the Clouds might not in many places do an infinite deal of mischief, before a Force could be brought together to repel them?" [15] Jefferson's speculations upon the balloon imply similar conclusions (see Chapter 3).

V I

Another controlling principle of Jefferson's scientific thought and activities was to have America benefit from everything that science anywhere in the world had to offer. Jefferson was second to no man in his love of his country. He took pride in every evidence of scientific genius in his fellow countrymen. He vigorously defended America against the imputations of Buffon, Raynal, and others (see Chapter 7). He looked upon America as the great hope of the world, and envisaged a virtually illimitable future progress for his country. During his own lifetime he exerted every effort to see that the United States made the best of her opportunities at home and received the best that Europe had to offer.

His patriotism may be seen in the pride he took in the orrery (forerunner of the planetarium) constructed by his fellow scientist, David Rittenhouse, in 1767. The orrery represented the motions of the sun, moon, and planets, and hence illustrated the "solar and lunar eclipses and other phenomena 'for a period of 5000 years, either forward or backward.' " [16] This marvelous mechanical device, Jefferson felt, disproved European claims that America could not produce geniuses. Therefore, in January of 1783, he moved that the American Philosophical Society commission Rittenhouse to make an orrery to be presented to the King of France. The orrery was despatched to France through Barbe-Marbois, secretary to the French legation in

Philadelphia.[17] Jefferson also argued that it was probably in America and not in England that the idea of making the rim of a wheel from a single piece of wood originated. It had been suggested in Homer, he says, and must have been noticed by a Jersey farmer, since "ours are the only farmers who can read Homer." At another time, he expressed the hope that Churchman, an American, had anteceded a European in devising a new compass. Also, he felt that if his fellow countryman Mr. Jacob Isaacs had actually discovered a new method of making fresh water from sea water, it would be "a new flower in the American wreath" —in which, however, he was unfortunately disappointed.

Commenting on Jefferson's tireless labors for the cultural and scientific interests of his native country during his embassy in Paris, the *Edinburgh Review* wrote: "Every thing he sees seems to suggest to him the question whether it can be made useful in America." The *Review* advised a similar assiduity in the diplomatic representatives of England.[18] For similar efforts at home Jefferson received widespread recognition from his contemporaries (see Chapter 10).

And, indeed, Jefferson's plans and promotional activities in the interest of his country were endless. In a letter to George Washington, in speaking of his project to bring Genevan scientists to Virginia, Jefferson mentioned Lhuilier, mathematician (whom he rated second only to Lagrange), Senebier, botanist and plant physiologist, Pictet, mathematician, physicist, and meteorologist, the de Saussures, father and son, chemists, naturalists, and geologists, and Prevost, philosopher and physicist. During the War of 1812 he hopefully predicted that British science would migrate to America as Britain crumbled. Jefferson also wished to bring to America the artisan he met in Paris who had devised standardized parts for the making of firearms.

Jefferson's patriotism differed from the narrower, more provincial type that characterized nineteenth-century

America. He recognized the necessity for America's kee
ing abreast of the intellectual currents of Europe. "Science," he wrote in 1821, "is more important in a republican
than in any other government. And in an infant country
like ours, we must much depend for improvement on the
science of other countries, longer established, possessing
better means, and more advanced than we are. To prohibit
us from the benefit of foreign light, is to consign us to long
darkness." Hence, though he had earlier advocated some
import duties on books, he later feared that too high a tax
—or any tax at all—would make most books unavailable "to
the practical man when he wishes a recurrence to them for
the uses of life." He was always delighted, he told Dr.
Wistar, to see America's capable sons "emulating the
European quarter in its brightest ornament"—science.

While abroad, Jefferson served as a one-man information
bureau, to keep America abreast of European science. His
letters provided a rich source of scientific information to
his friends back home. They covered virtually every scientific and technological development in Europe, from "a
cheap method of extricating inflammable air from pitcoal"
to speculation on the volcanoes on the moon. He was scientific correspondent to the presidents of Harvard, Yale, and
William and Mary. The latter wrote him: "It is certainly
of great importance to us to know what is done in the
philosophical World:—but our Means of Information are
confined almost entirely to you."

In a letter to the Reverend Madison, from Paris, dated
October 2, 1785, Jefferson described a new fire engine built
in Paris, epitomized and discussed the contents of certain
leading French scientific journals, passed on the latest information on the planet Herschel had discovered, along
with the most recent count of the number of double stars
in the heavens, spoke of new developments in aeronautics,
and described the propelling of a boat by a screw turning

against the air, and a "machine for copying letters at a single stroke." The subjects dealt with in a letter to President Willard of Harvard (March 24, 1789) included a French translation of the seventh book of Ptolemy's *État des étoiles fixes au second siecle,* "the designation of the same stars by Flamstead and Beyer, and their position in the year 1786"; Lagrange's *Mechanique analytique;* the Italian naturalist and physiologist Spallanzani's "On Digestion and Generation" ("valuable," Jefferson thought); Clavigero's *History of Mexico* (which, he pointed out, corrects the errors of the Scotch historian Robertson); the delay in the publication of de la Lande's fifth volume; "the chemical dispute over the conversion and reconversion of air and water"; new chemical nomenclature (which Jefferson argued against); Tom Paine's iron bridge (which should be much cheaper than stone and capable of a greater arch); Rumsey's latest steam-power devices; and finally, the promotion of scientific studies in America.

Jefferson also sent to America, sometimes by request, the latest European scientific publications. To John Bartram he sent a new edition of Linnaeus's *Systema Vegetabilium,*[19] and to Ezra Stiles, President of Yale, a copy of the *Bibliothèque physico-economique,* the *Connaissance des temps* for the years 1781, 1784, 1785, 1786, 1787 (Jefferson remarks that even in such old almanacs one finds "some of the most precious things in astronomy," and analyzes the value of the contents). To David Rittenhouse went a "dissertation, by De la Sauvagere, on the spontaneous growth of shells," issues of the *Connaissance des temps,* and a copy of Fourcroy's work on chemistry. Issues of the *Encyclopédie* also went to Monroe, Franklin, and numerous others. Three boxes of books were sent to the Reverend Madison, Franklin, and William Hay. To the College of Philadelphia Jefferson sent the *Bibliothèque physico-economique;* and two trunks of books went to William and Mary College. To his friend Ralph Izard of South Carolina went the prospectus of an engineering school in Paris. The list could go on and on.

Mechanical devices, along with gifts of a more personal nature, were also despatched on the hazardous ocean voyage to America. To a lady Jefferson humorously offered to fill a "box with caps, bonnets, &c." from a stylish French house. The latest thing in matches, a new watch, a pocket telescope, a walking stick, a chemical box, a portable copying machine, and a pedometer (one of Jefferson's delights) went to Madison; spectacles to his friend Charles Bellini (three or four pair adapted to the different periods of life, each marked with a number); crayons to Francis Hopkinson; and new lamps to R. H. Lee and Charles Thomson.

Of apparatus or pieces of machinery that he could not send over he managed to get all the pertinent facts, usually examining it personally and making mental or written notes. In Italy, he inspected the rice machine in use there, with the intention of increasing America's rice production. He also advised American tourists to keep their eyes open for whatever might be useful for adoption in the United States. In a set of "Travelling Notes for Mr. Rutledge and Mr. Shippen, June 3, 1788," Jefferson instructed them to look into (the order is his): Agriculture, mechanical arts—"so far as they respect things necessary in America, and inconvenient to be transported thither ready-made, such as forges, stone quarries, boats, bridges, (very especially,) etc. etc."—lighter mechanical arts, manufactures, gardens, architecture ("worth great attention" for its usefulness), painting and statuary, politics and law courts.

He hoped to see samples of the whole world's agricultural productions tested in the United States for suitability to soil and climate. Among the hundreds of foreign agricultural products he thought might be thus adapted and which he often personally helped to introduce are cane, coffee, oil, wine, vetch, various grasses, Siberian barley, melons, peaches, Jerusalem wheat (to resist the Hessian fly), better varieties of corn, the yellow-flowered locust, cork oaks (he himself brought back a cork seedling from Paris, but it died), pistachio nuts, almonds, figs, grapes, improved turnips, broccoli, cauliflower, South American pumpkins, kale from Germany, large Jamaican lima beans, the Tahitian mulberry, lupinella from Italy, potatoes from Liverpool, various seeds from Mexico, Spanish broom, Jerusalem artichokes, the breadfruit tree, seven hundred species of seeds from France, another group of 107 species of grains, cereals, trees, and legumes, also from France (these last two lots from his old friend André Thouin, director of the French National Garden)—a complete catalogue would appear endless.[20] Jefferson distributed these all over the country, to friends, to people recommended to him, to skilled gardeners, to societies.

He was equally interested in indigenous agricultural products that might be developed to bring America abundance and make her independent of foreign importations. From seed brought back from the Lewis and Clark expedition he himself grew plants in his gardens at Monticello. Others he sent to well-known professional gardeners, for experimental cultivation.

Jefferson particularly desired to introduce the olive to America. "Of all the gifts of heaven to man," he said, "it is next to the most precious, if it be not the most precious. Perhaps it may claim a preference even to bread, because there is such an infinitude of vegetables, which it renders a proper and comfortable nourishment." He saw in olive oil a great future source of wealth for all America and a boon to the poor in particular. The failure of his long and persistent efforts to grow it in South Carolina and Georgia was one of his major disappointments. He had a number of trees sent to the South Carolina Agricultural Society, wrote numerous letters to stimulate interest, arranged for a Frenchman near Marseilles to grow young, well-grafted trees and ship them annually to America, gave specific directions for their packing and shipment—but the venture failed.

Jefferson also promoted the growing of upland mountain rice in America, as a means of increasing America's agricultural income and avoiding the unhealthful conditions of lowland rice growing. Having read that the upland rice raised in Africa had originated in Cochin China, he arranged with a prince from that country, whom he met in France, to send him some Cochin China rice. The prince failed him and Jefferson arranged with a ship's captain to get him some rice from Africa—a thirty-gallon cask of it. This he divided between the South Carolina Agricultural Society and some Georgia planters. It proved only moderately successful. Jefferson, who tried some at Monticello, gave up because of difficulties with husking.

He was more successful with rice grown in northern Italy. While on his trip into south France and the Piedmont section of Italy, in 1787, Jefferson examined the rice-cleaning machine used in Italy and found it "absolutely the same as ours." From this he concluded that American rice was inferior not because of its processing but because of the quality of the seed. So he decided to get some Piedmont rice—despite the law prohibiting "the exportation of rough rice on pain of death." He brought out as much rice as his "coat and surtout pockets would hold"—and "took measure with a muleteer to run a couple of sacks across the Appennines to Genoa." Jefferson sent this rice to America, and was pleased when it turned out successful.

His own evaluation of these efforts is to be seen in the estimate he made of his life achievements not long after he returned from France. Along with such accomplishments as the Declaration of Independence and the establishment of religious freedom in Virginia, he listed his importation of olive trees and dry rice to America. "The greatest service which can be rendered any country," he

concluded, "is to add an useful plant to its culture; especially, a bread grain; next in value to bread is oil."

Jefferson also sought to introduce Algiers bantams to
America, and rabbits, partridges, pheasants, and other birds
from Europe, especially the nightingale, which he called a
"delicious bird" (in a purely aesthetic sense!), and exclaimed, "what a bird the nightingale would be in the climates of America! we must colonize him thither. . . ."[21]
On the ship taking him to Paris in 1784, Jefferson arranged
with an English fellow passenger to send to America hares,
rabbits, pheasants, and partridges. (The creatures died en
route.) Jefferson also advised his American traveling com-
panions, Shippen and Rutledge, to keep an eye out for
"Useful and agreeable animals which might be transported
to America." He was among those who wished to introduce into America good strains of European hogs and
Merino sheep.

V I I

It was also a principle of Jefferson's that government
should be made useful to science and science should be
made useful to government. Through government, science
should be made useful to society.

Using the term *science* both broadly and specifically, he
declared that "science is important to the preservation of
our republican government, and that it is also essential to
its protection against foreign power. . . ." Though primarily an advocate of States' Rights and fearful of the
consequences of centralized government, Jefferson felt dif-
ferently about governmental diffusion of cultural and scientific knowledge and the employment of science and men
of science for the national good. In his letter to President
Willard of Harvard on the teaching of science to college
students, he wrote that we older men "have spent the prime
of our lives in procuring them the precious blessing of

liberty. Let them spend theirs in showing that it is the great parent of *science* and of virtue; and that a nation will be great in both, always in the proportion as it is free."

Freedom with Jefferson, it should be re-emphasized, included freedom of scientific investigation. Government was to use and encourage science—but never to interfere with the freedom of the scientist to arrive at independent and unrestricted conclusions supported by proper scientific observation and experiment.

He wrote George Washington that "liberty can never be safe but in the hands of the people themselves," and in accepting the presidency of the American Philosophical Society he expressed his "ardent desire to see knowledge so disseminated through the mass of mankind, that it may at length reach even the extremes of society, beggars and kings." But the people must have highly competent leaders. To that end Jefferson advocated not only the education of the masses, but the selection and training by the state, in all the higher reaches of knowledge, nature's *aristoi,* her geniuses. With Joel Barlow he planned a national university. To Du Pont de Nemours he wrote that the national government would probably have to erect such an institution "on the comprehensive basis of all the useful sciences." Jefferson's definition of utility, as we have seen, included social utility in political, legal, cultural, and moral fields. But more than any great political leader of his day in America, Jefferson called for attention to science. In his own state-supported institution he saw to that.

Science came high on Jefferson's list of those branches of learning and activity in which he thought government should take a direct hand. The "introduction of new cultures, and especially of objects of leading importance to our comfort, is certainly worthy the attention of every government, and nothing short of the actual experiment should discourage an essay of which any hope can be entertained."

Recognizing the national benefits of a survey of America's coastal waters, he recommended such a survey to Congress in 1806. This proposal was not implemented during his administration, but his sponsorship led to future surveys. In his promotion of the exploration of the western parts of North America, Jefferson's interest was largely expansionist, but it was also scientific. While Ambassador to France, he persuaded the explorer John Ledyard to seek a passage eastward from the West Coast of America. Arrangements had been made for Ledyard's transit through Russia and he was well along on his journey when Catherine the Great changed her mind and had Ledyard arrested. In 1792, while Secretary of State, Jefferson secured the backing of the American Philosophical Society for an expedition by the French botanist André Michaux, to which he personally subscribed money. This also fell through, Michaux being recalled by his government when he reached Kentucky. But the notable explorations of Freeman, Pike, and Lewis and Clark all took place during Jefferson's Presidency.

Jefferson's scientific interests are reflected in the instructions he drew up for his explorers. Michaux was to study the soil, rivers, mountains, products, and inhabitants of the country he traversed, and—two of Jefferson's favorite preoccupations—the language of the Indians and traces of the "mammoth." This latter was "particularly recommended," along with information as to "whether the Lama or Paca of Peru, is found in those parts of this continent, or how far north they come." Before Meriwether Lewis started on his famous expedition, Jefferson had him go to Philadelphia, to be instructed in astronomy (for ascertainment of "the geography of the country with the precision desired"), botany, mineralogy, zoology, and "Indian history." Lewis's instructions went on:

Other objects worthy of notice will be, the soil and face of the country, its growth and vegetable productions, especially those not of the United States, the animals of the country generally, and especially those not known in the United States; the remains and accounts of any which may be deemed rare or extinct; the mineral productions of every kind, but particularly metals, limestone, pit-coal and salt petre; salines and mineral waters, noting the temperature of the last, and such circumstances as may indicate their character; volcanic appearances; climate, as characterized by the thermometer, by the proportion of rainy, cloudy, and clear days, by lightning, hail, snow, ice, by the access and recess of frost, by the winds prevailing at different seasons, the dates at which particular plants put forth or lose their flower or leaf, times of appearance of particular birds, reptiles or insects. . . .

Lewis also received the following humane instructions concerning his relations with the Indian tribes he should meet: "Carry with you some matter of the kine pox; inform those of them with whom you be, of its efficacy as a preservative from the small pox; and instruct and encourage them in the use of it. This may be especially done wherever you winter."

Jefferson's concern that technological progress be made available to the masses led him, as we have seen, to seek such government control of patents as to prevent their becoming permanent monopolies of individuals.

Jefferson's feeling about the interrelations of science and government may be seen in his own close reliance upon scientists and scientific societies such as David Rittenhouse and the American Philosophical Society, while he was Secretary of State. He secured Rittenhouse's aid in his work upon coins, weights, and measures. As we have seen he called upon members of the American Philosophical Society in deciding a patent grant on a process for developing fresh water from salt water. While President he lent Charles Willson Peale a Navy pump to remove water from excavations for "mammoth" bones. During

the Embargo Jefferson issued special permits for the importation of Merino sheep. In every public office he held
he used the American diplomatic corps for the exchange
of seeds and plants, and he used government vessels for
similar purposes. Even during the Embargo permission
was granted for the use of the *Mentor* to bring over "a
valuable machine which spins cotton, wool, and flax
equally."

In smaller ways we catch glimpses of Jefferson the
statesman submerged in Jefferson the scientist. On receiving a package of seed from Paris, he "franked" it and
sent it to the Botanical Garden of New York. While Ambassador to France he sent acorns of the cork oak to
members of Congress, and while President he personally
distributed to members of Congress some Gloucester hick-
ory nuts he had gotten from the Osage Indians.[22] There
was no end to his efforts to distribute the good things of
the world, both privately and officially.

V I I I

Unlike many eighteenth-century progressivists, Jefferson was no radical visionary, blandly ignoring discouraging
realities. Yet his ideas were founded on the optimistic
belief that the "light which has been shed on the mind
of man through the civilized world, has given it a new
direction, from which no human power can divert it."
He saw America headed rapidly toward "destinies beyond
the reach of mortal eye." Through America's example and
indirect influence he believed that democracy—the *sine
qua non* of progress—was destined to become the leading
form of government in all Europe and South America.

Similar beliefs in progress were entertained by many
of his contemporaries, some to a lesser, some to a greater,
degree. Among the former were Ben Franklin and John

Adams; among the latter, Ethan Allen, Elihu Palmer, Philip Freneau, Joel Barlow, and Tom Paine. Democratic America was also idealized abroad, particularly in France.

Behind Jefferson's progressivist hopes and his faith in democracy was his belief in man's "reason" and "moral sense." As an instrument signifying the "intelligence," the reason was capable of progressive advancement; from this would result a continued progress in such phases of society as science, technology, and an enlightened leadership necessary for good government. As an instrument capable of making common-sense or easy intuitive inductions, the reason guaranteed a continuous substratum of social morality and universal, elemental wisdom derived from "self-evident" natural moral principles.

But it was chiefly in the substantive faculty designated as the "moral sense" that Jefferson saw the moral basis of society. He regarded it both as a judicial faculty and as an emotional urge toward altruism and useful social conduct. The Stoics, said Jefferson, erred in stressing merely the suppression of all individual passion; hence "the moderns are far advanced beyond them in this line of science." In any case all conduct is to be judged by its "*utility* to man."

In the individual, restraint of evil passions, cultivation of the moral sense, and the effects of education, Jefferson thought, would assure the progress of private morality. But individual perfectability will proceed "to an indefinite . . . not to an infinite degree." The *aristoi*—nature's aristocracy of virtue and talent, capable of the highest development of the intelligence, "reason," and moral sense— would serve as models.

To attain the utmost in human happiness, Jefferson sought to stimulate every type of human endeavor through education and the accumulation of knowledge. He also sought an increasing use of deeds rather than creeds in religion for the furtherance of social harmony through altruistic service to others; and he emphasized the maintenance and perfection of the democratic state as the only form of government which permits the full expression of individual potentialities and advances human happiness.

Upon such moral, educational, religious, and political foundations did Jefferson base his confidence in the value of science and technology. Jefferson always posited material progress upon a sound moral and democratic way of life.[23]

3

Inventions

•

As we have seen, whenever opportunity presented itself in his travels, Jefferson inspected the latest inventions and, where possible, talked with the inventor. He continuously took notes of mechanical devices and filled his memoranda and letters with news of technological progress. He loved to handle tools, made some inventions himself, and altered others to suit his needs. Returning from England to Paris in 1786, he secured permission from the French government to bring in, among other articles, "A box containing small tools for wooden & iron work, for my own amusement." [1] Jefferson's moments of leisure were often devoted to tinkering.

In a letter to Robert Fulton in 1810 he wrote: "I am not afraid of new inventions or improvements, nor bigoted to the practices of our forefathers. . . . Where a new invention is supported by well-known principles, and promises to be useful, it ought to be tried." Three years later he expressed a "wish to see new inventions encouraged and old ones brought again into useful notice." He favored ingenious, cheap, small mechanical devices "applicable to our daily concerns." He considered labor-saving machinery peculiarly suitable to the United States, "a country where there is more to do than men to do it." Among the things he planned for in the educational system of Virginia was a proliferation of "the useful arts," of "inventions for saving labor and increasing our comforts."

One of the most spectacular scientific events of Jefferson's day was man's first conquest of the air by means of balloons. On June 5, 1783, the brothers Joseph and Etienne Montgolfier, of Annonay, France, gave a public demonstration of a balloon filled with ordinary air rarefied by heating. The balloon rose to about six thousand feet. On August 27, the physicist J. A. C. Charles inflated a balloon with hydrogen and sent it up from the Champ de Mars, in Paris. In October the French scientist J. F. Pilâtre de Rozier made the first flight ever performed by man. He went up eighty feet in a captive Montgolfier-type balloon and stayed up over four minutes. About five weeks later (November 21) de Rozier and a fellow passenger, the Marquis d'Arlandes, made the first flight into the air in a free balloon filled with air. They flew about five and a half miles over Paris and landed outside the city. On the first of December, the physicist Charles and a passenger flew twenty-seven miles in a hydrogen-filled balloon. The world was in a ferment over these spectacular events, and in France the excitement was tremendous. There were nearly a half million "awe-stricken" spectators of the flight of de Rozier and d'Arlandes. Benjamin Franklin wrote to a friend from Paris, on December 16, 1783: "We think of nothing here at present but of Flying; the balloons engross all attention."

Even before Jefferson's departure in July, 1784 to serve as Ambassador to France, American interest in balloons had begun. His friend Francis Hopkinson wrote from

Philadelphia, on March 31, 1784: "Congress imagined that when they removed to Annapolis to *pout* we should all be in deep Distress—& for every Pout return a Sigh—but the Event is far otherwise—the Name of Congress is almost forgotten—& for one Person that will mention that respectable Body, a hundred will talk of an Air baloon." In May Hopkinson wrote Jefferson describing the release of several balloons in Philadelphia "to the great Amusement of the Spectators—they rose twice or perhaps three times the Height of the Houses, & then gently descended, without Damage; they were open at Bottom, & of Course, the Gas soon wasted. . . ." Hopkinson was, he added, "contriving a better Method of filling them." In Philadelphia before proceeding to Boston to take ship for Europe, Jefferson himself had had the "pleasure" of seeing three balloons ascend. "The largest," he wrote to James Monroe, "was of 8 feet diameter and ascended about 300 feet."

Like others, Jefferson speculated on the international effects of the balloon. In a semi-humorous vein he wrote to Hopkinson from France on February 18, 1784, that balloons "really begin to assume a serious face. The Chevalr Luzerne communicated to me a letter received from his brother who mentions one which he had seen himself. The persons who ascended in it regulated its height at about 3000 feet, and passed with the wind about 6 miles in 20 minutes, when they chose to let themselves down, tho' they could have traveled triple the distance. [This was the flight of de Rozier and d'Arlandes, November 21, 1783.] This discovery seems to threaten the prostration of fortified works unless they can be closed above, the destruction of fleets & what not. The French may now run their laces, wines &c to England duty free. The whole system of British statutes made on the supposition of goods being brought into some port must be revised. Inland countries may become *maritime* states unless you chuse rather to call them *aerial* ones as their commerce is in future to be carried on

through that element—But jesting apart I think this discovery may lead to things useful. For instance there is no
longer a difficulty how Congress may move backwards &
forwards. . . ." [2]

Jefferson's correspondence from France kept his friends
informed of the progress in ballooning. To Francis Hopkinson he sent word of the successful crossing of the English Channel by Blanchard and John Jeffries on January 7,
1785. He informed several friends of the fall and death of
de Rozier and Romain in their attempted Channel crossing
in June of that year. Jefferson feared this would "probably
damp the ardor with which aerial navigation has been
pursued . . . and deter very many from the experiments
they would have been disposed to make." He was confident
that means of controlling the rise and descent of the balloon without loss of gas or air and of steering the balloon
while in flight would be found. He followed and passed the
news on to his friends of every experiment for solving this
"great desideratum in the use of the balloon." We "may
certainly expect that this desideratum will be found," he
wrote to Charles Thomson in October, 1785. "As the birds
& fish prove that the means exist, we may count on human
ingenuity for its discovery."

To his friend, the Reverend James Madison, President
of William and Mary, he described efforts to extract "inflammable air" (hydrogen) from pit coal, which would reduce the cost of ballooning. He also thought a screw
propeller he had seen demonstrated on the Seine might
be "used also for the balloon." He described it as "a very
large screw, the thread of which was a thin plate two feet
broad applied by it's edge spirally round a small axis. It
somewhat resembled a bottle brush if you will suppose the
hairs of the bottle brush joining together & forming a spiral
plane. This, turned on it's axis, in the air, carried the
vessel across the Seine." There was so much loss of power

that Jefferson thought it might be better to apply the screw to the water itself.

In return Jefferson's correspondents reported aeronautical progress in America. The Reverend Madison informed him of the flights of small balloons at Williamsburg filled with hydrogen, and of larger ones, about twenty feet in diameter, filled with heated air. Madison suggested scientific uses for balloons such as ascertaining the density and temperature of the air at different altitudes, "Propagation of Sound, Descent of Bodies," and so forth. He also felt that these "aerostatic Machines" might in time "be applied to other purposes than as mere philosophical Experiments." Unless a way to conserve gas and to steer the balloon could be found another correspondent, Charles Thomson (in a letter written in 1786) feared that, in time, the balloon would "only furnish a figure in poetry or Oratory, like Phaeton's attempt to guide the Chariot of the Sun." "The people of Europe and America," he continued, "seem to be pursuing different amusements. While the former are diverting themselves with bubbles of air and quarreling with one another for toys and rattles, the latter are employed in the encrease of their Species & providing the means of subsistance [sic]."

Jefferson, then Secretary of State, had an opportunity to see the flight of the famous French aeronaut Jean Pierre Blanchard from the Walnut Street Prison Court, Philadelphia, January 9, 1793. With an American, Dr. John Jeffries, Blanchard had set the world agog by flying across the English Channel. He had made forty-four flights in Europe, in Hamburg, Leipzig, Berlin, Warsaw, and Vienna, as well as in France.

The entire country appears to have been excited over Blanchard's venture, thousands of spectators lined the streets of Philadelphia on the morning of the flight. According to Dr. Benjamin Rush, many "had come from New York, Baltimore, and other distant parts. . . . The city was so crowded that it was difficult for strangers to get lodgings at taverns, and the theatre was so crowded this evening that several hundred people returned without getting in." Cannon began firing at dawn on the ninth and continued every quarter hour until the ascent. President George Washington arrived at nine o'clock and was saluted by fifteen guns. Inflation of the showy yellow silk bag began, accompanied by music from a band. Governor Mifflin introduced Blanchard to the President, who presented the flier with an aerial passport recommending "to all citizens of the United States and others that in his passage, descent, return, or journey elsewhere, they oppose no hindrance or molestation to the said Blanchard: and that on the contrary, they receive and aid him with that humanity and good will which may render honor to their country and justice to an individual so distinguished by his efforts to establish and advance his art in order to make it useful to all mankind." [3]

At five minutes past ten the balloon was released and away went Blanchard and the small black dog which accompanied him. According to William Dunlap's *American Daily Advertiser,* when the balloon began to rise "the majestical sight was truly awful and interesting,—the slow movement of the band added solemnity to the scene." Blanchard, "dressed in a plain blue suit, a cock'd hat and white feathers," waved the colors of France and the flag of the United States and "flourished his hat to the thousands of citizens from every part of the country who stood gratified and astonished at his intrepidity." Dr. Rush thought the sight "truly sublime." When Blanchard appeared above the Walnut Street Prison walls, Dr. Rush recorded, "there was an universal cry of, 'Oh! Oh! Good voyage!' &c. from several thousand spectators. . . ." [4]

Down the road galloped several gentlemen on horseback in an effort to follow Blanchard in his flight. But these were soon lost sight of by the aeronaut. Blanchard's trip carried him a distance of fifteen miles. He landed in a little woods east of Woodbury, New Jersey, after forty-six minutes in the air. His maximum altitude had been 5,812 feet. During his flight he had made several observations of a scientific nature which a number of friends had commissioned him to do. He had filled bottles with the air of the upper region; he had counted his pulse beat at different heights; he had tested the power of the loadstone at higher altitudes; he had made barometric readings; and he had noted variations in temperature. Then he had "strengthened" his stomach "with a morsel of biscuit and a glass of wine." By six-thirty that night Blanchard was back in Philadelphia. He paid his respects to Washington, thanked him for his passport, which had been of considerable service to him, and presented him with the colors of France, "which he politely accepted, and thereby acquired a fresh claim to my gratitude," Blanchard recorded in his *Journal*.[5] Thus ended the first successful flight of man in America.

Jefferson seems to have had little to say about this great venture, though it roused a wish for a balloon in which he might escape the turmoils of public life to the retirement of his beloved Monticello. To his daughter Martha he wrote: "We were entertained here lately with the ascent of Mr. Blanchard in a balloon. The security of the thing appeared so great, that everybody is wishing for a balloon to travel in. I wish for one sincerely, as instead of ten days, I should be within five hours of home."

Jefferson's earlier interest in the balloon had led him to some speculations which he had set down in 1784. He had enumerated these possibilities of future usefulness: "1. transportation of commodities under certain circumstances. 2. traversing deserts, countries possessed by an enemy or ravaged by infectious disorders, pathless and inaccessible mountains. 3. conveying intelligence into a besieged place, or perhaps enterprising on it, reconnoitering an army, etc.

4. throwing new lights on the thermometer, barometer, hygrometer, rain, snow, hail, wind and other phenomena of which the Atmosphere is the theatre. 5. the discovery of the Pole which is but one day's journey in a balloon, from where the ice has hitherto stopped adventures. . . ."

But as the years went by and ardent expectations of the balloon's usefulness failed to materialize, Jefferson's interest in aeronautics, like that of others, faded before the seemingly insoluble problem of controlling the flight of a balloon. Some three years before he died, he replied to an inquirer: "That there are means of artificial buoyancy by which man may be supported in the air, the balloon has proved, and that means of directing it may be discovered is against no law of nature, and is therefore possible as in the case of birds. But to do this by mechanical means alone in a medium so rare and unresisting as air must have the aid of some principle not yet generally known." All was not hopeless—but it would have to be left up to future generations to solve the problem.

More fruitful was Jefferson's interest in dry docks. His plans for these reflect his concern for economy, particularly where the Navy was concerned, and his tendency to modify mechanical devices to specific needs. During his presidency there was considerable controversy over expanding the American Navy, to which Jefferson's contribution was a proposal for the use of dry docks, in which he thought it possible to keep a navy in preservation for years and ready for instant launching during war, thereby cutting down expenses.

In Venice he reported, "there were then ships, lying on their original stocks, ready for launching at any moment, which had been so for eighty years, and were still in a state of perfect preservation; and that this was effected by disposing of them in docks pumped dry, and kept so by constant pumping. It occurred to me that this expense of constant pumping might be saved by combining a lock with the common wet dock, wherever there was a running stream of water, the bed of which, within a reasonable distance, was of a sufficient height above the high-water level of the harbor. This was the case at the navy yard, on the eastern branch at Washington, the high-water line of which was seventy-eight feet lower than the ground on which the Capitol stands, and to which it was found that the water of the Tyber creek could be brought for watering the city. My proposition then was as follows: Let *a b* be the high-water level of the harbor, and the vessel to be laid up draw eighteen feet water. Make a chamber A twenty feet deep below high water and twenty feet high above it, as *c d e f,* and at the upper end make another chamber, B, the bottom of

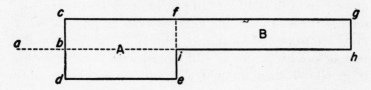

which should be in the high-water level, and the tops twenty feet above that. *g h* is the water of the Tyber. When the vessel is to be introduced, open the gate at *c b d.* The tide-water rises in the chamber A to the level *b i,* and floats the vessel in with it. Shut the gate *c b d* and open that of *f i.* The water of the Tyber fills both chambers to the level *c f g,* and the vessel floats into the chamber B; then opening both gates *c b d* and *f i,* the water flows out, and the vessel settles down on the stays previously prepared at the bottom *i h* to receive her. The gate at *g h* must of course be closed, and the water of the feeding stream be diverted elsewhere. The chamber B is to have a roof over it of the construction of that over the meal market at Paris, except that that is hemispherical, this semi-cylindrical."

It was obviously possible, Jefferson explained, to have chamber B large enough to accommodate several vessels at a time. In this and similar dry docks elsewhere, Jefferson proposed to have "a proper number of vessels always ready to be launched, with nothing unfinished about them, except the planting their masts, which must of necessity be omitted, to be brought under a roof."

Jefferson had a model of his dry dock made and exhibited at the Presidential Mansion for inspection by members of Congress. His plans were referred to a committee of which his friend, Dr. Samuel L. Mitchill of New York, was chairman. This group's favorable report was killed by Congress. Great was the ridicule heaped upon Jefferson for such a "visionary," "philosophical," and generally "impractical" idea. In a letter to Tench Coxe written in 1807 Jefferson had declared that "there ought never to be another ship built until we can provide some method of preserving them through the long intervals of peace which I hope are to be the lot of our country." And in 1825, the year before his death, he still looked with favor upon his proposal. "I then thought and still think the measure wise," he wrote.

Jefferson's plans to keep larger vessels in a partial state of completion in dry docks are also reflected in his ideas for the use of gunboats for coastal and river defense. Here too economy was a consideration. He wrote to Tom Paine (who was also interested in gunboats and had sent Jefferson a plan and model for a new type): "gunboats are the only *water* defence which can be useful to us, and protect us from the ruinous folly of a navy."

Though his ideas varied under the pressure of events, in 1805 his over-all plans for these relatively inexpensive "floating batteries" envisaged the construction of two hundred and forty over a period of ten years, "unless circumstances should force it sooner." Some were to be kept afloat and fully manned, ready for immediate action. Others were to be kept afloat and partly manned; in times of emergency these would draw the remainder of their crew from the town near which they were stationed. The remainder, by far the greatest number in times of international quiet, were to be kept "Hauled up under a shed, in readiness to be launched and manned by the seamen and militia of the town on short notice."

In a special message to Congress in 1807 Jefferson dwelt on the efficacy of these vessels and their use throughout the navies of the world. He estimated that the United States should build two hundred of them and listed the approximate numbers to be assigned to each important coastal area. He called for the construction of a "proper proportion" of larger-sized gunboats, "such as those heretofore built," and of a residue of smaller vessels, "less furnished for accommodation, and consequently less costly." In times of world peace "it would not be proposed that more than six or eight of these vessels should be kept afloat." He repeated his previous plans for manning them, and again insisted that at all times "those unemployed would be withdrawn into places not exposed to sudden enterprise, hauled up under sheds from the sun and weather, and kept in preservation with little expense for repairs or maintenance." Congress appropriated money for construction of a number of gunboats. But Jefferson's ideas for smaller ones, kept under sheds when not in use, again drew abusive criticism.

Jefferson was one of the earliest public figures to see the possibilities of the submarine. We have noted his interest in the possibility of screw propulsion under water, which had further reminded him of the experiments of David Bushnell of Connecticut with underwater craft—"Bushnell's Turtle"—during the American Revolution. In letters to Ezra Stiles and George Washington he asked for all available information about Bushnell's device and attempts to explode vessels beneath their water line. In 1813 he criticized a recent history of the American Navy for not

giving sufficient emphasis to Bushnell's idea. He considered
Bushnell's invention "excellently contrived, and might perhaps, by improvement, be brought into real use."

He commended Fulton's similar ideas for destroying
enemy craft, declaring, in 1813, that he had "more hopes
of the mode of destruction by the submarine boat than any
other." Jefferson saw in the submarine an inexpensive and
effective method of national defense and a means of dis-
pensing with the costs consequent upon maintaining a
large navy. The submarine, he wrote, is "not beyond the
laws of nature; and whatever is within these, is not to be
despaired of. It would be to the United States the consum-
mation of their safety."

Fulton's proposal to protect harbors from enemy naval
craft by what he called "torpedoes"—a kind of underwater
mine—also appealed to Jefferson. Used in conjunction
with the submarine they might be very effective, he
thought. In letters written to Fulton in 1810 he declared
that "torpedoes will be to cities what vaccination has been
to mankind" and hoped "sincerely" that they would become effective in "putting down navies." Jefferson gave
what aid he could to further Fulton's experiments. In 1807
he even expressed a wish to see "a corps of young men
trained to the service." "The very name of a corps of submarine engineers," he wrote to the Secretary of the Navy,
"would be a defense." During the War of 1812 he advised
President Madison to give serious consideration to Fulton's
proposals, which appear to have included the use of "sub-
aqueous guns, torpedoes, or diving boats." To Fulton he
expressed the hope that he would achieve complete success
and that this would come "by the aid of government."

While in France, Jefferson was impressed with the new
developments and future possibilities of steam power.
In letters to his friend Charles Thomson, written in 1786,
he remarked that though the power of steam had long
been known it was but then "beginning to be applied to

the various purposes of which it is susceptible," and stated that he had "little doubt" that it would come to be "applied generally to machines, so as to supersede the use of water ponds, and of course to lay open all the streams for navigation."

While in London, that year, Jefferson singled out, among so much technological progress that he could write "volumes" on it, the application of steam power to a grist mill made by Watt and Boulton. Jefferson wanted to inspect so marvelous a contrivance, but Boulton "made a secret of his mill" and Jefferson was allowed to see it "only superficially." Jefferson came away without knowing whether the mill operated by the direct application of steam power or whether it pumped up water and used this as its power. Nevertheless, he was told that it was turning eight pair of stones, that it consumed one hundred bushels of coal a day, and the use of thirty pair of stones was planned.

When Boulton visited Paris in 1786, Jefferson talked with him about fuel consumption and the advantages of steam over other sources of power. He wrote Thomson that Boulton "compares the effect of steam with that of horses, in the following manner: Six horses, aided with the most advantageous combination of the mechanical powers hitherto tried, will grind six bushels of flour in an hour; at the end of which time they are all in a foam, and must rest. They can work thus, six hours in the twenty-four, grinding thirty-six bushels of flour, which is six to each horse, for the twenty-four hours. His steam mill in London consumes one hundred and twenty bushels of coal in twenty-four hours, turns ten pair of stones, which grind eight bushels of flour an hour each, which is nineteen hundred and twenty bushels in the twenty-four hours. This makes a peck and a half of coal perform exactly as much as a horse, in one day, can perform." Such statistics must have confirmed Jefferson in his previous feeling that America, with its abundance of fuel, was likely to make extensive use of this new source of power.

Jefferson did not, however, envisage the inauguration, through steam, of a great industrial revolution in America, accompanied by the growth of factories, the expansion of cities, and a reduced role for agriculture. He thought of steam power in an accessory role—in navigation (as in Fulton's steamboats in which he saw a "permanent blessing" to America), grist mills, small home manufactures, and the relief of household chores and other forms of drudgery, and perhaps partly to free man for agricultural pursuits. In a letter to George Fleming, in 1815, Jefferson explains that he is not competent to comment upon the technical problems involved in Fleming's idea for modifying the steam engine. He has not, he says, been able to keep up with technological progress in this field. However, he likes Fleming's idea because, besides the apparent correctness and soundness in its calculations, it combines the "valuable properties of simplicity, cheapness and accommodation to the small and more numerous calls of life." Such an engine should prove of great importance because "a smaller agent, applicable to our daily concerns, is infinitely more valuable than the greatest which can be used only for great objects."

Jefferson himself had once conceived a device which might be useful and economical—a small steam engine attached to a "common pot" or to a "cistern" at the back of the chimney. While the kitchen fires were burning, the steam thus generated would "give a stroke from time to time" to the engine. Water thus pumped from a well to the top of the house could be stored in tanks to supply running water to all the different rooms of the house for ordinary family use, and serve as a "resource against fire." Jefferson thought his scheme might have other applications, which he listed in a letter of 1815: ". . . to wash the linen, knead the bread, beat the hominy, churn the butter, turn the spit, and do all other household offices which require only a regular mechanical motion." Furthermore, the "unproductive hands now necessarily employed in these might then increase the produce of our fields." "Of how much more value would this be to ordinary life," Jefferson declared, "than Watts and Boulton's [*sic*] thirty pair of mill-stones to be turned by one engine. . . ." Jefferson sought to interest the American inventor James Rumsey ("the most original and the greatest mechanical genius" Jefferson had ever seen) in this scheme, along with the statesman, mechanical virtuoso, and steamboat magnate, Robert R. Livingston (partner of Robert Fulton).

In his travels in Europe, wherever he was intrigued with what he saw, Jefferson set down careful descriptions. He made the following notation after a visit to Kew:

Kew. Archimedes' screw for raising water. A horizontal shaft made to turn the oblique one of the screw by a patent machinery of this form:

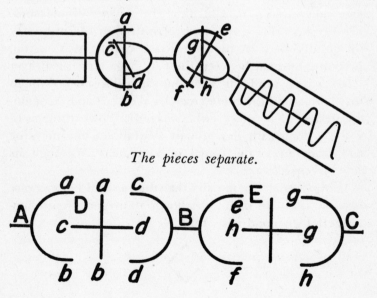

The pieces separate.

A is driven by its shank into the horizontal axis of the wheel which turns the machine.

B is an intermediate iron to connect the motion of A and C.

C is driven by its shank into the axis of the screw.

D is a cross axis, the ends, *a* and *b,* going into the corresponding holes *a* and *b* of the iron A, and the ends, *c* and *d,* going into the corresponding holes *c* and *d* of the iron B.

E is another cross axis, the ends, *e* and *f,* going into the corresponding holes *e* and *f* of the iron B, and the ends, *g* and *h,* going into the corresponding holes *g* and *h* of the iron C.

In Italy he made an elaborate inspection of the local rice machines. In southern France he took notes on wagons and mules. He inspected the famous Canal of Languedoc and after discussing canal locks with Monsieur Pin and others, he suggested to them an idea of his own: the use of "a quadrantal gate, turning on a pivot, and lifted by a lever like a pump handle, aided by a windlass and cord, if necessary." They promised to try it and inform him of the results. Back in Paris, he wrote George Washington, proposing a canal between the Cuyahoga and Big Beaver rivers, which would, he thought, "infallibly turn through the Potomac all the commerce of Lake Erie, and the country west of that, except what may pass down the Mississippi." Along with this he sent Washington the notes he had made upon the Canal of Languedoc "through its whole course."

In Amsterdam he noticed that the joists of houses were placed, "not with their sides horizontally and perpendicularly, but diamond wise, thus:

first, for greater strength; second, to arch between with brick, thus:

"

He was also impressed with windows which opened so as to admit air and not rain. He drew a sketch of them:

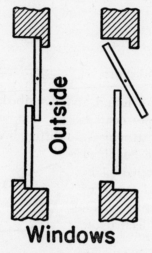

Outside

Windows

He likewise sketched and wrote out directions for using a device for fixing a flagstaff onto the mast of a vessel. Dining tables in Amsterdam also interested him. He found some which would let down "with single or double leaves, so as to take the room of their thickness only with a single leaf when open,

open thus:

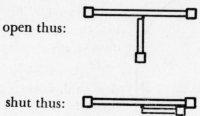

shut thus:

or thus [open]:

or thus [shut]:

double leaves open:

[double leaves] shut:

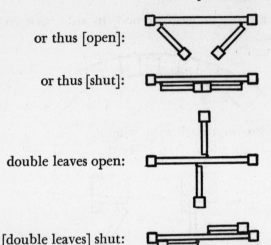

In Holland he also found and described a machine for drawing light empty boats over a dam, a unique use of camels (watertight structures) for lifting boats in the water, wind sawmills (he bought a book full of detailed plans for these), several types of bridges, an interesting aviary, and a "Dutch wheelbarrow . . . in this form":

In Germany he made sketches of ruins, monuments, towers. At Mannheim he took notes on an "economical curtain bedstead" which looked like this (left):

Elsewhere he noted down a peculiar method of twisting stove flues for ornamental purposes. Back in France the crudeness of the plows in use spurred him to design a better one.

Beautiful, convenient, and novel furniture appealed to Jefferson—

and in some cases the more novel the better. Dumb-waiters (in the form of portable stands set between guests at table) were in vogue when Jefferson was in France. He had five at his Paris residence. Since they made servants unnecessary for certain courses, table conversation could go on with fewer interruptions. His introduction of one of these in the Presidential mansion in Washington caused comment.[6]

During Jefferson's first administration, a visitor to the President's residence was shown about by Mrs. Madison. Among the interesting things noted by the visitor was an "odd but useful contrivance for hanging up jackets and breeches on a machine like a turnstile." [7] Another contemporary describes a set of circular shelves so contrived in the wall "that on touching a spring they turned into the room loaded with the dishes placed on them by the servants without the wall." When another visitor lingered over a singular piece of furniture, Jefferson touched a spring upon it and little doors flew open disclosing a goblet of water, a decanter of wine, a plate of light cakes, and a night-taper. The President explained that he used this when he sat up late and did not wish to bother a servant.[8]

In his own home at Monticello, Jefferson indulged his taste for special tables, clocks, desks, chairs, etc. Even in Washington, in the famous unfinished East Room of the President's House, he had kept a set of carpenter's tools and garden implements, "from the use of which he derived much amusement," in the words of a contemporary.[9] At Monticello he appears to have had a kind of workshop which, according to biographer Randall, was originally the eastern extremity of his library. His overseer testified that Jefferson was forever busy upon some plan, diagram, or model. Marie Kimball, a close student of Jefferson's interest in furniture, points out that Jefferson's skilled furniture makers at Monticello made numerous pieces from his drawings. "Jefferson's personal papers," says Mrs.

Kimball, "abound with sketches of tables and chairs, and with minute calculations for their construction. The master of Monticello had, furthermore, a tireless passion for introducing ingenious features into his furniture . . . it may safely be said that any so-called Jeffersonian furniture showing ingenuity of design may very likely have come from Monticello." [10]

One such piece was a revolving or swivel chair, probably made in his own workshops.[11] This novelty became the butt of contemporary satirists. His grandson described another of his devices, "a walking stick . . . composed of three sticks, which being spread out and covered with a piece of cloth made a tolerable seat." He used to carry this little folding stool into Charlottesville with him to sit on while supervising the construction of the University of Virginia. As an extension of his swivel chair Jefferson often used an elongated padded leg rest. Reclining comfortably upon this, as on a chaise longue, he could write upon his special table with a revolving top, constructed to fit over his leg rest. Upon this table he often placed and used his writing device, the polygraph.

Then there were ingenious music stands. One of these could be adjusted to any height desired, or converted into a table. When used as a stand, the slope of its music rack could be slanted to any desired angle; when used as a table, it lay flat. Another music stand sat on top of the music cabinet. This stand was remarkable in that it could revolve and had four racks, any or all of which could be raised or lowered, so that the stand could be used for anything from a solo to a quartet.

Jefferson also had a writing desk, the top of which could be tilted to any angle. When pulled out, its drawer had a special pair of legs to support it. This drawer had a sliding top; thus one could get into the drawer, or avail himself of additional writing surface. Most interesting of all Jefferson's desks was the portable one upon which he wrote the Declaration of Independence. A "writing-box" Jefferson called it. And so it was, in a way. It was a little flat box with a drawer for writing materials. Its folding lid opened up like a book and then tilted slightly to form a convenient writing surface. Jefferson had had this made from his own drawing by the Philadelphia cabinetmaker, Benjamin Randolph, with whom he lodged in 1776.

In 1825, the year before Jefferson's death, his granddaughter, Ellen W. Coolidge, suffered the loss of all her baggage on her way to Boston. Among the things which went down with the ship was a beautiful desk made for her by Jefferson's Negro cabinetmaker, John Hemings. Jefferson sent her and her husband the little desk which we have just described, observing that it "claims no merit of particular beauty. It is plain, neat, convenient, and, taking no more room on the writing table than a moderate quarto volume, it yet displays itself sufficiently for any writing. Mr. Coolidge must do me the favor of accepting this. Its imaginary value will increase with years, and if he lives to my age, or another half-century, he may see it carried in the procession of our nation's birthday, as the relics of the saints are in those of the Church."

Jefferson was among the first in America to use the dumb-waiter in the form of a lift. He had a small one installed in each end of the mantelpiece in his dining room. While empty wine and liquor bottles went down, full ones came up from his cellar below. A panel door neatly closed the aperture in the mantel when the dumb-waiter was not in use. For one of his double glass doors, Jefferson devised and hid in the paneling a mechanism which caused both doors to open automatically when one was used. It was also from his own sketch and specifications that the clock in his study was made. It was constructed in France after Jefferson's return to America, and was a modification of a clock he had owned but had lost through theft.[12]

The famous clock over the main entrance to Monticello was also built to Jefferson's specifications by a Swiss clock-maker in his employ. It had one face inside the house and one on the porch. It was wound once a week and its weights were cannon balls. As one of these moved down the side wall of the room, it passed by plates indicating the days of the week. It contained a bell upon which the hours were struck. Since a ladder was necessary to wind the clock, Jefferson devised one whose uprights were so grooved and the rungs so hinged that it all folded into a single, slender piece.

Another of Jefferson's devices facilitated his meteorological observations. Attached to the weather vane over the east portico of Monticello was a rod which ran down through the roof to a dial placed in the ceiling below. Upon this dial Jefferson could observe the direction of the wind while remaining indoors.

Illustrative of Jefferson's observation and study of technical improvements is a letter of 1812 in which he discusses "fire-proof cielings [sic]." Benjamin Harris had proposed improvements in the fire-proofing of ceilings and had requested Jefferson's opinion of them. Jefferson replied: "I will state to you three kinds of fire-proof cielings which I have known. The first is by planting

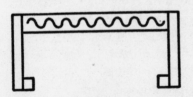

slips of lath on the inside of every joist at bottom laying short planks on these and filling the interval between them & the floor with brick & mortar. this is usual to the Northward under the name of countersealing, and is used in my own house, and has once saved my house by the floor resisting the taking fire from a coat of sawdust spread over it, and burning on it a whole night. the 2.^{d} was that of David Hartley the British minister. he laid, on his sleepers and joists, floors of sheet iron, and a floor of planks close on them, nailing them thro to the joists by holes punched thro the iron. he built a room in the fields near London, & in the presence of the royal family and a great concourse of spectators made a large fire on the lower floor of the room, which burnt out without communicating the fire to the naked planks below or cieling above. I had this revelation from himself. he had a patent for it, and I believe it has been practised in London. the 3.^{d} method I saw in use in Holland. It was nothing but an arch of common brick turned between the joists. your method has the advantage of covering the underside of the joists, and saving the expense of lathing to plaister on."

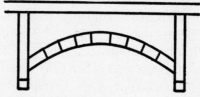

Jefferson sometimes found his beautiful home rather chill. Once, in fact, as he sat writing a letter, the ink froze in his pen. So when he heard of a marvelous improvement in fireplaces made by a Mr. Quincy of New York, who claimed that one-tenth of normal fuel burned only one hour in every five would keep a room at "summer temperature," Jefferson was naturally interested. He wrote to his friend Robert Fulton in his "affection to improvements" to look up Mr. Quincy and his new device. With his friend Benjamin Harris, Jefferson also discussed a new modification in the construction of cisterns which he had devised and built at Monticello.

An interesting Jeffersonian gadget is described by Edmund Bacon, his overseer. It was a machine for measuring one's strength. According to Bacon, few who tried it proved to be stronger than Jefferson's son-in-law Randolph—except Mr. Jefferson himself.

Jefferson collected a veritable museum of instruments, gadgets, and inventions of all kinds, useful to him in his practical pursuits or valued by him because of his scientific interests. The collection included the telescope, magnifying glasses, bifocal spectacles, the thermometer, barometer, artificial horizon (for measuring altitudes of the sun and so forth), lunette (for optical work), quadrant, "a fine theodolite and equatorial both by Ramsden, a Hadley's circle of Borda, a fine meridian," a "pocket sextant of miraculous accuracy, considering its microscopic graduation," a camera obscura, a copying press, a polygraph, an odometer, and a pedometer. Most of these he kept at Monticello.

Jefferson was also keenly interested in advances made in musical instruments, sometimes apparently even more than in the music itself.[13] Mention of the violin, harpsichord, pianoforte, footbass, harmonica, and a kind of metronome and other instruments and musical accessories run in and out of his correspondence. Jefferson was among the first Americans to become interested in the piano, then a novelty. While in Paris, as we have seen, he got an inventor to make him one of his metronomes (if such it may be called). When he tested the pendulum he found it to vibrate 52 times for Largo, 60 for Adagio, 70 for Andante, 95 for Allegro, and 135 for Presto. He encouraged his friend Francis Hopkinson in his efforts to improve the quilling of the harpsichord and to apply the use of keys to and extend the range of the "harmonica," or "musical bells" as they were frequently called.[14] Franklin had devised an ingenious way to use these "musical bells" or glasses partly filled with water and played with wet fingers—a fad of the eighteenth century. Jefferson thought that if Hopkinson succeeded in equipping them with keys the result would be "the greatest present which has been made to the musical world this century, not excepting the Piano-forte." He also eagerly followed Hopkinson's progress on a device to use keys in the playing of bells, an instrument Hopkinson proposed to call the "Bellarmonica," which also, Jefferson thought, would be "a great present to the Musical world." [15]

A gadget that interested Jefferson in Paris was the pedometer. He was so intrigued with it that he sent one to James Madison and, in characteristic fashion, provided minute instructions for its operation. "By Mr. Warville I send your pedometer," he wrote in 1788. "To the loop at the bottom of it, you must sew a tape, and at the other end of the tape, a small hook, (such as we use under the name of hooks and eyes) cut a little hole in the bottom of your left watch pocket, pass the hook and tape through it, and down between the breeches and drawers, and fix the hook on the edge of your knee band, an inch from the knee buckle; then hook the instrument itself by its swivel hook, on the upper edge of the watch pocket. Your tape well adjusted in length, your double steps will be exactly counted by the instrument, the shortest hand pointing out the thousands, the flat hand the hundreds, and the long hand the tens and units. Never turn the hands backward; indeed, it is best not to set them to any given place, but to note the number they stand at when you begin to walk. The adjusting the tape to its exact length is a critical business, and will cost you many trials. But once done, it is done for ever. The best way is, to have a small buckle fixed on the middle of the tape, by which you can take it up, and let it out at pleasure. When you choose it should cease to count, unhook it from the top of the watch pocket, and let it fall down to the bottom of the pocket."

Another instrument for measuring distance which interested Jefferson during his stay in Europe was the odometer. While on his trip to southern France and northern Italy in 1787, he made a note in Milan: "Count del Verme tells me of a pendulum odometer for the wheel of a carriage." Back in Paris he corresponded with Benjamin Vaughan in England about this new instrument. While serving as Secretary of State under Washington, he bought an odometer in Philadelphia for ten dollars before leaving that city for a visit to Monticello, September 2, 1791. With this attached to the wheel of his phaeton, he kept a minute record of the distances between all the towns and villages through which he passed, and so arrived at the exact distance from the nation's capital to his home. Along with this tabulation went notes about the time consumed between the different towns, as well as an account of the country through which he passed and of the places where he lodged and ate.

Arrived at Monticello, he discovered a slight inaccuracy in his odometer. "These measures," he wrote, "were on the belief that the wheel of the Phaeton made exactly 360 revolutions in a mile, but on measuring it accurately at the end of the journey it's circumference was 14 ft. 10½ I. and consequently made made 354.95 revol^{ns} in a mile. these numbers should be greater then in the proportion of 71:72 or a mile added to every 71." Within less than a week after his arrival at Monticello, he had used his odometer to measure one of his "roundabouts" and found it to be .837 of a mile.[16]

During his second administration Jefferson heard of a new and improved odometer made by a Mr. James Clarke. It was built and attached to the carriage in a manner Jefferson had, himself, attempted to perfect but without success. Jefferson immediately got in touch with the inventor, and was soon in possession of one of these newer instruments. Some eleven years later, Clarke was considering patenting his new device and asked Jefferson's opinion. Jefferson had received so much "pleasure and satisfaction" from the one he had that he wrote Clarke an enthusiastic recommendation. He had found it, he stated, "as simple as we can expect such a machine to be . . .

inconsiderable in weight and volume, and of convenient application to the carriage." Furthermore, Jefferson had seen no other odometer like Clarke's either in Europe or America and hence could vouch for its originality. He concluded: "I continue still to use it, finding great satisfaction in having miles announced by the bell as by milestones on the road."

It may well be that the odometer suggested to Jefferson the possibility of constructing "a machine that could lay down the platt of a road by the traveling of a carriage over it." Jefferson gave it up as impracticable, but wrote to Clarke about it. The latter did devise just such an instrument, which was attached to his carriage wheel and with which he surveyed "a triangle of road, about twelve miles in circumference."

Jefferson was the outstanding American advocate of the decimal system used in our coinage. He proposed its adoption, also, for our weights and measures.[17] Interestingly enough, his beloved odometer proved his point, he remarked, in a letter to Thomas Cooper in 1808. "The iron-founder," he explained, "deals in tons; let him take the ton for his unit, and divide it into 10ths, 100ths and 1000ths. The dry-goods merchant deals in pounds and yards; let him divide them decimally. The land-measurer deals in miles and poles; divide them decimally. . . . I have lately had a proof of how familiar this division into dimes, cents, and mills, is to the people when transferred from their money to anything else. I have an odometer fixed to my carriage, which gives the distance in miles, dimes, and cents. The people on the road inquire with curiosity what exact distance I have found from such a place to such a place; I answer, so many miles, so many cents. I find they universally and at once form a perfect idea of the relation of the cent to the mile as a unit. They would do the same as to yards of cloth, pounds of shot, ounces of silver, or of medicine."

Official and private correspondence demanded an excessive amount of both his time and his energies. The older he grew, the more burdensome this became. "From sunrise to one or two o'clock, and often from dinner to dark, I am drudging at the writing-table," he wrote to John Adams in 1817, in an effort to reply to "strangers and others, who, in the most friendly dispositions, oppress me with their concerns, their pursuits, their projects, inventions and speculations, political, moral, religious, mechanical, mathematical, historical, etc., etc., etc." Some years later he counted the letters he had received in a single year and found the total to be 1,267. Answering all these was, Jefferson thought, but to live "the life of a mill-horse, who sees no end to his circle but in death."

Since Jefferson tried to keep duplicate copies he was naturally interested in any duplicating device. Before leaving America for France, he had heard of the copying press, a device by means of which, when the proper ink is used with the original letter and a special kind of paper is then pressed down upon this ink, one can make a copy of what he has written. Finding the larger copying press in Paris not suitable to his needs, Jefferson set about devising a portable one. On his trip to England in 1786, he had one made to his own specifications drawn up after "some experiments." He was delighted with it when it arrived in Paris—so much so that he had several more made right away by a Paris artisan and distributed them to several of his friends, among them James Madison and the Marquis de Lafayette. His press was "in such demand" that the workman had "his hands full," Jefferson reported happily to Madison in 1787. Jefferson continued using his copying press until the latter part of his first term as President. Then he acquired a new writing instrument—the polygraph.

Jefferson was so excited over this new machine that in 1806 he pronounced it "the finest invention of the present age," and considered it "so much superior to the copying machine" that the latter would be discarded by anyone who tried the new device. To a man in public affairs it was "a most precious possession"—a secretary who could not reveal state and personal secrets.

The polygraph was a writing desk with from two to five pens attached to and suspended from a mechanism above the desk in such a way that any movement made by one pen was exactly and simultaneously duplicated by the others. Jefferson used one with two pens; thus he made an original letter and a facsimile for his files. The machine worked, as Jefferson expressed it, "without the least additional embarrassment or exertion to the writer." It was invented by John Hawkins of Philadelphia, close friend of Charles Willson Peale, to whom the inventor turned over his American rights (except for a royalty of ten per cent) before leaving for England in 1803. Both men expected a promising return on this new writing aid, but were greatly disappointed.

A scarcity of customers for the polygraph was not President Jefferson's fault. In fact his vociferous enthusiasm for "these delightful machines" made him one of Peale's best advertising agents. He went so far as to write a testimonial for Peale's use in sales promotion and he suggested their use in the government departments. He often sent friends the duplicates instead of the originals of his letters to demonstrate how good this writing device was. He sent polygraphs to his friends, after trying them out himself. Along with these went glowing statements about this "inestimable invention." In this way they came into the hands, among others, of such people as Constantin Volney, James Bowdoin, United States Minister to Spain, the Bey of Tripoli (a silver-mounted one), and Commodore Edward Preble. Jefferson's secretary also had one.

Jefferson and Peale carried on a continuous correspondence about the polygraph. Jefferson suggested improvements which Peale incorporated in his later models. Jefferson's own inventiveness is to be seen in one of his letters to Peale. He had, he said, adopted Peale's idea of having the polygraph sit on one's writing table in the form of a desk, and not in the form of a box to be closed when not in use. He had also reduced the size, devised a method of guarding against the warping of one of the parts, and a new type of cover. Later he suggested the use of a "double spring" to hold the paper in place; and as late as 1822 he thought Peale might try "a cord of elastic gum" in place of "the spiral springs of silver wire which suspend the penframe." This would be so simple, he felt, that "any bungler" could "prepare & adjust it."

The polygraph has now become a museum piece. But students of history have it to thank for the survival of much of Jefferson's correspondence.[18]

Throughout Jefferson's own writings and those of his contemporaries concerning him, one is struck by the attention given to conveyances, machinery, implements, and so forth, useful in domestic life and manufacture, and to the efficient and progressive conduct of agriculture. There are references to the "cranked-axle" for two-wheeled carriages, the problem of making the axletree turn with the wheel, and the construction of wheel rims from single pieces of wood. There is talk about and plans for constructing or altering carriages, carriage tops, gigs, and wagons; the blacksmith shop, cabinet-making shop, hemp-breaking machine, carding machine, fulling machine, looms with the flying shuttle, cotton gin, spinning jenny, nailery (at one time Jefferson had a very profitable one), gristmill, sawmill, rice mill, benne oil press, and hominy beater. There is interesting information about threshing machines, a box for sowing seed, drills, corncob crushers, corn shellers, a straw-cutting machine, the dynamometer, and the plow. In some cases the object was entirely of

Jefferson's design; in others, it was what was currently available, often altered to suit his own fancy and needs.

"He planned his own carriage, buildings, garden and fences and a good many other things," said his overseer. His carriage, made after he left the Presidency, by his own workmen, was drawn by five fine horses, four pulling the carriage and one ridden by his faithful servant Burwell, behind. It was not the first. On the trip to Philadelphia during which he wrote the Declaration of Independence, he had driven to the city in a gig of his own design. He had also designed a light wagon for farm use.[19] Randall records his contriving, in 1815, "a leather top for a carriage, which could be readily arranged to exclude rain, or leave the vehicle entirely uncovered—and which worked essentially on the plan of the . . . extension-top carriage."

Jefferson had first opposed manufactures of almost any kind in America. He preferred agriculture as a way of life for his countrymen. But time and the course of history —particularly the immediate stimulus of the War of 1812— caused him to modify his former position. In 1785 who could have foreseen how things would be altered in the second decade of the nineteenth century, he asked Benjamin Austin in 1816. "We must now place the manufacturer by the side of the agriculturist. Shall we make our own comforts, or go without them, at the will of a foreign nation? He, therefore, who is now against domestic manufacture, must be for reducing us either to dependence on that foreign nation, or to be clothed in skins, and to live like wild beasts in dens and caverns. I am not one of these; experience has taught me that manufactures are now as necessary to our independence as to our comfort; . . . in so complicated a science as political economy, no one axiom can be laid down as an expedient for all times and circumstances, and for their contraries." Jefferson appears to have had in mind manufacturing within the home. He once inquired of Eli Whitney whether his cotton machines could be adapted to "family use." He desired no more expansion of larger manufacturing establishments in cities than was necessary for domestic use; he was against manufacturing for export.

He wrote to his and America's old friend, the Polish patriot Thaddeus Kosciusko: "We have reduced the large and expensive machinery for most things, to the compass of a private family, and every family of any size is now getting machines on a small scale for their household purposes. Quoting myself as an example, and I am much behind many others in this business, my household manufactures are just getting into operation on the scale of a carding machine costing $60 only, which may be worked by a girl of twelve years old, a spinning machine, which may be made for $10, carrying 6 spindles for wool, to be worked by a girl also, another which can be made for $25, carrying 12 spindles for cotton, and a loom, with a flying shuttle, weaving its twenty yards a day. I need 2,000 yards of linen, cotton and woolen yearly, to clothe my family [this term included his slaves, of course], which this machinery, costing $150 only, and worked by two women and two girls, will more than furnish. For fine goods there are numerous establishments at work in the large cities, and many more daily growing up. . . . In other articles we [that is, Americans as a whole] are equally advanced, so that nothing is more certain than that come peace when it will, we shall never again go to England for a shilling where we have gone for a dollar's worth. Instead of applying to her manufacturers there, they must starve or come here to be employed."

By 1813 Jefferson had two spinning machines and more than one loom at work. By 1815 he had thirty-five spindles going. He declared categorically this same year: "I have come to a resolution myself as I hope every good citizen will, never again to purchase any article of foreign manufacture which can be had of American make be the difference of price what it may."

So much machinery gave Jefferson an opportunity to bring into play his inventive ability, as in the case of his machine for breaking and beating hemp into fiber. In a letter of 1815 he explained that flax was so unproductive and so injurious to the land that he had never raised any. Hemp, on the contrary, grew well; but the drudgery of breaking and beating it by hand had proved too slow and distasteful for his laborers and he had given hemp up and bought cotton for making into shirts. Cotton had so risen in price, however, that he had been driven to devise a machine with which hemp might be prepared for manufacture.

"To a person having a threshing machine," he wrote, "the addition of a hemp-break will not cost more than twelve or fifteen dollars. You know that the first mover in that machine is a horizontal horse-wheel with cogs on its upper face. On these is placed a wallower and shaft, which give motion to the threshing apparatus. On the opposite side of this same wheel I place another wallower and shaft, through which, and near its outer end, I pass a crossarm of sufficient strength, projecting on each side fifteen inches in this form:

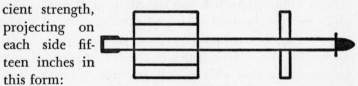

Nearly under the cross-arm is placed a very strong hemp-break, much stronger and heavier than those for the hand. Its head block particularly is massive, and four feet high, and near its upper end, in front, is fixed a strong pin (which we may call its horn); by this the cross-arm lifts and lets fall the break twice in every revolution of the wallower. A man feeds the break with hemp stalks, and a little person holds under the head block a large twist of the hemp which has been broken, resembling a twist of tobacco, but larger, where it is more perfectly beaten than I have ever seen done by hand. If the horse-wheel has one hundred and forty-four cogs, the wallower eleven rounds, and the horse goes three times round in a minute, it will give about eighty strokes in a minute. I had fixed a break to be moved by the gate of my saw-mill, which broke and beat at the rate of two hundred pounds a day. But the inconveniences of interrupting that, induced me to try the power of a horse, and I have found it to answer perfectly. The power being less, so also probably will be the effect, of which I cannot make a fair trial until I commence on my new crop. I expect that a single horse will do the breaking and beating of ten men." He went into a further discussion of the hemp-break in a letter to Peale.

His modesty and concern for the common welfare are reflected in the concluding passage: "Something of this kind has been so long wanted by the cultivators of hemp, that as soon as I can speak of its effect with certainty, I shall probably describe it anonymously in the public papers, in order to forestall the prevention of its use by some interloping patentee."

For his homespun, Jefferson rigged up a fulling machine, which he described to his friend Charles Willson Peale: "For fulling in our families we use the simplest thing in the world. We make a bench of the widest plank we can get, say half a yard wide at least, of thick and heavy stuff. We cut notches crosswise of that 2 inches long and 1 inch deep; the perpendicular side of the notch fronting the middle one from both ends; on that we lay a 4 inch board, 6 feet long, with a pin for a handle in each end, and notched as the under one. A board is nailed on each side of the under one, to keep the upper in place as it is shoved backwards and forwards, and the cloth, properly moistened, is laid between them. Two hands full 20 yards in two hours." He thought that some day he might even

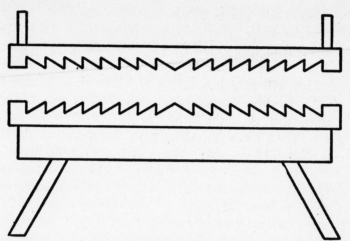

attach a mechanism to this and so increase its efficiency.

A purchased carding machine was altered by putting "a six-inch whirl in place of the handle of the great cylinder, to be driven by a two-foot wheel and band so that the hand will make one revolution where it now makes four," thereby producing "a less fatiguing composition of force and velocity." With a device affixed to his sawmill he beat his corn into hominy. Finding that benne oil, which he was promoting as a native substitute for olive oil, required a special press, he devised one.

He showed similar resourcefulness in his farming equipment. In 1793 he imported one of the latest models of the Scotch threshing machine—the first to be introduced into Virginia.[20] Along with it came the workman who had made it and who now expected to settle in America. Jefferson directed him to proceed immediately to Richmond, where he was to place Jefferson's machine on exhibit. Jefferson's intention was thus to secure new orders for this machine for its maker, and spread its use. As usual, Jefferson was not entirely satisfied and made his own improvements. He wrote to George Washington, in June of 1796, that he was having a new machine made, modeled upon

the original one, except that he had "put the whole works
(except the horse wheel) into a single frame, movable
from one field to another on the two axles of a wagon.
It will be ready in time for the harvest which is coming
on, which will give it a full trial." The time he saved
with this machine helped him forestall the wheat moth,
the insect scourge of the farmer in that day.[21]

Of Jefferson's new threshing machine, the Duke de la
Rochefoucauld-Liancourt, who spent a week at Monticello in 1796, wrote: "Mr. Jefferson possesses one of those
excellent threshing machines which a few years since were
invented in Scotland, and are already very common in
England. This machine, the whole of which does not weigh
two thousand pounds, is conveyed from one farm to
another in a wagon, and threshes from one hundred and
twenty to one hundred and fifty bushels a day. A worm
[the weevil], whose eggs are almost constantly deposited
in the ear of the grain, renders it necessary to thresh the
[grain] a short time after the harvest; . . . Mr. Jefferson
hopes that this machine, which has already found some
imitators among his neighbors, will be generally adopted
in Virginia."

Jefferson was greatly taken by a new "drill-plough"
invented by T. C. Martin of Virginia, and sent to him by
his friend John Taylor of Caroline. Jefferson wrote Taylor
in acknowledgment: "A good instrument of this kind is
almost the greatest desideratum in husbandry," because
of its saving in seed and the greater evenness in the sowing. He wrote about a "Jersey drill" that he had and
referred Taylor to a description of it in the "N.Y. agricl.
transactions." [22]

Jefferson's enthusiasm for Martin's drill led him to
write minute descriptions of it to a number of correspondents, among them Sir John Sinclair, President of the
London Board of Agriculture. Sinclair was informed that
Martin's machine was a "drill-plough" in which the in-

ventor had "used the band of buckets for elevating the grain from the box into the funnel, which let them down into the furrow." Furthermore, the inventor had employed "bands with different sets of buckets adapted to the size of peas, of turnip seed, etc." Moreover, this "instrument" opened its furrow, sowed its seed, and covered it. Finally, it was simple, easy to repair, perfect in performance, and so cheap it could be made for nine dollars. To promote the use of so "perfect" an invention Jefferson did not stop with verbal descriptions; he sent the machines themselves. One went to Sir John Sinclair, and another to the Agricultural Society of the Seine. This latter traveled by a government-owned boat in 1808 since, because of the Embargo, private shipping was virtually at a standstill.

His resourceful mind contemplated improvements even in this "perfect" machine. He planned to enlarge it so that it would plant more than one row at a time, or to alter it to plant a wider variety of seed than it was first designed for. He thought the "Jersey drill" might be made to drill eight rows at a time instead of its present four. He suggested to the inventor Martin that either he or Jefferson alter his drill to sow "four rows at a time, twelve inches apart," instead of one. In 1813 he wrote that he had used Martin's drill primarily for sowing peas, turnips, and benne seed, but that he proposed to add a separate band of buckets for corn and another for wheat.

For some four or five years, according to a notation of 1798, Jefferson had used a seed box for sowing clover seed. He described it to Sir John Sinclair as being seven feet long, six inches wide, three inches deep, and divided by partitions into seven equal cells. In the bottom of each cell were holes of the proper size and of such number and arrangement that when the box was carried over a field by the sower an area about nine feet in breadth was covered with seed. One man could thus sow from eight to ten acres a day, with never any interferences from the wind. Where hand-sowing used a gallon of seed to the acre, this box used only three pints, and with a far more even distribution. In 1795 he found that his "machine" had reduced his costs for sowing clover "from six shillings to two shillings and three pence the acre."

Jefferson's reference to the plow brings us to his really notable contribution in agricultural implements. This was a new form of the moldboard which he worked out by theoretical principles, discussed with his scientific friends, tested, demonstrated to others, operated, modified, and improved until he had what he believed to be, as he wrote Robert Fulton, "the finest plough which has ever been constructed in America." . . . "The plough is to the farmer what the wand is to the sorcerer," he wrote. And since the farmer produced the most essential things of life, the plow was therefore "the most useful of the instruments known to man."

Aside from his own improvement of the moldboard and his use of a chain in front of the plow so that it might better turn under the weeds, he did his best to promote Jethro Wood's excellent plows and a new plow devised by his son-in-law, John Randolph, for contour-plowing. Greater simplicity, lower costs, and increased utility were what he sought in plows. When these requirements were met, his enthusiasm was unbounded. Since Randolph's new implement promised to stop the ravages of soil erosion, Jefferson considered this use of the plow "equal in value almost to its services before known."

Jefferson's interest in plows was stimulated during his stay in Europe. While in Paris, he paid three francs to see a plow drawn by a windlass, without horses or oxen. To Jefferson, this seemed but a "poor affair," a complicated apparatus by means of which "four men could do the work of two horses." It was while journeying through western Germany and northern France in 1788, however, that he really began thinking seriously upon the "awkward figure" of the moldboards then in use and worked out a theory for its improvement.

"The offices of the mould-board," he wrote in his memoranda, "are to receive the sod after the share has cut under it, to raise it gradually, and to reverse it. The fore-end of it, then, should be horizontal to enter under the sod, and the hind end perpendicular to throw it over; the intermediate surface changing gradually from the horizontal to the perpendicular. It should be as wide as the furrow, and of a length suited to the construction of the plough." Following this statement of principles, he next described for himself, with diagrams, precisely how a proper moldboard might be cut from a solid block of wood to achieve these desired ends. These efforts eventuated in a lighter and more easily made implement that would plow a much deeper furrow than the usual eighteenth-century plow, with the expenditure of far less force.

In 1790, when he was back in New York acting as George Washington's Secretary of State, Jefferson sent his son-in-law Randolph a model of his moldboard. By 1794 he appears to have tried out his invention at Monticello. One of its advantages was that it could be made "by the most bungling carpenter," who could not "vary a hair's breadth in its form, but by gross negligence." Jefferson was soon busy demonstrating and promoting this useful discovery. Mr. William Strickland of England, to whom Jefferson showed his moldboard, was so impressed that he "took drawings of it" and later interested the English Board of Agriculture in it. Jefferson wrote John Taylor in 1798 that it had been "greatly approved" in Philadelphia and by "very good judges" at Monticello, where he himself had "used it for five years with entire approbation." Where practical demonstrations were impossible, Jefferson sent models (sometimes by request), to interested people and organizations. One went to John Taylor, one to Robert Patterson, one to Robert R. Livingston. Along with the last went a block of wood in the form from which the moldboard was cut out of it. Others went to Philip Tabb, to A. Thouin of the French Jardin des Plantes, to Du Pont de Nemours in Paris, and to the English Board of Agriculture.

Toward the end of his second term as President, Jefferson had made a small alteration in the toe of his moldboard. This permitted the shortening of the share some six or eight inches, a change which he reported the farmers preferred. Not long afterward, by using a dynamometer, which he had managed to borrow from Robert Fulton, he had scientifically tested the amount of force used in operating his plow. And, as we have seen in his letter to Peale, by 1815 he had "lately" had his moldboard cast in iron and fitted to a plow so light that two small horses could pull it with less effort than he had "ever before seen necessary." It plowed a furrow nine inches wide and six inches deep, did "beautiful work," and was "approved by every one."

Thus did Jefferson, as he expressed it, make "the combination of a *theory* which may satisfy the learned, with a practice intelligible to the most unlettered laborer." It received universal recognition. His detailed diagrammatic explanation of his moldboard appeared in the *Transactions* of the American Philosophical Society. The instrument itself was exhibited before the Philadelphia Society for the Promotion of Agriculture. From France he received a gold medal for it from its principal agricultural society.

Jefferson never took out a patent for it. To Charles Willson Peale he wrote: "You will be at perfect liberty to use the form of the mouldboard, as all the world is, having never thought of monopolizing by patent any useful idea which happens to offer itself to me. . . ."

4

Megalonyx, Mammoth, and Mother Earth

•

In 1796 Jefferson came into possession of some fossilized bones of a large animal heretofore unknown to American scientists. The bones had been found in a saltpeter cave in Greenbriar County, Virginia, now West Virginia. Upon receipt of them Jefferson sent a brief description to David Rittenhouse, President of the American Philosophical Society. Rittenhouse was actually dead at the date of this letter, July 3, 1796, though the news had not yet reached Monticello. Jefferson ascribed the bones to "the family of the lion, tyger, panther etc. but as preeminent over the lion in size as the Mammoth is over the elephant." In fact, the size of the claw and general bulk of the animal led him to name this unknown creature "the Great-claw, or, Megalonyx." He expressed his ultimate intention to deposit the bones with the Society.

Curiosity about prehistoric creatures was, in fact, constantly increasing during this period with both laymen and scientists in America and throughout the world. Man was just beginning to piece together satisfactorily the broken threads of the past history of the earth and its inhabitants. Investigations of the bones of ancient vertebrates and other evidences of nature's previous life-forms were naturally not new by the middle 1790's. But by this date excitement over the discovery, collecting, and examination of such remains had grown tremendously.

Jefferson's discovery naturally created great interest among his scientific friends in Philadelphia. Benjamin Smith Barton wrote him on August 1 that his account of these bones would be "very acceptable" to the American Philosophical Society for publication in the forthcoming volume of the *Transactions,* if it were received in time.

Jefferson's excitement over his new discovery and his eagerness to have his account published in the *Transactions* glows through his letter to Dr. Benjamin Rush of January, 1797: "What are we to think of a creature whose claws were eight inches long, when those of the lion are not 1½ inches; whose thighbone was 6¼ diameter; when that of the lion is not 1½ inches? Were not the things within the jurisdiction of the rule and compass, and of ocular inspection, credit to them could not be obtained. . . . I wish the usual delays of the publications of the Society may admit the addition to our new volume, of this interesting article, which it would be best to have first announced under the sanction of their authority."

When Jefferson rode to Philadelphia to assume his duties as Vice-President of the United States, he carried with him his collection of bones and the article he had written about them. In Philadelphia, he discovered something that challenged his identification of this unknown animal, his *Megalonyx,* as a carnivore belonging to the lion or tiger family. This was "an account published in Spain of the skeleton of an enormous animal from Paraguay, of the clawed kind, but not of the lion class at all; indeed, it is classed with the sloth, ant-eater, etc., which are not of the carnivorous kinds; it was dug up 100 feet below the surface, near the river La Plata. The skeleton is now mounted at Madrid, is 12 feet long and 6 feet high."

The discovery Jefferson refers to had been made in South America in 1789. It was, in actuality, an extinct ground sloth of herbivorous habits whose habitat had been both North and South America. Its remains have been found in Pleistocene deposits.[1]

Though his own identification was now in doubt, Jefferson went ahead with his original plans. His paper was read before the American Philosophical Society on March 10, 1797, and was published in the fourth volume of its *Transactions,* in 1799. The bones which he had—a radius, an ulna, the second, third, and fifth metacarpals, a second phalanx of the index finger, and a third phalanx of a thumb[2]—he deposited with the Society. Jefferson added a postscript to his paper, commenting on the similarities between his animal and the giant sloth (*Megatherium*), and concluded that positive identification must await the discovery of missing parts of the skeleton. In the meantime he was unwilling to change his own identification.

This decision was consistent with Jefferson's own demand that scientific conclusions be reached with greatest caution after the most careful investigation of all facts. Perhaps he considered his postscript sufficient notice that the identification was tentative. Interestingly enough, an essentially accurate identification of Jefferson's animal as a species of ground sloth was made by Dr. Caspar Wistar, Philadelphia physician, later professor of anatomy at the University of Pennsylvania and a recognized authority in American vertebrate paleontology during this period, and was also published in the fourth volume of the *Transactions* of the American Philosophical Society.

In his article, "The Beginnings of Vertebrate Paleontology in North America," [3] George Gaylord Simpson, the American paleontologist, points out Jefferson's strengths and weaknesses as a paleontologist and as a pioneer of this

science in America. He praises Jefferson for raising the
study of fossils to respectability in this country and
stimulating the collecting of specimens. He finds Jefferson's
work upon the *Megalonyx,* however, unscientific in its
methods, viewpoints, and conclusions. Wistar's memoir of
1799, on the contrary, is described as "a model of cautious,
accurate scientific description and inference, an achieve-
ment almost incredible in view of the paleontological
naivete of his associates and of the lack of comparative materials." No "essential point" in Wistar's conclusions concerning the bones has had to be corrected by later scientists.
It should be noted, however, that Jefferson himself accorded Wistar the very high place he deserved in American
paleontology. Jefferson's name for the animal, Megalonyx,
or Great Claw, has been kept to this day.

In his memoir upon the Megalonyx, it should be noted
that Jefferson argues against the extinction of species. This
problem was a controversial issue of the day. Such important figures as Franklin, Buffon, and Daubenton (Buffon's
assistant at the *Jardin des Plantes*) held that species do not
become extinct, and their view prevailed until Cuvier and
others popularized the contrary opinion at the turn of the
century. Jefferson's thought upon this problem underwent
some changes but he maintained, until the very last years
of his life, that if a race of animals should disappear the
void thus left in the hierarchy of nature would be again
filled by the "intelligent and powerful Agent" which lies
behind the universe and which will not permit it to be
"reduced to a shapeless chaos."

Jefferson's argument against the extinction of species is
based upon the old idea of the "great chain of being," [4]
which regards the created universe as an infinite series of
"links" in a chain, running from inanimate nature and the
very lowest order of being up through man, the angels, and
God himself. The chain as a whole constitutes a beautiful,
ordered, and fixed harmony. Should any link be allowed to

disappear, the order of the series would be wrecked and give way to chaos. It was from this beautiful design in creation that many eighteenth-century men looked "through nature up to nature's God." Jefferson used this chain-of-being concept to argue that the *Megalonyx* and mammoth must range somewhere in the western wilds of North America, and he searched Indian and other traditions for evidence that these huge animals inhabited impenetrable forests still unexplored by white men.

Such a discovery would further have gladdened his heart for its value in refuting ideas held by Buffon and other European scientists that nature in America was too impotent to sustain life upon the grand scale required by the larger vertebrates—another point touched on in his article. This problem (given fuller treatment elsewhere in this book) was another controversial issue of that time.

Jefferson's greatest popular fame in the field of paleontology came from his work with the so-called "mammoth," a huge prehistoric animal whose remains attracted international attention during Jefferson's day. Jefferson's interest in the mammoth appears to have begun when he was collecting material for his *Notes on Virginia,* that is, about 1780.[5]

In his *Notes,* Jefferson points out that the mammoth must have been the largest of American quadrupeds. Remains "of unparalleled magnitude," he says, have been found rather recently on the Ohio River and in many parts of America further north. Indian tradition, Jefferson noted with satisfaction, has it that such a huge, carnivorous creature still roams the northern parts of America. Jefferson then argues that, contrary to certain European opinion, ascribing these remains to the hippopotamus or elephant, or to both, they cannot belong to either.

Though they definitely belong to one animal only, the tusks, frame, and teeth of these remains prove that this animal was not a hippopotamus. Nor could it have been an elephant since (1) its skeleton bespeaks an animal "five or six times the cubic volume of the elephant," (2) the "grinders are five times as large, are square, and the grinding surface studded with four or five rows of blunt points" and hence quite different from those of the elephant, (3) no elephant grinder has been found in America, (4) the elephant could not have lived in those regions where these remains are now discovered—unless one is willing to suppose some great difference in the earth in past ages, which Jefferson feels no one given to "cautious philosophy" could do. The habitat of the elephant, he points out, is from 30° south of the equator to 30° north of the equator; that of the mammoth must have begun at 36½° north latitude and probably extended to the pole itself. This "largest of all terrestrial beings" was built upon a scale so vast that it should never have been confused with the elephant by European naturalists.

The mammoth's great superiority over the elephant in size was insisted upon by Jefferson time and again during his ambassadorship to France. In arguing that the remains of this huge creature could not have belonged to the hippopotamus or to the elephant, he challenged the opinion of Daubenton, Buffon, and other leading naturalists of this period.

Further evidence of Jefferson's interest in this great creature and other prehistoric animals appeared during the early days of his presidency of the American Philosophical Society. At its first meeting over which he presided (May 19, 1797), "A Plan for Collecting Information Respecting the Antiquities of N. A." came under consideration. On April 6, 1798, a second report upon this plan was gone into in great detail and a committee consisting of Jefferson, George Turner, Caspar Wistar, Dr. Adam Seybert, C. W. Peale, James Wilkinson, and Joh. Williams was appointed. By the end of the year this committee reported that a

circular letter had been "extensively distributed" throughout the country soliciting help in accomplishing, among
other things, the following: the procuring of "one or more
entire skeletons of the Mammoth, so called, and of such
other unknown animals as either have been, or hereafter
may be discovered in America." [6]

Fossils were among the treasures brought back by the
Lewis and Clark Expedition of 1804–1806. At about this
time Jefferson and Dr. Caspar Wistar also tried, but without success, to procure for the American Philosophical
Society a large collection of bones dug out by a Dr. William Goforth at Big Bone Lick, famous source of prehistoric animal remains located in what is now the State of
Kentucky. Jefferson expected Goforth's findings to include
the skull of a mammoth—so desperately needed by the
American Philosophical Society to complete its collection
of the bones of this huge vertebrate. He was also hopeful
(as he wrote to Dr. Samuel Brown, in July, 1806) that
there would be bones of the Megalonyx. But Goforth sold
his collection to an adventurer who took them to England. [7]
Therefore President Jefferson had to undertake a private
paleontological venture. He arranged with the owner of
the Big Bone Lick for Clark to go there in 1807 and do
some excavating at Jefferson's expense. Clark "employed
ten laborers several weeks" and unearthed some three
hundred bones, which he shipped down the Mississippi to
New Orleans, from whence they were forwarded to Jefferson in Washington.

On receiving Clark's letter with the news of the collection he had made, Jefferson immediately invited Dr. Caspar
Wistar to Washington to see the bones as soon as they arrived. Jefferson confides to him his plans for their disposal.
There is to be "a tusk and femur which General Clarke
[*sic*] procured particularly at my request, for a special kind
of cabinet I have at Monticello." But his primary purpose
has been "to procure for the society as complete a supple-

ment to what is already possessed as that Lick can furnish at this day." Hence Wistar is to select what bones the American Philosophical Society may desire, and the rest are to go to the National Institute of France.

The odd cargo arrived at the Presidential mansion in Washington early in 1803. "The bones are spread in a large room [the unfinished East Room]," Jefferson immediately informs Wistar, "where you can work at your leisure, undisturbed by any mortal, from morning till night, taking your breakfast and dinner with us. It is a precious collection, consisting of upwards of three hundred bones, few of them of the large kinds which are already possessed. There are four pieces of the head, one very clear, and distinctly presenting the whole face of the animal. The height of his forehead is most remarkable. In this figure, the indenture of the eye gives a prominence of six inches to the forehead. There are four jaw bones tolerably entire, with several teeth in them, and some fragments; three tusks like elephants; one ditto totally different, the largest probably ever seen, being now from nine to ten feet long, though broken off at both ends; some ribs; an abundance of teeth studded, and also those of the striated or ribbed kind; a fore-leg complete; and then about two hundred small bones, chiefly of the foot. This is probably the most valuable part of the collection, for General Clarke, aware that we had specimens of the larger bones, has gathered up everything of the small kind. There is one horn of a colossal animal. . . . Having sent my books to Monticello, I have nothing here to assist you but the 'Encyclopédie Methodique.'"[8] All this during the desperate days of the Embargo!

Wistar delayed his trip to Washington partly because of health and partly to study all available information about the mammoth. On his arrival at the Capital, he confirmed Jefferson's estimate of the value of the collection.

After Wistar had made his selection, Jefferson sent the remainder of the bones, together with a few other articles, by a government dispatch boat to the National Institute of France. The captain had instructions to leave them with the American Consul at whatever port in France he should put into. From thence they were to be forwarded to the American legation at Paris for delivery to the well-known scientist Count de La Cépède. Jefferson's contribution was "highly valued by the naturalists of Paris," the Secretary of the American legation wrote him, and he was sent a formal letter of thanks. La Cépède and Cuvier were appointed to examine the bones, some of which remained on exhibition in the Museum d'Histoire Naturelle in the Jardin des Plantes at least up to the Second World War.[9]

Useful as Jefferson's contribution was, a final, correct identification of the huge animal had already been arrived at by Cuvier several years earlier. As Simpson sums it up: "The elephant-like animals then known from North America were really of two kinds. Both were related to the living elephant but both belonged to separate, wholly extinct species. One, the 'mammoth' of the Americans, the 'mastodonte' of Cuvier (in 1806 and later), was quite unlike the mammoth of Siberia. The other was like, if not identical with, the latter. The mammoth of Siberia was also extinct and not of the same species as any living elephants. All these forms were herbivorous. They could live in the north because they were northern species and not the same as the tropical forms of today." Cuvier's statement of the case "has proved permanently valid, aside from unimportant details." [10]

These interests of Jefferson were strengthened by his friendship with Charles Willson Peale, painter, member of the American Philosophical Society, and founder of the justly famous Philadelphia Museum,[11] which served to dramatize to the American public, as no other single thing did, the wonders of natural history in general and of paleontology in particular.

Peale's interest in museum work began soon after the American Revolution, when he came into possession of mammoth bones from the Big Bone Lick, a paddle fish from the Allegheny River, and an Angora cat from France, the latter a gift from Franklin. The growth of his collection made roomier accommodations necessary. In 1794, the American Philosophical Society rented him the so-called Philosophical Hall in its own building. In 1811 Peale's exhibits were moved to Independence Hall, where they remained until his death, in 1827.[12] Through private gifts, purchases, and exchanges with European museums and collectors, Peale built a museum of great public renown and scientific value.

Peale was a delightful fellow, pursuing with ardor anything that caught his fancy—painting, inventing, Jeffersonian democracy, museum building.[13] He was also a showman and knew how to excite public interest in his museum. This is to be seen in the way he moved his collection from his home to its first exhibit hall. "To take advantage of public curiosity," he wrote, "I contrived to make a very considerable parade of the articles, especially those which were large. As boys are generally very fond of parade, I collected all the boys of the neighborhood. At the head of the parade was carried on men's shoulders, the American buffalo, the panthers, tiger cats; and a long string of animals carried by the boys. The parade from Lombard Street to the Hall brought all the inhabitants to their doors and windows to see the cavalcade. It was fine fun for the boys. They were willing to work in such a novel removal and saved me some expense in moving the delicate articles." [14]

Although Peale found it advisable, largely for business reasons—the admission was twenty-five cents, not an inconsiderable fee in those days—to add occasional attractions outside the field of natural history—paintings of famous men, magic mirrors, an organ, musical recitals, and a "physiognotrace" (a profitable mechanical device for making silhouettes of customers)—he was serious about his museum work. One of his motives was the patriotic one of providing the United States with a museum that would, as he wrote Jefferson in 1797, become the equal of any in Europe and "an honour to my Country." Other motives were the scientific, moral, and religious utility he perceived in such a museum. In a letter to Jefferson in 1802, he wrote: "Such a museum, easy of access, must tend to make all Classes of the People, in some degree, learned in the science of Nature, without even the trouble of Study. Whether a diffused knowledge of this kind, may tend to mend their Morals, is a question of some import.—Furnishing the Idle and disapated with a great and new source of amusement, ought to divert them from frivolous and pernicious Entertainments—It is fully demonstrated that viewing the wonderful structure of a great number of *beings best formed for their respective stations,* elevates the mind to an Admiration and Adoration of the Great Author!—I have seen folly stopped in its carier, by the Sight of a few articles in this Repository. . . ."

Seen in its heyday, roughly the first quarter of the nineteenth century, the Museum was indeed a place where almost anyone might find something of interest. Framed scriptural texts on the walls left no doubts of Peale's religious purpose, while framed catalogues provided the scientifically minded with information of the orders and classes of the quadrupeds, generally in the Linnaean system. Reality was added by a habitat arrangement for many specimens—then an advanced step—the effects often achieved by painted backgrounds. By thus showing "the nest, hollow, cave or a particular view of the country" from which the specimens came, wrote Peale, "some instances of the habitats may be given." [15]

In preparing specimens for display, care was taken to

preserve absolute lifelikeness. The limbs of some were
carved in wood so that their muscles appeared beneath the
skin when placed over these wooden imitations. Where
possible, animals were shown in lifelike attitudes. A llama
from South America reared up "in the act of spitting
through the fissure of his upper lip." A snake was shown
"charming a stuffed bird with its bead eyes," while another
was busy "swallowing a toad or frog with the hind quarters
projecting from the mouth." And a gray wolf was to be
seen "with bloody fangs . . . rending a lamb" whose
papier-mâché entrails added a gruesome touch of reality.
In lighter vein were monkeys posed as craftsmen. Some
freaks also were displayed, a cow with two tails, five legs,
and six feet, which gave milk to a two-headed calf. These
were incidentals. Peale's main object was to promote the
scientific and—as he saw it—religious knowledge to be in-
culcated by his quadrupeds, insects, minerals, marine life,
birds, and the natural harmony they indicated. Of special
interest to Jefferson was the Model Room, where one
might see such products of mechanical genius, in specimens
or models, as a clothes washer, threshing machine, dry dock,
spinning wheel, and Tom Paine's iron bridge.[16]

Mrs. Anne Royall has left an interesting contemporary
account. "It may readily be supposed," she says, "that the
idea of seeing a place so celebrated as the museum of
Philadelphia, inspired me with no common curiosity."
There, she found "ten thousand things wonderful and
pleasing." What Mr. Jefferson had said of the Natural
Bridge of Virginia could be applied also to Peale's Museum—"it was worth a trip across the Atlantic" to view
its 1,100 different kinds of birds, 250 quadrupeds, 3,450
insects, and 200 portraits of distinguished men! And such
excellent preserving and mounting! Even the gloss on the
feathers had been retained! There was a remarkable sea
lion with glass eyes, "very large, full, fierce, and as natural
as though it were living; even the eye lash was entire."

Portrait of Thomas Jefferson by Charles Willson Peale in Independence Hall, Philadelphia. (*Courtesy of the City of Philadelphia Department of Public Works*)

Two of Jefferson's architectural achievements. *Above:* The main house at Monticello. *(Courtesy of Popular Science Monthly.) Below:* The University of Virginia from a drawing by William Goodacres in 1824. (*Courtesy of Proceedings of the American Philosophical Society*)

The shaft of the weathervane (*shown above*) was connected to a dial (*shown below*) affixed to the ceiling of the enclosed porch. This enabled Jefferson to make observation of wind drift while indoors. (*Courtesy of Popular Science Monthly*)

Clock (*above, left*) operated by a set of cannon balls whose slow descent marked the days (*above, right*). Affixed high up on the wall the clock was reached for winding by a collapsible ladder (*below, left*). All were made to Jefferson's designs.

Above: Moldboard for a plow, Jefferson's most notable invention. Its streamline principle is continued in modern plows. *Center:* Spectacles worn by Jefferson (*left*) beside a modern pair. Made from instructions and drawings furnished to the optician by Jefferson. *Below:* This camera obscura used by Jefferson did not take pictures. It reflected traceable images on a plate of ground glass. (*Courtesy of Popular Science Monthly*)

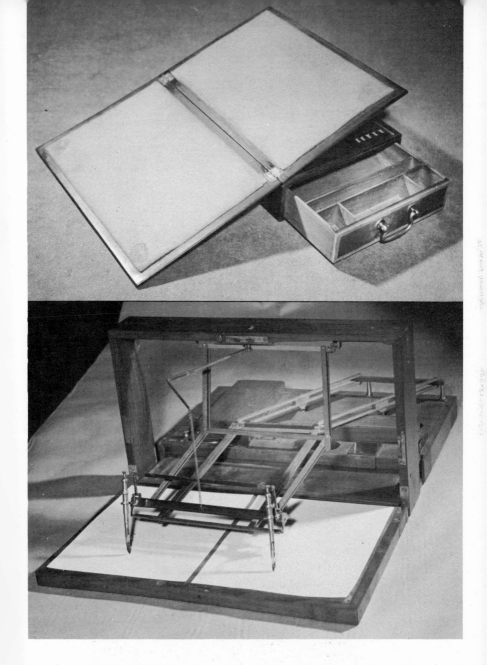

Above: Jefferson designed this portable writing desk with a drawer for writing materials and a tilting top. The Declaration of Independence was written on it. *Below:* The Polygraph, a device which made an automatic copy with a pen attached to the pen used by the writer. After he substituted the Polygraph for a copying press of his own invention Jefferson made a number of improvements on the original design. (*Courtesy of Popular Science Monthly*)

Above: The Odometer. Attached to the hub of a carriage wheel it measured travel distance. *Center:* This adjustable musicstand was made to Jefferson's design. *Below:* The stand was convertible into a table by lowering the rack. (*Courtesy of Popular Science Monthly*)

Jefferson's adjustable architect's drafting desk. *Top, left:* The desk with the top tilted up. *Bottom, left:* Serrations at the back to secure the desired tilting angle. *Above, right:* The drawer's sliding top could be used as an auxiliary table when closed. (*Courtesy of Popular Science Monthly*)

Jefferson's dumbwaiter, said to have been the first in America. Built into the side of the mantel, behind a panel door, it delivered wine from the cellar below. (*Courtesy of Popular Science Monthly*)

A modified form of the swivel chair, used by Jefferson. It revolved but did not swing freely. Fitted to it were a padded bench on which Jefferson could stretch his legs, and a writing table. (*Courtesy of Popular Science Monthly*)

Destruction of the forests. Burning fallen trees in a girdled clearing. Early painting by George Harvey. (*Courtesy of Proceedings of the American Philosophical Society*)

Scene at the excavation, near Newburgh, N.Y., of the bones of Charles Willson Peale's mastodon. (*Courtesy of Proceedings of the American Philosophical Society*)

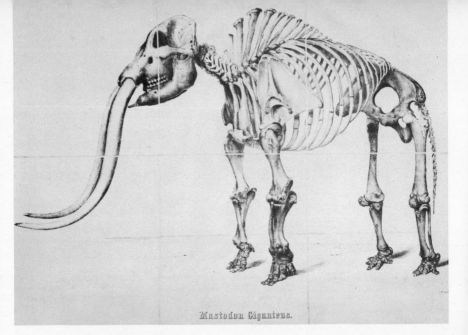

Mastodon Giganteus.

Plet. II.

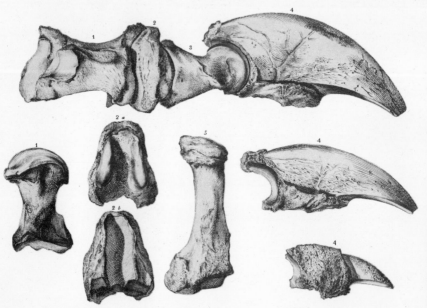

Engraved by James Akin from Chalk Drawings made (the size of the Bones) by Doct.' W. S. Jacobs.—

Above: Reconstructed skeleton from mastodon bones unearthed by Charles Willson Peale. *Below:* Toe bones of *Megalonyx jeffersoni,* subject of a paleontological essay by Jefferson. (*Courtesy of Proceedings of the American Philosophical Society*)

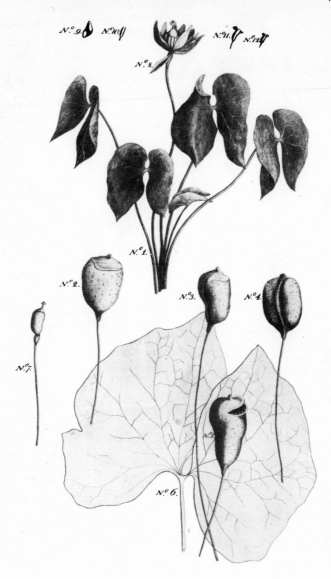

The *Jeffersonia diphylla*, a plant named in tribute to Jefferson's contributions to Botanical science. (*Courtesy of Proceedings of the American Philosophical Society*)

Above, left: Portrait of Jefferson by Mather Brown. *Above, right:* Portrait of Benjamin Rush by Charles Willson Peale. *Below, left:* Portrait of Benjamin Franklin by Thomas B. Welch. *Below, right:* Portrait of David Rittenhouse by Charles Willson Peale. From the collection at Independence Hall, Philadelphia. (*Courtesy of the City of Philadelphia Department of Public Works*)

The devilfish was a sight indeed! Twelve feet long, fifteen feet around the body, and weighing "upwards of 2000 pounds!" One huge sheep alone was worth "ten dollars" to see. Then there were a great Missouri bear, the largest of buffalo bulls, the whole family of the deer kind, and an old buck elk "with his tremendous horns on his head." The exhibit excited Mrs. Royall's imagination as "something like a furious combat of the most awful looking wild beasts, amongst which the tiger, and the lion, which last with his dreadful jaws extended, seems to threaten the whole affair of them with instant destruction."

Mrs. Royall commented on the "fury and vengeance" in "the hyena's eyes," the realism of the wolf's gorging upon the lamb whose bowels "looked as though they had that instant been torn out of the body, and the blood besmeared upon the whole seemed yet warm." The monkeys, who appeared to be "looking you in the face," were "a subject of much amusement to the country people," observed Mrs. Royall, "particularly two of those human-looking animals who are dressed in clothes, sitting on stools engaged at shoemaking." There were strange birds— the ostrich, crane, pelican, and Patagonian penguin; there were Chinese and Persian shoes and hats, "a pair of pantaloons made of the intestines of the whale," an Indian workbasket, the shoe and stocking of the Irish Giant Obrian (who was eight feet, seven and a half inches high), a shoe of Simon Pap the dwarf (who was but twenty-eight inches high), portraits, shells, amphibious animals, coins from all parts of the world. Mrs. Royall was a satisfied customer. She thought the exhibit "well worth ten times the money demanded."

But Mrs. Royall met with one disappointment. The great mammoth failed to live up to her expectations. "The skeleton is indeed as large as is represented, but it had not that formidable, dread-inspiring aspect which my romantic turn led me to expect, and with which I expected to be overwhelmed: I beheld it without surprise or emotion." Two gentlemen who were also viewing this great creature were likewise disappointed. One stooped beneath the rail for a closer examination, scraped a part of the skeleton with his penknife, and "swore 'it was nothing but wood.'" The over-all appearance, thought Mrs. Royall, was that of "old smoky-looking hard white oak"; in many parts the skeleton was even "quite black."

Nevertheless the mammoth, for some time, remained a wonder of the scientific world. In 1801 Peale read a newspaper account of some mammoth bones dug up in Orange and Ulster Counties, New York. He promptly visited the scene to get a description which he might present to the American Philosophical Society. John Masten, owner of the bones, many of which were badly broken because of the crude methods used in excavation, had them on exhibit in his granary for a small fee. The remains, of which Peale made charcoal sketches, so excited him that he offered Masten two hundred dollars for the lot, with an extra hundred dollars for rights to dig for others. The terms were agreed upon but a rifle for Masten's son and gowns for his daughters had to be thrown in. The bones were then packed up and shipped to Philadelphia.[17]

There, Peale took stock of his collection. He wrote Jefferson on July 24 about the greatly damaged condition of many of the bones, of which "some essential pieces [are] yet wanting, which Doct^r Wistar & several members of the Philosophical Society urge me to procure."

Peale then explained to Jefferson his need for a pump to remove water from the pit on Masten's farm. Could Jefferson procure an order for him to get one from a government frigate at Philadelphia or New York? Replying on July 28, Jefferson congratulated Peale on his plans and informed him that "Mr. Smith, the Secretary of the Navy will give orders immediately to the Navy agent at New York to lend you a pump." Orders had also gone to General Irvine at Philadelphia to lend Peale "a couple of tents." Jefferson expressed his mortification that his duties had kept him from taking an active hand in the project. Peale's departure from Philadelphia, however, was too hurried for Jefferson's proffered help to reach him. With a five-hundred-dollar loan hastily made him by the American Philosophical Society, Peale hurried northward on his greatest scientific adventure.

To drain the water from the pit Peale constructed a large wheel which, when revolving, supplied power by means of a rope to "a chain of Buckets carried round an axis." At the top of the chain, each bucket poured its contents into a trough which conducted the water to a nearby "Bason." The wheel which supplied the power was "20 feet diameter, of a width for men to walk within, as Squirrils in a Cage." With "2 or 3 men walking slowly" this ingenious device carried off "1440 Gallons of Water every hour" thus enabling Peale, despite fast-flowing springs of cold water, "to emty the Ponds and keep them free of Water, while the Men removed the Mud." Piles had to be driven down to prevent the banks from caving in. The mammoth remains then unearthed by Peale included a tusk (it was broken but could be fitted together), parts of the upper head, part of a breast bone, "all the Vertebraes," part of the "os sacrum," all the ribs, a tibia and fibula not in the previous collection, and many small bones. With missing parts imitated with carved wooden pieces, Peale felt that he would have "a tolerable compleat Skeleton."

But he was in a fever to find other missing parts, especially an under jaw. So he moved to another likely source, some sixteen miles away. Here, after eight or nine days, he came upon numerous bones of the feet and tail, two tusks, many ribs, some vertebrae, and a blade bone, but still no lower jaw. He moved to another site about five miles away, where other bones had been unearthed, but found only some ribs and foot bones. Things began to look hopeless. Then after digging up the ground "to a very considerable distance round in the moment when dispairing of getting any more bones, and thinking to discharge the labourers—By means of a spear which we used, we luckily discovered other Bones—which uncovered prooved to be a fore leg, beneath which was an intire under Jaw not a part deficient, except one of the Upper grinders, which appears to have been lost while the Animal lived." Parts of a foot and of an upper portion of a head were also uncovered.

Peale's son Rembrandt, in his *Historical Disquisition on the Mammoth,* published while he was in England, gives us a few details about how fossil excavations were then conducted. After Masten's accidental discovery, for "the two succeeding days upwards of an hundred men were actively engaged, encouraged by several gentlemen, chiefly physicians, of the neighbourhood, and success the most sanguine attended their labours; but, unfortunately, the habits of the men requiring the use of spirits, it was afforded them in too great profusion, and they quickly became so impatient and unruly, that they had nearly destroyed the skeleton; and, in one or two instances, using oxen and chains to drag them from the clay and marle, the head, hips, and tusks were much broken."

Peale's excavation was handled more scientifically, but it was a great attraction, just the same. The attention of travelers along the road was caught by "the coaches, waggons, chaises, and horses, which animated the road, or were collected at the entrance to the field: rich and poor, men, women, and children, all flocked to see the operation." When Peale finally unearthed the under jaw, all were "extremely grateful . . . and the unconscious woods echoed with repeated huzzas, which could not have been more animated if every tree had participated in the joy. 'Gracious God, what a jaw! how many animals have been crushed between it!' was the exclamation of all: a fresh supply of grog went round, and the hearty fellows, covered with mud, continued the search with encreasing vigour."

Peale's finds turned out to be nearly enough for two complete skeletons. Where parts were missing, Rembrandt Peale worked with "his Chizil to carve in wood all the deficiencies." Peale finally had a skeleton the general dimensions of which he sent to Jefferson in April, 1803. Along the tusks and back, to the tip of the tail, extended 30 feet, 6 inches. The perpendicular height at the shoulders was 11 feet, 10 inches, while at the hips it was 9 feet, 1 inch.

The fame of the mammoth spread throughout the country. The word *mammoth* became a popular adjective. Sellers, in his study of Peale (p. 143), notes that "a Philadelphia baker offered 'Mammoth Bread' for sale" and "at Washington a 'Mammoth Eater' dispatched forty-two eggs in ten minutes." The Peales being decided Jeffersonians and Jefferson's interest in paleontology being known, the affair, as we shall see, took on a strong political flavor as well.

Peale's museum now became profitable. And overseas the French scientist Cuvier noted that Europe had only fragments to examine whereas Peale, in America, had assembled two whole skeletons.[18] Raphael and Rubens Peale took the second skeleton to England for exhibition, but the venture was not financially successful, and the skeleton was brought back. It finally became part of a museum which Rembrandt started in Baltimore in 1814.

The mammoth in the Philadelphia museum was "the first fossil skeleton ever mounted in America" and "probably the second in the world"—the first being a Megatherium skeleton mounted in the Royal Cabinet, Madrid, in 1795.[19] It was a drawing of the latter which had shaken Jefferson's confidence in the identification he had made of his *Megalonyx*.

Peale's Museum played a considerable role in America's

cultural development. As early as 1789 the Reverend Nicholas Collin, in a talk before the American Philosophical Society, had illustrated a point by referring to a "double-headed" snake to be seen in Peale's Museum. Dr. Benjamin Rush cited a picture of a Virginia leper displayed in Peale's museum. Jefferson had a high opinion of the Museum's educational function. In a letter to Wistar in 1807, he declares that he will send his grandson, Thomas Jefferson Randolph, to Philadelphia for his education because "there are particular branches of science, which are not so advantageously taught anywhere else in the United States as in Philadelphia. The garden at the Woodlands for Botany, Mr. Peale's Museum for Natural History, your Medical school for Anatomy, and the able professors in all of them, give advantages not to be found elsewhere." Young Randolph stayed in Peale's home from 1808 to 1809.

Jefferson had become a member of the original Board of Visitors of Peale's Museum, back in 1792 when Peale entertained the idea of converting his museum into a national institution. This Board of Visitors acted as adviser-patrons. With two exceptions, they were all members of the American Philosophical Society. Not even Jefferson's influence, however, was sufficient to have Congress take it over for the nation.

Jefferson never lost interest in Peale's activities in natural history. In 1795, he acted as intermediary between the Spanish Prince of Parma and Peale for an exchange of specimens. He recommended correspondents to Peale. He assisted Peale in efforts to secure some large bones from Greenbriar County, Virginia (both Peale and Jefferson supposed them to be additional remains of the Megalonyx). He sent Peale a "prickly lizard" secured from the Osage Indians. He forwarded to Peale material sent back by Lewis and Clark, and later placed a large part of the Lewis and Clark collections in Peale's hands.[20] When Peale considered selling his museum in 1815, Jefferson voiced the hope that its contents would not thus be "separated" and its great value lost.

In addition to this interest in prehistoric forms of life (though to him they were not strictly prehistoric, since he thought it likely that the mammoth and *Megalonyx* still existed), Jefferson also had some interest in the history of the earth itself—this despite two objections he had to geology—its lack of utility and its uncertainty. His objections have already been touched upon. He thought geology useful, however, as an aid in prospecting for minerals.

Furthermore the range of Jefferson's scientific interest was too great to leave out geology. We find him speculating on the formation of mountain ranges and whether they are generally parallel with the earth's axis; on the origin of the Natural Bridge; on the possibility of American rivers having once been inland lakes which broke through their mountain dams and made their ways to the ocean (as in the case of the Potomac, Shenandoah, and Delaware rivers); on the possibility of the Gulf of Mexico having been formed by an ocean current; on the general history of the topography of America; on the Flood recorded in the Bible; on the occurrence of sea shells in places far distant from the ocean; and on the origin and history of the earth itself. In 1797 he urged the American Philosophical Society to promote "researches into the Natural History of the Earth, the changes it has undergone as to Mountains, Lakes, Rivers, Prairies, etc." [21]

Concerning the origin of the universe and of the earth, Jefferson opposed mechanistic interpretations which ruled out a divine Creator. When one looks at the creation, Jefferson said, with its order, harmony, beauty, and wonderful design, one cannot help perceiving a God behind it. This eighteenth-century concept was particularly held by that group of thinkers known as "deists." As a matter of fact, the heavens had long ago declared the glory of God, and the firmament had shown His handiwork. But in more traditional religious belief a knowledge of God and of His purposes—and even a knowledge of the functioning of the universe itself—could be derived from Revelations. Jefferson maintained that a sufficient understanding of God's nature and God's will could be secured from observation of nature itself. He pointed out that in his belief in a superintending Regulator or Agent he was in opposition to Timaeus, Spinosa, Diderot, and D'Holbach. The fundamentalists of his day were quick to show that he was also in opposition to the Bible as they interpreted it, and the authority of Revelations as God's word.

One of the clearest expressions of Jefferson's belief is contained in a letter to John Adams in 1823:

. . . I hold, (without appeal to revelation) that when we take a view of the universe, in its parts, general or particular, it is impossible for the human mind not to perceive and feel a conviction of design, consummate skill, and indefinite power in every atom of its composition. The movement of the heavenly bodies, so exactly held in their course by the balance of centrifugal and centripetal forces; the structure of our earth itself, with its distribution of lands, waters and atmosphere; animal and vegetable bodies, examined in all their minutest particles; insects, mere atoms of life, yet as perfectly organized as man or mammoth; the mineral substances, their generation and uses; it is impossible, I say, for the human mind not to believe, that there is in all this, design, cause and effect, up to an ultimate cause, a Fabricator of all things from matter and motion, their Preserver and Regulator while permitted to exist in their present forms, and their regeneration into new and other forms. We see, too, evident proofs of the necessity of a superintending power, to maintain the universe in its course and order. . . . So irresistible are these evidences of an intelligent and powerful Agent, that, of the infinite numbers of men who have existed through time, they have believed, in the hypothesis of an eternal pre-existence of a Creator, rather than in that of a self-existent universe. Surely this unanimous sentiment renders this more probable, than that of the few in the other hypothesis.

This "intelligent and powerful Agent" had created the universe and our world in substantially its present form, with, possibly, some minor subsequent changes.

During his ambassadorship to France, Jefferson had studied the ideas of the "Vulcanists," who argued that mountains and valleys were the products of vast upheavals caused by the tremendous pressure of internal steam and gases in past ages of the earth. In refutation Jefferson wrote:

But I give one answer to all these theorists. That is as follows. They all suppose the earth a created existence. They must suppose a creator then; and that he possessed power and wisdom to a great degree. As he intended the earth for the habitation of animals and vegetables, is it reasonable to suppose, he made two jobs of his creation, that he first made a chaotic lump and set it into rotatory motion, and then waited the millions of ages necessary to form itself? That when it had done this, he stepped in a second time, to create the animals and plants which were to inhabit it? As the hand of the creator is to be called in, it may as well be called in at one stage of the process as another. We may as well suppose he created the earth at once, nearly in the state in which we see it, fit for the preservation of the beings he placed on it. But it is said, we have a proof that he did not create it in its present solid form, but in a state of fluidity; because its present shape of an oblate spheroid is precisely that which a fluid mass revolving on its axis would assume.

I suppose that the same equilibrium between gravity and centrifugal force, which would determine a fluid mass into the form of an oblate spheroid, would determine the wise creator of that mass, if he made it in a solid state, to give it the same spheroidical form. A revolving fluid will continue to change its shape, till it attains that in which its principles of contrary motion are balanced. For if you suppose them not balanced, it will change its form. Now, the same balanced form is necessary for the preservation of a revolving solid. The creator therefore, of a revolving solid, would make it an oblate spheroid, that figure alone admitting a perfect equilibrium. He would make it in that form, for another reason; that is, to prevent a shifting of the axis of rotation. Had he created the earth perfectly spherical, its axis might have been perpetually shifting, by the influence of the other bodies of the system; and by placing the inhabitants of the earth successively under its poles, it might have been depopulated; whereas, being spheroidical, it has but one axis on which it can revolve in equilibrio. Suppose the axis of the earth to shift forty-five degrees; then cut it into one hundred and eighty slices, making every section in the plane of a circle of latitude, perpendicular to the axis: every one of these slices, except the equatorial one, would be unbalanced, as there would be more matter on one side of its axis than on the other. There could be but one diameter drawn through such a slice, which would divide it into two equal parts. On every other possible diameter, the parts would hang unequal. This would produce an irregularity in the diurnal rotation. We may, therefore, conclude it impossible for the poles of the earth to shift, if it was made spheroidically; and that it would be made spheroidical, though solid, to obtain this end. I use this reasoning only on the supposition that the earth has had a beginning.

But this nice and logical system was shaken from time to time by observed facts—the discovery, for example, of "trees, &c., found far below the surface of the earth," discoveries which "seem to set the reason of man at defiance." Shells, and theories related to them, made trouble. In his *Notes on Virginia,* he commented that shells have been found in the Andes fifteen thousand feet above sea level. Many consider this "a proof of an universal deluge." But there could never have been such a deluge, Jefferson maintains. The weight of the atmosphere and all its contents "never exceeds that of a column of mercury of thirty-one inches height, which is equal to one of rain water of thirty-five feet high." Even if the atmosphere had been all water and this had descended upon the earth and hence had poured into the oceans, they would have risen to a height of only fifty-two and a half feet above their present level. There may have been "some instances of a partial deluge in the country lying round the Mediterranean sea." But a deluge which would account for shells in very high places seemed to Jefferson "out of the laws of nature."

He also argued against a second theory to account for shells in high places: that "the bed of the ocean, the principal residence of the shelled tribe, has, by some great convulsion of nature, been heaved to the heights at which we now find shells and other marine animals." But Jefferson cannot conceive "any natural agents, within or without the bowels of the earth, of force sufficient to heave, to the height of fifteen thousand feet, such masses as the Andes."

Jefferson was more hospitable to a third contemporary explanation, Voltaire's theory that shells grow just as do "crystals, plants, animals." Jefferson did not feel that Voltaire had sufficiently established the *fact,* though he had cited as proof a case of shell growth reported in southern France. Characteristically Jefferson kept this in mind when he visited the south of France, and sought to check on Voltaire's facts. Near Tours he talked with a Monsieur Gentil, with whom an introduction had been arranged through the Marquis de Chastellux.

Monsieur Gentil had been interested in this problem, and had corresponded with Voltair about it. He considered Voltaire's informant reliable, and Monsieur Gentil's own observations had convinced him that shells do actually grow. Jefferson listened carefully, reviewed the opposing arguments, and returned to the conclusion he had reached in his *Notes.* As he now stated it: "One . . . who had rather have no opinion than a false one, will suppose this question one of those beyond the investigation of human sagacity; or wait till further and fuller observations enable him to decide it."

Not long after his return from southern France to Paris, Jefferson sent David Rittenhouse the article Monsieur de la Sauvagiere, Voltaire's informant, had written on the growth of shells. With it went an explanation that the best Jefferson could say for the theory was that it was "not impossible"—though he himself could not accept it.

As we see Jefferson did not dismiss geology. He later induced Samuel L. Mitchill, professor of geology at Columbia College, to translate Cuvier's *Essay on the Theory of the Earth*.[22] And though he gave it a secondary place, he included geology in the curriculum of the University of Virginia.

5

Meteorology

•

With the possible exception of agriculture, gardening, and allied matters, no other scientific field held Jefferson's interest like meteorology, in which he appears to have made himself the best-informed American of his day. Even before the Revolutionary War he held that knowledge of the weather is to be accurately established only through simultaneous observations made at considerable distances apart. In this he was far in advance of the practices of his time.[1]

There had been climatological observations in America before Jefferson. The Reverend John Campanus of the Swedes' Fort near Wilmington, Delaware, had kept weather records as early as 1644–1645. Paul Dudley, Chief Justice of Massachusetts, had kept records at Boston for 1729–1730. Dr. John Lining of Charleston, South Carolina, had recorded temperature, pressure, humidity, and precipitation from 1738 to 1750, and Professor John Winthrop of Harvard College, physicist and astronomer, had kept meteorological records from 1742 to 1778.[2] Benjamin

Franklin had interested himself in such matters as the origin of our northeast storms, land temperature and temperatures of the Gulf Stream, and the relative humidity of America compared with that of Europe. Lewis Beck, too, had made significant contributions to America's knowledge of her climate.

During Jefferson's lifetime the American Philosophical Society and the Surgeon General's Office of the United States Army also concerned themselves with the problems. Before the end of the War of 1812, Dr. James Tilton, Physician and Surgeon General of the Army, issued a directive to hospital surgeons to make weather recordings. But it was not until after the reorganization of the Army in 1818 that the new Surgeon General, Dr. Joseph Lovell, put Dr. Tilton's plans into extensive operation. The initiator of vaccination into America, Dr. Benjamin Waterhouse, "hospital surgeon and director of Department No. 2, Northern Division" of the Army, had kept a meteorological journal, dated July, 1816, the earliest preserved in the Army Medical Library. The year of Jefferson's death, 1826, the first meteorological publication by the Medical Department of the Army appeared.[3]

It was Jefferson himself, however, who had taken the lead in meteorological investigations. Wherever the reader of Jefferson turns, he meets evidences of Jefferson's excited interest in and detailed knowledge of climate. A letter to William Short about America's new Constitution opens with some observations on the weather. A letter to President James Madison on problems of the War of 1812, concludes with the statement that at Monticello "we have had three days of excessive heat. The thermometer on the 16th was at 92°, on the 17th 92½, and yesterday at 93°. It had never before exceeded 92½° at this place; at least within the periods of my observations." During the tremendous events of early July, 1776, Jefferson recorded that on July 2 at 6:00 A.M. the temperature was at 78°, whereas at 9:00 P.M. it was at 74°; on July 3 at 5:30 A.M. the thermometer stood at 71½° and at 8:10 that night it stood at 74°; and on July 4 at 6:00 A.M. it was at 68°, while at 9:00 that night it was at 73½°. The Fourth of July, 1776, was obviously a pleasant day; the highest reading recorded by Jefferson (at 1:00 P.M.) was 76°. Jefferson was also busy at this momentous time equipping himself with proper instruments. On July 4 he "pd Sparhawk for a thermometer . . . £3 /15" and on July 8 he "pd Sparhawk for a barometer . . . £4 /10"—high prices, indicating instruments of high quality.[4]

On board the *Ceres* bound for Paris in 1784, as we have seen, Jefferson recorded temperature readings. Among the notes on a tour of southern France in 1787, were the following: "Ten morning observations of the thermometer, from the 20th to the 31st of March inclusive, made at Nismes, St. Remis, Aix and Marseilles, give me an average of 52½°, and 46° and 61° for the greatest and least morning heats. Nine afternoon observations, yield an average of 62⅔°, and 57° and 66° the greatest and least." Away from home, he delegated his daughters to keep up the weather recordings at Monticello. Other of his interests, the flights of birds, the appearance of insects, the leafing of trees, and so forth, were correlated with his interest in weather data.

He became an unofficial weather bureau. Friends wrote for information which he supplied from his own multitudinous records or from data he had collected from other sources. It was to him that Volney turned for material on the climate of America, to receive accurate records covering the winters of 1779, 1789, 1793, 1796, and 1797. The diaries he kept during his two terms as President contain many notations on the climate. Referring to them he was able to inform Dr. Nathaniel Chapman, founder of the Medical Institute of Philadelphia and first President of the American Medical Association, that from 1802 to

1809 inclusive "the average fall of snow of the seven winters was only fourteen and a half inches, and that the ground was covered but sixteen days in each winter on an average of the whole. The maximum in any one winter, during that period, was twenty-one inches fall, and thirty-four days on the ground."

His records were kept replenished by a constant stream of information from friends and correspondents. The planter William Dunbar, who was also a scientist and explorer, sent him data from near Natchez, Mississippi, entitled "Meteorological Observation for One Year from Jan. 31, 1800. Made at The Forest Four and a Half Miles Northeast of the Mississippi." Jefferson had this account published in the American Philosophical Society's *Transactions* and Dunbar elected a member. These data "were the earliest meteorological records in the Mississippi Valley." [5] Jefferson received from Dr. Hugh Williamson a similar account of climatic conditions at Quebec. Comparing Quebec with Natchez, he wondered how anybody could choose to live where it was so cold.

Jefferson's own *Weather Memorandum Book* was kept up from 1776 to 1820. These records show that on January 21, 1810, the thermometer in his greenhouse registered 21.3°, whereas his bedroom was 37° and the outside air 9¾°.[6]

This interest may have started in his student years at Williamsburg (1760–1767), where he had the advantage of intimate association with such "philosophical" gentlemen as the naturalist and mathematician, Professor William Small, George Wythe, the scholarly lawyer in whose office he studied, and Francis Fauquier, colonial Governor of Virginia, who was interested in meteorology and, among other things, had written an account of an unusual hailstorm in Williamsburg for the Royal Society of England. Professor Dumas Malone, in his *Jefferson the Virginian,* surmises that Jefferson "may have gained from Fauquier his first ideas about the regular recording of the temperature and winds." [7] In 1772 Jefferson and his friend Reverend James Madison, later President of William and Mary College, began a five-year program of simultaneous weather observations at Williamsburg and Monticello— 1772 to 1777.

Jefferson used these observations in his *Notes on Virginia,* in a passage written in a response to a request for information from the French inquirer Barbé-Marbois. For the sake of simplicity Jefferson here digests his entire five-year data into monthly averages, with some explanatory accompanying comments. (See p. 136)

Observations upon wind direction were made two or three times a day, or, as we can see in the table, 337 times in the five Januaries recorded, 276 in the five Februaries, etc.

From information largely derived from other sources, Jefferson informs Barbé-Marbois that proceeding along the same parallel of latitude westwardly, the climate of Virginia becomes colder until the summit of the Alleghenies is reached. From that point, the trend is reversed until one reaches the Mississippi River which, according to travelers, is warmer than the seacoast. In further proof certain of its vegetables and animals are not found along the coast. Catalpas "grow spontaneously on the Mississippi, as far as the latitude of 37°, and reeds as far as 38°. Parroquets even winter on the Scioto, in the 39th degree of latitude." In the summer of 1779 the thermometer reached 90° at Monticello, 96° at Williamsburg, and 110° at Kaskaskia.

According to Jefferson's and Madison's figures, Monticello's temperature averaged 6⅓° cooler than Williamsburg's, but some allowance must be made for the fact that Monticello is 52' and 22" north of Williamsburg. There is also a difference in their barometer readings. Taking "contemporary observations of between five and

Months	Fall of rain, etc., in inches.	Least and greatest daily heat, by Fahrenheit's thermometer	Winds.								
			N.	N.E.	E.	S.E.	S.	S.W.	W.	N.W.	Total.
Jan...	3.102	38½ to 44	73	47	32	10	11	78	40	46	337
Feb..	2.049	41 to 47½	61	52	24	11	4	63	30	31	276
Mar..	3.95	48 to 54½	49	44	38	28	14	83	29	33	318
April.	3.68	56 to 62½	35	44	54	19	9	58	18	20	257
May	2.871	63 to 70½	27	36	62	23	7	74	32	20	281
June..	3.751	71½ to 78¾	22	34	43	24	13	81	25	25	267
July..	4.497	77 to 82½	41	44	75	15	7	95	32	19	328
Aug...	9.153	76½ to 81	43	52	40	30	9	103	27	30	334
Sept..	4.761	69½ to 74¼	70	60	51	18	10	81	18	37	345
Oct...	3.633	61¼ to 66½	52	77	64	15	6	56	23	34	327
Nov..	2.617	47¾ to 53½	74	21	20	14	9	63	35	58	294
Dec..	2.877	43 to 48¾	64	37	18	16	10	91	42	56	334
Total.	47.038	8 A.M. to 4 P.M.	611	548	521	223	109	926	351	409	3,698

six weeks" as his basis, Jefferson finds the air at Monticello .784 of an inch lighter than at the coast, but again allowance must here be made for Monticello's altitude—500 feet.

He found "the most remarkable difference" in the winds. He reduces 421 simultaneous observations on wind direction, made over a period of nine months, to the following tabulation:

	N.E.	S.E.	S.W.	N.W.	Total
Williamsburg	127	61	132	101	421
Monticello	32	91	126	172	421

Thus the northeast wind predominates at Williamsburg, the northwest wind at Monticello. The different effect of these two winds upon a human being, he observes, is very great. The northeast "is loaded with vapor," brings with it "a distressing chill," and is "heavy and oppressive to the spirits." But the northwest wind is "dry, cooling, elastic, and animating."

Jefferson next calls Barbé-Marbois's attention to the problem of air pockets, unexpected "bodies of warm air." They pass too quickly for scientific investigation, he says, but he judges their temperature to be approximately that of the human body. They seem to be "about twenty to thirty feet in diameter horizontally." Their height is not known but it appears probable to Jefferson that they are "globular volumes wafted or rolled along with the wind." "Their cause," he feels, "must be sought for in the atmosphere itself" rather than in any source like forest fires and so forth. He notes these "constant circumstances: . . . a dry air; a temperature as warm, at least, as that of the spring or autumn; and a moderate current of wind. They are most frequent about sun-set; rare in the middle parts of the day; and I do not recollect having ever met with them in the morning."

Comments upon barometric readings follow. "Variation in the weight of our atmosphere . . . is not equal to two inches of mercury," observes Jefferson, citing observations made by himself and Reverend Madison, and by "a gentleman, who has observed his barometer many years." Simultaneous observations at Monticello and Williamsburg showed "the variations in the weight of air" to be "simultaneous and corresponding in these two places."

Changes in and extremes of heat and cold next engage Jefferson's attention. These he finds to be "very sudden and great." In the summer of 1766 the mercury at Williamsburg reached 98°; in the winter of 1780 it dropped to 6°, the highest temperatures occurring at 4 P.M., the lowest at dawn. Such extremes are "very distressing," Jefferson admits, but he argues, patriotically, that such matters are relative, "a Siberian would have considered them as scarcely a sensible variation." Jefferson observes that: "At Jenniseitz . . . in latitude 58°27', we are told that the cold in 1735 sunk the mercury by Fahrenheit's scale to 126° below nothing; and the inhabitants of the same country use stove rooms two or three times a week, in which they stay two hours at a time, the atmosphere of which raises the mercury to 135° above nothing. Late experiments show that the human body will exist in rooms heated to . . . 347° of Fahrenheit's, and 135° above boiling water." By that standard Virginia's range, from 6° to 98°, was indeed insignificant.

Frosts do not appear to "depend merely on the degree of cold; much less on the air's being at the freezing point." White frosts frequently occur at 47°, have killed young corn at 48°, and have been known to occur even as high as 54°. Black frost and ice have occurred even at 38½°. Therefore "other circumstances must be combined with this cold to produce frost." The lack of frost on mountains must be due partly to "the want of dew" at such high altitudes, as he has confirmed by "twelve years' observations" of this phenomenon!

Some people, Jefferson remarks, may find a "more satisfactory estimate of [Virginia's] climate . . . by noting the
plants which grow here." He lists the fig, pomegranate,
artichoke, and European walnut. No shelter is required
for lettuce and endive in mild winters, he points out,
though generally they do need a slight covering. The aloe
lived in Williamsburg even through the severe winter
of 1779–1780.

Jefferson declares that a "change in our climate . . .
is taking place very sensibly. Both heats and colds are become much more moderate within the memory even of
the middle-aged." Snows also are "less frequent and less
deep." Nor do they remain on the ground as long as
formerly. Old people have told him, he says, that "the
earth used to be covered with snow about three months
in every year." This has proved disadvantageous to fruits,
whose budding was formerly delayed long enough to
prevent damage by a late cold spell. Now it is not rare
for fruit to be killed in the bud. Another observed change
in Virginia climate is in wind drift. Winds from the east
and southeast "have advanced into the country very
sensibly within the memory of people now living. They
formerly did not penetrate far above Williamsburg. They
are now frequent at Richmond, and every now and then
reach the mountains. They deposit most of their moisture,
however, before they get that far. As the lands become
more cleared, it is probable they will extend still further
westward." No problem connected with the climate of
America came in for more discussion in Jefferson's day
than these changes. Land clearance and its effects on climate were debated up and down the entire eastern seaboard of the United States and even in Europe.

Finally Jefferson discusses the phenomenon of "looming," the principal effects of which are to distort distant
objects or to make them appear larger than they actually
are. This phenomenon has often been observed at Monti-

cello. "A solitary mountain about forty miles off in the South" is shaped like "a regular cone," but through looming, "it sometimes subsides almost totally in the horizon; sometimes it rises more acute and more elevated; sometimes it is hemispherical; and sometimes its sides are perpendicular, its top flat, and as broad as its base." Neither refraction nor concomitant atmospheric conditions can explain it, Jefferson having found "no particular state, either in the weight, moisture, or heat of the atmosphere, necessary to produce this." The "only constant circumstances are its appearance in the morning only, and on objects at least forty or fifty miles distant."

On its publication Jefferson's *Notes on Virginia* drew world-wide attention to him as a true scientist as well as a statesman.

As we have seen Jefferson's exactness and interest in simultaneous observations carried over into his correspondence. In a letter written in 1790, from New York, to his son-in-law Thomas Mann Randolph, he noted:

We have had here a series of as disagreeable weather as I have seen. It is now raining and snowing most furiously, & has been doing so all night. As soon as I get into the house I have hired, which will be the 1st. of May, I will propose to you to keep a diary of the weather here & wherever you shall be, exchanging observations from time to time. I should like to compare the two climates by contemporary observations. My method is to

1790			Monticello		
Feb.	Morning		Afternoon		Miscellaneous
1	39	c	—	far	
2	46	r		c	
3	29	c	31	c	
4		carhs	—	far	
5	30	f	—	c	
6	25	f	30	5	
7	54	f	—	f	
8	42	f	43	c	

make two observations a day, the one as early as possible in the morning, the other from 3. to 4. oclock [*sic*], because I have found 4 oclock the hottest & day light the coldest point of the 24. hours. I state them in an ivory pocket book in the following form, & copy them out once a week.

The 1st column is the day of the month & 2d the thermometer in the morning. The 4th do. in the evening. The 3d the weather in the morning. The 5th do. in the afternoon. The 6th is for miscellanies, such as the appearance of birds, leafing & flowering of trees, frosts remarkably late or early, Aurora borealis, &c. In the 3d and 5th columns, a. is *after:* c, cloudy: f, fair: h: hail: r rain; s, snow. Thus, carhs, means, *cloudy after rain, hail, & snow:* whenever it has rained, hailed or snowed between two observations I wrote it thus, far (i.e. fair afternoon) cas (cloudy after snow) &c. Otherwise the falling weather would escape notation. I distinguished weather into fair or cloudy, according as the sky is more or less than half covered with clouds. I observe these things to you, because in order that our observations may present a full comparison of the two climates, they should be kept on the same plan. I have no barometer here & was without one at Paris. Still if you chuse to take barometrical observations you can insert a 3d. morning column and a 3d. afternoon column.[8]

Jefferson's most ambitious early scheme for ascertaining the climate of the United States and its probable causes was recalled in a letter from Monticello to his friend Volney in 1797. Had his idea been carried out, we should have had the beginnings of a weather service upon a national scale even before the American Revolution. Jefferson's letter also indicates his early recognition of the potential role of scientific organizations.

I am sorry you have received so little information on the subject of our winds. I had once (before our revolution[ary] war) a project on the same subject. As I had then an extensive acquaintance over this State, I meant to have engaged some person in every county of it, giving them each a thermometer, to observe that and the winds twice a day, for one year, to wit, at sunrise and at four P.M. (the coldest and the warmest point of the twentyfour hours,) and to communicate their observations to me at the end of the year. I should then have selected the days in which it appeared that the winds blew to a centre within the State, and have made a map of them, and seen how far they had analogy with the temperature of the air. I meant this to be merely a specimen to be communicated to the Philosophical Society at Philadelphia, in order to engage them, by means of their correspondents, to have the same thing done in every State, and through a series of years. By seizing the days when the winds centred in any part of the United States, we might, in time, have come to some of the causes which determine the direction of the winds, which I suspect to be very various. But this long-winded project was prevented by the war which came upon us, and since that I have been far otherwise engaged.

Jefferson's activities made him impatient over the slow advance of meteorology. "Of all the departments of science," he wrote in 1822, "no one seems to have been less advanced for the last hundred years than that of meteorology. The new chemistry indeed has given us a new principle of the generation of rain, by proving water to be a composition of different gases, and has aided our theory of meteoric lights. Electricity stands where Dr. Franklin's early discoveries placed it, except with its new modification of galvanism. But the phenomena of snow, hail, halo, aurora borealis, haze, looming, etc., are as yet very imperfectly understood."

In a letter from Monticello, July, 1824, which Jefferson wrote to Lewis Beck, a physician who achieved note as a scientist, we see that even in extreme old age Jefferson still cherished plans for the recording of weather data on a national scale and the discovery of meteorological laws.

Thanking Beck for receipt of his recent pamphlet on the climate of the West (the area more generally designated today by our term "Midwest"), which he has read "with great satisfaction," he applauds it as a step toward a "satisfactory theory" of the climate of America. "Mine was," he remarks about his own earlier work, "perhaps the first attempt, not to form a theory, but to bring together the few facts then known, and suggest them to public attention." But this was before the West had been opened up. Now, with increasing scientific knowledge of this vast territory, we may expect "after a few years more of observation and collection of facts . . . a theory of solid foundation." Jefferson next passes to an analysis of how such facts are to be gathered and what facts are pertinent to valid conclusions. "Years are requisite for this steady attention to the thermometer, to the plants growing there, the times of their leafing and flowering, its animal inhabitants, beasts, birds, reptiles and insects; its prevalent winds, quantities of rain and snow, temperature of fountains, and other indexes of climate."

Then he arrives at a favorite idea. We want, he says, a similar painstaking and complete observation "for all the States, and the work should be repeated once or twice in a century, to show the effect of clearing and culture towards changes of climate. My Notes [i.e., *Notes on Virginia*] give a very imperfect idea of what our climate was, half a century ago, at this place, which being nearly central to the State may be taken for its medium." He has recently completed "seven years of close and exact observation" and has prepared a new estimate of the climate of Virginia, "which may some day be added to the former work." Jefferson hopes that "something like this is doing in the other States, which, when all shall be brought together, may produce theories meriting confidence." He concludes with the desire that Beck himself "will not be inattentive to this service" in the future, that he will make a second set of observations in the West and "at the distance of another half century."

Nowhere do we find a better example of Jefferson's own work on climate than in his summary of the "seven years of close and exact observation" which he referred to in his letter to Beck. They are here presented as they appeared in

The Virginia Literary Museum, and Journal of Belles Lettres, Arts, Sciences, &c.

A table of thermometrical observations, made at Monticello, from January 1, 1810, to December 31, 1816.

	1810.			1811.			1812.			1813.			1814.			1815.			1816.			mean of each month.
	max.	mean	min.	max.	mean	min.	max.	mean	min.	max.	mean	min.	max.	mean	min.	max.	mean	min.	max.	mean	min.	
Jan.	5½	38	66	20	39	68	5½	34	53	13	35	59	16½	36	55	8½	35	60	16	34	51	36
Feb.	12	43	73				21	40	75	19	38	65	14	42	65	16	36	57	15½	41	62	40
Mar.	20	41	61	28	44	78	31½	46	70	28	48	71	13½	43	73	31	54	80	25	48	75	46
April	42	55	81	36	58	86	31	56	86	40	59	80	35	59	82	41	60	82	30	49	71	56½
May	43	64	88	46	62	79	39	60	86	46	62	81	47	65	91	37	58	77	43	60	79	61½
June	53	70	87	58	73	89	58	74	92½	54	75	93	57	69	87	54	71	88	51	70	86	72
July	60	75	88	60	76	89½	57	75	91	61	75	94½	60	74	89	63	77	89	51	71	86	75
Aug.	55	71	90	59	75	85	61	71	87	62	74	92	56	75	88	58	72	84	51	73	90	73
Sep.	50	70	81	50	67	81	47	68	75	54	69	83	52	70	89	45	61	82	54	63	90½	67
Oct.	82	57	82	35	62	85	39	55	80	32	53	70	37	58	83	38½	59	76	37	57	73	57
Nov.	27	44	69	32	45	62	18	43	76	20	48	71	23	47	71	20	46	70	24	46	71	45½
Dec.	14	32	62	20	38	49	13	35	63	18	37	53	18	38	59	12	36	57	23	43	69	37
mean of clear weather.	55			58			55			56			56⅓			55½			54½			55½

In the matter of climatic preferences, Jefferson was convinced that he could never learn to bear up under a cold climate. He agreed with Rittenhouse "that it is altogether unaccountable how any man can stay in a cold country who can find room in a warm one." To another correspondent he wrote: "The Canadian glows with delight in his sleigh and snow; the very idea of which gives me the shivers." It was his opinion that no poet can flourish north of the Alps, for "a poet is as much a creature of climate as an orange or palm tree." [9] In writing to John Adams about the decrepitudes of old age, four years before he died, he spoke of his enjoyment of the summer. But, he added, "I shudder at the approach of winter, and wish I could sleep through it with the dormouse, and only wake with him in spring, if ever."

For Jefferson his beloved Monticello and its vicinity had about the best climate to be met with anywhere, though he could be enthusiastic over the southern coast of France and speculated over the pleasures of living at Madeira. But his loyalty never swerved from the Monticello region, "the Eden of the U. S. for soil, climate, navigation & health." [10] Whenever he invited foreigners or others for a visit, he always cited the enjoyments they might expect because of the excellent climate at Monticello, its beauty and agreeableness, its freedom from agues and fevers, its healthfulness as attested to by its many "nonagenaires," the "robust constitution of its inhabitants, and their numerous families." Among the inducements he offered to Nathaniel Bowditch, New England mathematician and astronomer, to join the faculty of the University of Virginia, was the claim that "there is not a healthier or more genial climate in the world." Wherever he went it delighted him to learn that buds and birds appeared earlier at Monticello.

To have the best climate and soil in America was, as a matter of fact, one of the unwritten States' Rights of this period—sectionalism reflected in pronouncements upon climate. North and South were each convinced of its superior climate. Jefferson commented on "the prejudices of every State against the climates of all those States south of itself." He was a defender of the southern climate. Traveling near Lake Champlain in the summer of 1791, he wrote his daughter Martha that he found nothing "in point of climate, which Virginia need envy." The heat was as excessive as that of Georgia or Carolina and there were as many fevers, agues, and bilious complaints as one would find in the South.[11]

Writing of his American travels, Volney remarked that "the southern people will terrify [anyone] from fixing [settling] in the north, by dwelling on their long and dreary winters, the hardships of excessive cold, the expence and apparatus which a bleak air and churlish occasion in living or cultivating the earth." In his turn the Northerner "boasts much of his health, robustness, and activity, the gifts of labour, a sparing soil, and inclement skies; and rails against the pestilential bogs of the southern states, their sultry and incessant heats, their tormenting insects, the slothful and luxurious habits, and the crazy constitutions of the people, their gambling, drunkenness, and tyranny over their slaves: all produced by the very nature of their soil, and its luxuriant fertility." Then both would join in decrying the climate and soil of the middle states. Even within a given section our traveler noticed rivalries. He cited a Floridian who maintained that his state had a better air than did the Carolinas or Georgia since these states were cursed with more "noxious exhalations" and had not Florida's fresh running streams to prevent stagnating ponds.[12]

New Englanders appear to have been the most vociferous, climaxed perhaps by Jeremy Belknap's bizarre claim that drunkards among New Hampshire's immigrants do not die early, the climate, apparently, preserving them.

They railed against the "effeminate Southerner" and his "lazy plains" and "fevers."

Other Southerners besides Jefferson were vigorous in countercharges. Among them was one, F. Budd of South Carolina, who used Scriptural analogies. He pointed out that its climate was in the same latitude as that of Jerusalem, "a climate that produced so quick vegetation, that made it a land of plenty, 'a land that flowed with milk and honey.' It was in this blessed climate, God Almighty placed his chosen people."

But though Americans might score each other's climate, they took a united stand against any foreign aspersions.

And in the international rivalry over climate Jefferson led the American contingent. Let us now turn to the theory of the effect of climate upon men and animals which was such a battleground for many leading eighteenth-century thinkers.

6

Miserable New World

•

Certain "scientific" European ideas disparaged American nature and climate. These ideas passed from the realm of science into problems of religion, morals, politics, law, literature, and even international relations.

The ideas were derived from the following assumption. The natural surroundings in which men, animals, insects, and plants live exert a tremendous force upon their physical condition: upon their health, height, girth, color, beauty or ugliness, numbers, species, varieties, and so forth. In the case of men and animals, their very sexual potency may be affected. And on man himself, the effect of his physical environment is felt also in his intellectual, nervous, moral, and social nature. Hence the very state of his society, its form of government, its laws, its religion, its customs, its artistic productivity, its misery or its happiness, is conditioned by natural environment.

The term used for this environmental factor was "climate." As used by eighteenth-century philosophers and scientists, it signified about what it does to us today: temperature, winds, humidity, rainfall, snow, aridity, degree of sunlight, purity or impurity of the air. Not infrequently it was extended to signify "nature" in general. Climate was often considered a result of certain other physical phenomena—mountains, lakes, rivers, marshes, forests, vegetation, clearings, and conditions of the soil, whose vegetative products were believed to influence the air.

Many European theories about the climate of the New World stated it to have malevolent effects upon its vegetation and fauna. These theories were of particular interest to Jefferson and his contemporaries. In his *Sketch Book* Washington Irving touched ironically on this subject. One of his reasons for desiring to travel in Europe, he said, was "an earnest desire to see the great men of the earth. . . . We have, it is true, our great men in America: not a city but has an ample share of them. I have mingled among them in my time, and been almost withered by the shade into which they cast me. . . . But I was anxious to see the great men of Europe; for I read in the works of various philosophers, that all animals degenerated in America, and man among the number. A great man of Europe, thought I, must therefore be as superior to a great man of America, as a peak of the Alps to a highland of the Hudson; and in this idea I was confirmed, by observing the comparative importance and swelling magnitude of many English travellers among us, who, I was assured, were very little people in their own country. I will visit this land of wonders, thought I, and see the gigantic race from which I am degenerated."

Few European ideas about the New World so angered Jefferson and other American thinkers as the supposed degenerating effects upon animal and plants caused by the physical nature and climate of America.

But before we go into that delusion it may be well to point out an opposite one to which it was diametrically opposed. This was the view held by romanticists, primitiv-

ists, sentimentalists, believers in natural goodness, moralists, Rousseauists, utopians, escapists, social and political
revolutionaries, objectors to restraint, and other seekers for
simplicity or for they knew not what. They saw civilization
as decadence, and the primitive as man's highest state,
pointing to India, Tahiti, Paraguay, and the Indians of
North America as examples.

The Scottish thinker Lord Monboddo, for example,
maintained that man in the state of nature "is much hap-
pier than he is in his civilized life, as it is conducted at
present in the nations of Europe. And the reason is plain,
that man, as well as other animals in the natural state, is
governed by instinct, that is divine intelligence prompting
him to do everything that is necessary for the preservation
of the individual and the continuation of the kind." Monboddo eulogizes the "gravity, love of liberty, public spirit,
friendship, hospitality, etc." of the natives of North America.[1]

Typical, too, are the expressions to be found in the
letters to his mother of Lord Edward Fitzgerald, who had
visited America twice, in 1781 and 1788–1789, and had
been adopted by the Bear Tribe of Indians. "Savages," he
wrote, "have all the real happiness of life, without any of
those inconveniences, or ridiculous obstacles of it, which
custom has introduced among us." After a perilous voyage
down the Mississippi to New Orleans, he wrote: "I should
like to give you an account of my voyage, but it would be
too long: it has done me a great deal of good. I have seen
human nature under almost all its forms. Everywhere it is
the same, but the wilder it is the more virtuous." [2]

Better known than either was Chateaubriand whom
Irving Babbitt, bitter modern anti-romanticist, drew upon
for examples of the foolishly exaggerated reactions of the
romantic traveler in the American wilds. Upon entering
the virgin forests west of Albany, New York, writes
Chateaubriand, "I was seized by a sort of intoxication of

independence: I went from tree to tree, to right and left, saying to myself, 'Here are no more roads or cities or monarchy or republic or presidents or kings or men.' And in order to find out if I was restored to my original rights I did various wilful things that made my guide furious. In his heart he believed me mad." [3]

Against this background of romantic idealization of the American Indian and the life next to nature in the New World,[4] an almost exactly contrary opinion was held by certain other influential thinkers of the eighteenth century. Chief among them was Georges Louis Leclerc, the world-famous Comte de Buffon (1707–1788), considered by many the leading naturalist of his time.

Buffon's prestige and influence were enormous. His *Histoire naturelle,* which began publication in 1749 and was finally completed by a collaborator in 1804, totaled forty-four volumes, and was universally considered an extraordinarily important contribution to science.

In France he was Director of the Jardin du Roi (the Jardin des Plantes) and of the Royal Museum, one of the forty immortals of the French Academy and Treasurer of the French Academy of Science. His ideas were reflected in the works of the Abbe de Pauw. The Marquis de Chastellux termed Buffon the man whom Nature had chosen for her "confident and interpreter." One of the great scientist Cuvier's most formidable tasks was to refute the errors of Buffon.

In his elaborate refutation of Buffon's strictures on the Americas (*Storia Antica del Messico* (1780)), the Mexican historian Clavigero nevertheless terms Buffon "the most diligent, the most accurate, and most eloquent naturalist of the age; perhaps there never was in the world one who made such progress in the knowledge of animals as he has done. . . ." William Robertson of Scotland, king's historiographer and prominent author of several histories, relied heavily upon Buffon for his passages on the animals of the

New World in his *History of America* (1777),[5] which was roundly criticized in America. Similarly Oliver Goldsmith, whose knowledge of natural history, according to Dr. Samuel Johnson, extended no further than an ability to distinguish a cow from a horse, relied upon Buffon as gospel in his *History of the Earth and Animated Nature.*

Buffon had the status almost of a living classic. In addition to the honors accorded him in France he had been elected member of the Academies of London, Edinburgh, Berlin, Saint Petersburg, Florence, Philadelphia, Boston. He was one of the earliest foreigners elected (1768) to the American Philosophical Society. During the Revolutionary War, M. Buffon sent the Society an elegantly bound edition of his *Histoire naturelle des oiseaux.* The Society sent him in return a modestly printed copy of its *Transactions.*[6] When Buffon was elected to membership in the American Academy of Arts and Sciences, January 30, 1782, the letter informing him of this honor terms him "so illustrious a member of the royal Academy of Sciences of Paris, and a Gentleman so extensively celebrated in the republic of letters, and whose name must do honor to every Philosophic Society, in whose catalogue it is enrolled." [7]

Acquaintance with Buffon's works and theories was widespread in America. Jefferson knew Buffon's works well before he met the sage himself in Paris. In his *Notes on the State of Virginia* he termed Buffon "the best informed of any naturalist who has ever written," and in referring to some corrections Buffon had made in his *Histoire naturelle* Jefferson commented: "The wonder is, not that there is yet something in the great work to correct, but that there is so little." Upon numerous occasions Jefferson turned to Buffon for facts, tables, and statistics.

John Adams might feel that Buffon lacked common sense, was too fond of paradox, too materialistic and irreligious; but the works of Buffon were in his library and he frequently discusses Buffon (along with other French philosophers, who, it might be added, were not to Adams's taste). Benjamin Franklin, in his *Autobiography*, terms Buffon "a philosopher deservedly of great reputation in France, and, indeed, all over Europe." It was Buffon who advised D'Alibard to make a correct translation of Franklin's work on electricity, which was published in Paris early in 1752. He was also influential in having Franklin's experiments with lightning repeated near Paris in the same year.[8] Franklin and Buffon enjoyed "very cordial" relations in Paris, where they had a wide circle of common acquaintances. From America Franklin sent Buffon seeds for the Jardin des Plantes. A few days before his death, April 16, 1788, Buffon sent Franklin a new edition of his *Histoire naturelle*.[9]

Benjamin Smith Barton, Pennsylvania physician and naturalist, in discussing the progress of population in America, uses Buffon's tables of probabilities. Ira Allen, brother of Ethan Allen, wishing to prove that Vermont has her fair share of the world's four-footed animals, uses Buffon's figures on the total number of quadrupeds. A writer in the magazine *American Museum* cites Linnaeus, Buffon, and other "celebrated" writers, in a discussion of longevity. To refute the theory of the degeneracy of animals in America, Timothy Dwight uses the figures given by Buffon, himself, for the weights of European animals, and says that these "will therefore not be questioned." To identify specimens for his museum Charles Willson Peale turned to the works of Buffon. Francis Hopkinson writes to Thomas Jefferson, June 28, 1786, that he will send to M. Buffon in Paris (where Jefferson was then acting as Ambassador) the foot, feathers, and description of a remarkable bird recently shot in New Jersey, though he is fearful that this may be a waste of time, for: "After all, it is more than probable that this may be no Curiosity to so great a natural Historian as Mr Buffon."

Some of Buffon's ideas lasted well into the nineteenth century. As evidence of his influence in England a critic cites "the typical children's books about animals of the years 1880–1900." He comments: "Long after Darwin made earlier views of animal nature untenable, Buffon's optimistic moralism tempered in many minds the ferocious struggle for existence." Bernard Shaw, he points out, asserts that in the earlier 1880's "every literate child knew Buffon's Natural History as well as he knew Esop's fables." [10] George Gaylord Simpson, estimating the position of Buffon among his contemporaries, terms him "the pope of eighteenth century zoologists." [11]

In the newly discovered continents across the Atlantic Ocean, according to this pope of science, "there is some combination of elements and other physical causes, something that opposes the amplification of animated Nature: there are obstacles to the development, and perhaps to the formation of large germs." This "combination of elements and other physical causes . . . must be referred to the quality of the earth and atmosphere, to the degree of heat and moisture, to the situation and height of mountains, to the quantity of running and stagnant waters, to the extent of forests, and, above all, to the inert condition of Nature in that country."

America has less heat and a greater degree of cold than have similar latitudes in Europe and elsewhere in the world. At Quebec, in the same latitude as Paris, the rivers freeze several feet thick every year, snow blankets the land for months each year, the birds disappear each winter, and so forth—which does not happen at Paris. Even America's torrid zone is colder: in Senegal the sun is scorching, whereas in Peru an agreeable temperature prevails. All of this is true because "America is so formed and situated, that every circumstance occurs in diminishing the action of heat." America's huge mountain ranges "bound the continent towards the west," and, with other factors, bar off the "east wind, which flows perpetually between the Tropics," and is cooler, when it reaches America, than it is in "Senegal, Guinea, &c., where it arrives impregnated with the accumulated heat acquired from all the lands and burning sands in its passage through Asia and Africa." Thus, "from the situation of the land alone in the New Continent, the heat must be greatly inferior to that of the Old. . . ."

There is also "a greater degree of moisture in America." The huge mountains, highest in the world, condense all the "aerial vapours" of the winds. This causes an infinite number of springs and ultimately "the greatest rivers in the world." This volume of running water is increased "for want of proper drains or outlets," which the natives have done nothing to correct. Lakes, rivers, marshes, and "stagnating waters cover immense tracts of land, augment the moisture of the air, and diminish its heat." The thick vegetation and endless forests hinder evaporation, while the "transpiration of so many vegetables, pressed close together, produces immense quantities of moist and noxious exhalations."

Furthermore America is in reality a *new* world, for it has "continued longer than the rest of the globe under the waters of the ocean." Just beneath the vegetable stratum one finds sea shells and madrepores forming large masses of limestone much softer than the free-stone of Europe. Another proof is the thinness of native inhabitants in America. America is, therefore a "new land, still untouched by the hand of man, and in which Nature had not time sufficient to accomplish her plans, or to unfold the whole extent of her productions."

"In these melancholy regions," laments Monsieur Buffon, "Nature remains concealed under her old garments, and never exhibits herself in fresh attire; being neither cherished nor cultivated by man, she never opens her fruitful and beneficent womb. Here the earth never saw

her surface adorned with those rich crops, which demonstrate her fecundity, and constitute the opulence of polished nations. In this abandoned condition, every thing
languishes, corrupts, and proves abortive. The air and the
earth, overloaded with humid and noxious vapours, are
unable either to purify themselves, or to profit by the
influence of the sun, who darts in vain his most enlivening
rays upon this frigid mass, which is not in a condition to
make suitable returns to his ardour. Its powers are limited
to the production of moist plants, reptiles, and insects, and
can afford nourishment only for cold men and feeble
animals."

America's fauna are pitiful. To begin with, there are
fewer species in America than in the Old World. Buffon
may not be quite certain as to their origin but he is certain
of their paucity. Taking two hundred species of quadrupeds as the total for the entire world, we find above 130
of them in the Old World and less than seventy in the
New. Subtracting those common to both continents, we
find that the New World has not above forty native
species. Such is the impotence of nature in America!

Moreover creatures in the New World are "modelled
upon a small scale." Even the largest animals are twenty
times smaller than those of the Old World. Their forms
are also "imperfect," their figures "awkward," their bodies
and members "ill proportioned." This is found in almost
all the animals in South America, "which alone can be
regarded as peculiar to the New World." How miserably
the anteaters and sloths are formed! They "have hardly
the powers of moving, or of eating their food. With much
difficulty they drag out a painful and languishing life in
the solitudes of the desert. . . ." And the humble animals
of America are "of gentle, tractable, and timid dispositions, very few ferocious, and none formidable."

As an illustrative contrast Buffon points to differences
between the tapir of America and the elephant of the Old

World. The tapir, or *tapiierete,* of Brazil, the largest quadruped of South America, which may be considered "the elephant of the New World," does not exceed "the size of a calf six months old!" And the poor tapir is described as "solitary, gentle, and timid . . . a gloomy, melancholy animal. He comes abroad in the night only and delights in the water, where he dwells oftener than on the land."

How different from the noble elephant! "If the human species be excepted, the elephant is the most respectable animal in the world." He is larger, stronger, and longer-lived than all other terrestrial creatures, and his intelligence "makes as near an approach to man as matter can approach spirit." Continuing his elephant rhapsody Buffon recalls a lovely female elephant of his acqaintance. As in other species she was gentler than the male. The affectionate creature "even caressed people with whom she was unacquainted." Buffon regrets that the elephant cannot thrive in temperate and cold climates. He cites the case of a young male elephant four years old sent to Louis XIV in 1668. He died at the age of seven despite a diet "managed with the greatest attention," of a sheaf of corn, eighty pounds of bread, and two pails of pottage mixed with four or five additional pounds of bread. This latter was varied with two parts of boiled rice. And every day he had twelve pints of wine! Individual cases aside, however, it is the dimensions and power of the elephant in general which so well proves to Buffon the contrast of the powers of nature in the New and the Old Worlds.

The miserable condition of animals in America can be explained by their degeneration under the effects of inferior climate, soil, and food, and neglect by the native inhabitants. Degeneracy has affected both those animals which have voluntarily migrated to America and those brought there by Europeans. All alike "shrink and diminish under a niggardly sky and an unprolific land, thinly peopled with wandering savages," in "a general contraction of animated Nature throughout the whole continent."

Furthermore, in her antipathy toward her newer continents, Nature "seems to have cherished the reptile, and enlarged the insect tribes" in the Americas. Though Senegal has longer serpents and larger lizards than South America, the difference between these creatures is not nearly so great as that between the quadrupeds of these countries. It is certain that insects "are no where so large as in South America." The world's largest spiders, beetles, caterpillars, and butterflies are to be found near Cayenne. The numbers of species are also greater there and there is a "prodigious multiplication of individuals." Toads, frogs, and similar unpleasant creatures are also very large in America.

Europeans showed a particular partiality toward America's noxious insects. Isaac Weld, who traveled in America in the years 1795 to 1799, printed a tall tale, quoting George Washington, that the mosquitoes around Skenesborough, New York, "used to bite through the thickest boot." In defense, Timothy Dwight, terming Weld a man of "ill-natured petulance," declared that he had had it from a gentleman of great respectability that what Washington had actually said was that the mosquitoes "bit through his stockings above his boots." Washington Irving satirized Weld in *Salmagundi,* in a set of fictitious notes offered for use by British travelers: "Newark—noted for its fine breed of fat mosquitoes—sting through the thickest boot—story about Gallynippers. . . ." And some Americans used the insect argument to prove the inconsistency of European philosophers. Could a continent be called impotent that produced such hordes of huge insects?

Buffon's portrayal of the indigenous inhabitants of the New World is of a piece with his account of its animals. Stating as a principle, that "man, in the savage state, is only a species of animal," he pictures the Indians of America as "wandering savages, who, instead of using this territory as a master, had no property or empire; and, having subjected neither the animals nor the elements, nor conquered the seas, nor directed the motions of the rivers, nor cultivated the earth, held only the first rank among animated beings, and existed as creatures of no consideration in Nature, a kind of weak automatons, incapable of improving or seconding her intentions. She treated them rather like a stepmother than a parent, by denying them the invigorating sentiment of love, and the strong desire of multiplying their species. . . . In the savage, the organs of generation are small and feeble. He has no hair, no beard, no ardour for the female." His strength is less than that of the European. Though his sensations are less acute than the European, he is "more timid and cowardly." Also he "has no vivacity, no activity of mind." Minus his physical appetite for victuals and drink, he would remain on his couch whole days in "stupid repose."

His estrangement from society is due to his weak sexual desire, "the most precious spark of Nature's fire." Having "no ardour for women," he has of course no love for mankind. Lacking in this "most lively and most tender of all attachments" he suffers a weakening of his other sensations, so that he has almost no love for parents or for children. Families are small and their ties are weak. This coldness extends ultimately to all of society. The Indian's "heart is frozen," his "society cold," and his "empire cruel." Look at his treatment of women, who are but servants and beasts of burden.

It is evident, therefore, says Buffon, that "man makes no exception to what has been advanced. Nature, by denying him the faculty of love, has abused and contracted him more than any other animal." And since the weak and impotent native has done nothing toward subjugating animals, draining off bogs, clearing forests, and advancing in society, he shares the responsibility for the miserable condition of the New World.

Buffon's fantasies were reflected and elaborated upon in the work of numerous followers and popularizers. Among the most conspicuous were Corneille De Pauw, the Abbé Raynal, and William Robertson, the Scotch historian.[12] In his *Recherches philosophiques sur les Américains* De Pauw applied Buffon's ideas in such an exaggerated form that he may be credited with having precipitated the great eighteenth-century controversy over the American climate.

According to De Pauw immense areas of America are covered with "putrid and death-dealing waters" over which hang "fogs of poisonous salts." In the swamps grow "poisonous trees." America is "overrun with serpents, lizards, reptiles, and monstrous insects." Swollen with the poison they drink, these have grown to "prodigious size and multiplied beyond imagination." Frogs in Louisiana have "weighed thirty-seven pounds and bellowed like calves." America is so cold that in Illinois the ground is often frozen to a depth of thirty feet. America lacks large quadrupeds and her animals are "often ugly and deformed." Even domestic animals brought over from Europe have "either degenerated or failed to reproduce," with the hog as the only exception. Transplanted trees likewise have degenerated.

Syphilis, which originated in America, infects all human beings and many animals. In certain parts of the country one may contract the disease merely by "breathing the pestilential air." The natives have no physical strength. Their lack of virility is shown by the fact that many men have milk in their breasts. They are stoical under torture not because of their bravery but because "they are too weak and devoid of the finer sensibilities." The characteristic mental quality of the Indian may be termed "stupid insensibility."

All this is attributed to the cold moist air of America, the results of a new deluge "many centuries later than Noah's."

We may deal more briefly with William Robertson and the Abbé Raynal. Robertson's *History of America*, published in 1777, makes references to De Pauw and quotes Buffon as final authority, in reiterating their charges against America. Interestingly enough, Robertson points out the differences between the ideas of De Pauw and Buffon and those of Rousseau.

Abbé Raynal, in his *Histoire philosophique et politique des établissements et du commerce des européens dans les deux Indes* (1770), expresses some agreement but even greater disagreements. The Mexicans, he says, are the opposite of being cowardly and mentally deficient. "Animals and plants may have degenerated in America, but probably because of want of care, failure to renew stock, or 'the law of climate which wills every people, every animal and vegetable species to grow and flourish in its native soil.' " One of Raynal's statements which Jefferson found particularly offensive was that "America has not yet produced a good poet, an able mathematician, a single genius in a single art, or a single science." [13] However, Raynal's work furnished Europe with an array of data to support arguments against slavery and brought home "to the conscience of Europeans the miseries which had befallen the natives of the New World through the Christian conquerors and their priests." [14] And his account of the American conflict with England was favorable to the colonies.[15] Yet the extent to which he agreed with De Pauw made him a co-target of American counter attack. In later editions of Raynal's work, he retracted what he had said for North America, but not for South America.[16]

7

Jefferson vs. Buffon

•

To correct the misrepresentations of his country made by
Buffon, De Pauw, Raynal, and others was a task that appealed to Jefferson's love of truth, his distaste for theory
disassociated from facts, his scientific scruples, and—above
all—his patriotism. His was the first full-length refutation
of the theory of degeneracy made by a man of standing
in the New World, and he was long remembered by his
fellow countrymen for it.

His refutation appeared in his *Notes on the State of
Virginia,* written as a reply to a series of twenty-three
questions asked by the Marquis François de Barbé-
Marbois, secretary of the French legation in Philadelphia,
who had been delegated to secure this information by his
government. Soon after his retirement from the governor-
ship of Virginia, Jefferson went to work in earnest upon
his answers and had the manuscript in the hands of
Marbois by April, 1782.[1] Three years later, when Jefferson
was in Paris as Ambassador, his *Notes* were finally published. They went through many editions during his
lifetime.

Marbois's twenty-three queries sought information on Virginia's boundaries, rivers, seaports, mountains, falls, caverns, mines, vegetation, animals, Indians, meteorology, population, state constitution and form of government, laws, education, roads, religions, manufactures and commerce, agriculture, money, taxes, and state histories and papers. Marbois's request was opportune, for Jefferson had long been preparing to do just such a book. "I had always made it a practice," he wrote, in reference to his *Notes,* "whenever an opportunity occurred, of obtaining any information of our country which might be of use to me in any station, to commit it to writing." Through the drafts of the manuscript Jefferson sought additional or corroborative data from his friends, to whom he submitted the text for comments and additions. He sought to make his finished product as thorough and accurate as possible.

Professor Dumas Malone, in his *Jefferson the Virginian,* cites a letter from Jefferson to his explorer friend and neighbor Thomas Walker, to whom he had sent "that part [of his manuscript] particularly which relates to the position of Monsr. de Buffon. . . . I wish to have [it] very correct in matters of fact," he said. Calling attention to the table of animals he had made, he asked Walker to send him the heaviest weights of American animals that he knew, "from the mouse to the mammoth." He also turned to half a dozen qualified observers with what amounted to a questionnaire about the moose. At this stage, the bigger the animals the better. He sought precise information or reasonable conjectures.[2]

Summing up Buffon's theories for his readers, Jefferson wrote: "The opinion advanced by the Count de Buffon, is 1. That the animals common both to the old and new world are smaller in the latter. 2. That those peculiar to the new are on a smaller scale. 3. That those which have been domesticated in both have degenerated in America; and 4. That on the whole it exhibits fewer species.

And the reason he thinks is, that the heats of America are less; that more waters are spread over its surface by nature, and fewer of these drained off by the hand of man. In other words, that *heat* is friendly, and moisture adverse to the production and development of large quadrupeds."

Jefferson doubts that America is more humid than other continents, but feels that there is insufficient data to make any conclusions. However, for the sake of argument, he says, suppose that America actually is more humid; it must therefore follow that moisture is unfriendly to animal growth. Yet all experience contradicts this. Heat and moisture intensify vegetable growth, which is the food of animals. In humid climates we therefore find animals "not only multiplied in their number, but improved in their bulk." In fact, Monsieur Buffon himself says just this in another part of his own work, where he places the world's largest cattle in Denmark, the Ukraine, and other places where the climate is cold and humid. Thus cold and moisture have actually increased these animals' dimensions —"in direct opposition to the hypothesis" that their contraries, dryness and heat, are necessary for greatest growth! Further, America's latitude brings her more heat than Europe. Grant that Europe may be drier, balance these two facts, and we must conclude that these two parts of the world are "equally adapted . . . to animal productions."

Next he offers "a comparative view of the quadrupeds of Europe and America, presenting them to the eye in three different tables." The weights of the larger animals are expressed in pounds and decimals; those of the smaller in ounces and decimals. Those marked with an asterisk (*) "are actual weights of particular subjects, deemed among the largest of their species. Those marked thus +, are furnished by judicious persons, well acquainted with the species, and saying, from conjecture only, what the largest individual they had seen would probably have weighed."

The other weights are those given by Buffon and Daubenton, Buffon's assistant at the Jardin des Plantes, from specimens they have examined. "This circumstance," says Jefferson, "must be remembered where their weights and mine stand opposed; the latter being stated not to produce a conclusion in favor of the American species, but to justify a suspension of opinion until we are better informed, and a suspicion, in the meantime, that there is no uniform difference in favor of either; which is all I pretend."

The following is a selection made from items where Jefferson was able to give comparative weights:

	Europe, lb.	America, lb.
Bear	153.7	*410
Red deer	288.8	*273
Beaver	18.5	* 45
Otter	8.9	12
Marten	1.9	6
Flying squirrel	2.2 [oz.]	4 [oz.]

In his discussion following this table, Jefferson points out inconsistencies in Buffon's own figures and cites authorities who disagree with his data. He further berates the readiness of European philosophers to give credence to the reports of ignorant, unobservant, unskilled, inaccurate, and prejudiced travelers who have filled Europe with old wives' tales about America. We are yet "unripe," says Jefferson, for an accurate comparison of the animals of the two countries. Buffon himself has found it necessary to make revisions in his later editions. Jefferson commends his candor and his desire for accuracy.

Summarizing from his first table and his accompanying discussion, Jefferson concludes: "The result of this view then is, that of twenty-six quadrupeds common to both countries, seven are said to be larger in America, seven of equal size, and twelve not sufficiently examined. So that the first table impeaches the first member of the assertion, that of the animals common to both countries, the American are smallest, 'et cela sans aucune exception.' It shows it is not just, in all the latitude in which its author has advanced it, and probably not to such a degree as to found a distinction between the two countries."

Jefferson then turns to his second table: animals indigenous to one country only. The list for Europe includes:

	lb.
Wild boar	280
Wild sheep	56
Rabbit	3.4
Polecat	3.3
	oz.
Squirrel	12
Rat	7.5
Mole	1.2
Mouse	.6

The list for America includes:

	lb.
Tapir	534
Jaguar	218
Cougar of North America	75
Paca	32.7
Sloth. Unau	27.25
Raccoon	16.5
Great Gray Squirrel	+2.7
Fox Squirrel of Virginia	+2.625

In his accompanying discussion Jefferson retorts to Buffon's remark that the tapir, the "elephant" of America, is but the size of a small cow, by pointing out that "the wild boar, the elephant of Europe, is little more than half that size." Furthermore, analysis of the second table indicates that "there are eighteen quadrupeds peculiar to Europe; more than four times as many, to wit, seventy-four, peculiar to America; that the first of these seventy-four [the tapir] weighs more than the whole column of Europeans; and consequently this second table disproves the second member of the assertion, that the animals peculiar to the new world are on a smaller scale, so far as that assertion relied on European animals for support. [It should be noticed that Jefferson distinguishes between European and African]; and it is in full opposition to the theory which makes the animal volume to depend on the circumstances of *heat* and *moisture.*"

The third table, given here complete, lists animals domesticated in Europe and America:

	Europe, lb.	America, lb.
Cow	765	*2500
Horse	...	1366
Ass	...	....
Hog	...	*1200
Sheep	...	*125
Goat	...	*80
Dog	67.6	....
Cat	7	....

In his discussion accompanying the third table Jefferson admits that some of these animals in America may weigh less than their original stock. But this is attributable to poor feeding and care, not to climate. Where given proper care these domestic animals are as large as those of Europe. American breeders have even been known to improve upon imported stock within a two-year period. A horse standing four feet, eight and six-tenths inches high and weighing four hundred and thirty-six pounds is rated medium by Monsieur Daubenton but would be rated "small" in America. Daubenton has dissected a horse six feet, one and seven-tenths inches high, which is six inches taller than any Jefferson has seen, but he may not have seen the largest horses in America. Jefferson knows of bullocks in Connecticut and Rhode Island which, when

slaughtered, weighed 2,500, 2,200, and 2,100 pounds net.
He himself saw a hog in Williamsburg in April, 1769,
which weighed 1,050 pounds after the blood, entrails, and
hair had been removed. "Yet this hog was not within
fifty generations of the European stock." Asses, the most
neglected of all domesticated animals in America, are
nevertheless larger than those measured by Daubenton.
Goats, similarly neglected in America, are, however, prolific, bearing two to three times a year, and producing
from one to five kids at a birth.

Jefferson concludes that the weights listed in his third
table "will suffice to show, that we may conclude on probable grounds, that, with equal food and care, the climate
of America will preserve the races of domestic animals as
large as the European stock from which they are derived;
and, consequently, that the third member of Mons. de
Buffon's assertion that the domestic animals are subject
to degeneration from the climate of America, is as probably
wrong as the first and second were certainly so."

Attacking next the theory that nature, weakened by the
New World climate, had produced fewer species of quadrupeds than other continents, Jefferson points to the
refutations contained in his three tables, these show one
hundred species native to America. Buffon assumes there
are about two hundred species in the entire world. Let
us suppose that Europe, Asia, and Africa have 126 of
these—that is, the twenty-six common to Europe and
America and about one hundred not found in America.
"The American species, then, are to those of the rest of
the earth, as one hundred to one hundred and twenty-six,
or four to five. But the residue of the earth being double
the extent of America, the exact proportion would have
been but as four to eight." Hence America produces far
more than her share.

But for his chief argument Jefferson turned to America's
pride—the "mammoth." Americans loved the mammoth as

Buffon loved the elephant. To Buffon the elephant proved the physical superiority of the Old World; to Americans the mammoth proved the contrary.

Jefferson argued that of the American animals the mammoth must have been the largest. He based his argument on discoveries of bones, teeth, and tusks near the Ohio River and further north, and upon Indian reports that such a creature still lives in the northern parts of America. Contrary to the opinion of certain European scientists, these remains do not belong to the hippopotamus or to the elephant of Europe, but to an animal, as the dimensions indicate, five or six times the cubic volume of the elephant, as Buffon himself has admitted. Jefferson is particularly irked with Buffon for identifying this creature as the elephant. Elephants' teeth have never been found in America. Furthermore, the elephant could never have existed in such latitudes, nor does any acceptable geological theory justify any assumption that the northwest portions of America were ever habitable for the elephant. Beginning at 36½° north latitude we find the home of this huge creature, whose remains increase in numbers the further north we go, whereas the elephant cannot live north of 30° latitude.

Dead or alive, the mammoth is or was "the largest of all terrestrial beings." This "should have sufficed to have rescued the earth it inhabited, and the atmosphere it breathed, from the imputation of impotence in the conception and nourishment of animal life on a large scale; to have stifled, in its birth, the opinion of a writer [Buffon], the most learned, too, of all others in the science of animal history, that in the new world, 'La nature vivante est beaucoup moins agissante, beaucoup moins forte. . . .'" ("Living nature is far less active, far less strong.")

Jefferson was not alone in his use of the mammoth to refute notions of the degenerating effects of American nature and climate. Dr. Hugh Williamson of North Carolina and Samuel Williams of Vermont, both scientists known abroad as well as in America, Jedidiah Morse, father of Samuel F. B. Morse, author of the well-known *American Geography*, Timothy Dwight, Rembrandt Peale, touring England with one of the two skeletons of the mammoth he and his father had assembled, and others joined in the counter-attack.

To them it may be added the Mexican, Abbe Francisco Clavigero, who, in his *History of Mexico*, cites Buffon to the effect that there was in America an animal seven times larger than the elephant, "called by Mr. Muller the *Mammout;* but in Europe there never was, nor can be, any quadruped of such size." According to Clavigero's source this creature would be 133 feet long and 105 feet high. Clavigero thinks such a monster a satisfactory disproof of the attacks on the potency of nature in America.

Nor was this animal sluggish or timid. On the contrary, he was reported to be exceptionally active and fierce. Indian legend emphasized this quality of his nature, and an American commentator remarked: "With the agility and ferocity of the tiger; with the body of unequalled magnitude and strength, it is possible the Mammoth may have been at once the terror of the forest and of man!—And may not the human race have made extirpation of this terrific disturber a common cause?"

Jefferson next turns to European attacks upon man in America. Quoting Buffon's blistering comment upon American natives, he declares it an "afflicting picture, indeed, which for the honor of human nature, I am glad to believe has no original." Admitting a lack of knowledge of South American aborigines, he refuses to accept as facts the "fables" published about them. He stands on what he has seen and known himself or what he has read or heard from "enlightened" commentators and observers.

The Indian, declares Jefferson, "is neither more defective in ardor, nor more impotent with his female, than the white reduced to the same diet and exercise." And his bravery is beyond all question. Furthermore "he is affectionate to his children, careful of them, and indulgent in the extreme." His affections also "comprehend his other connections" and "his friendships are strong and faithful to the uttermost extremity." Nor is there any impairment of his mental qualities, for "his vivacity and activity of mind is equal to ours in the same situation." Women, it is true, are "submitted to unjust drudgery." But this is true of all barbarous people, with whom force is law. Civilization alone places women "in the enjoyment of their natural equality," and if we were in the Indian's state of barbarism our females would also be drudges. Indian males are weaker than white males, but on the contrary, their women are stronger than ours. This is due to work habits. That they have fewer children than the whites is due to social circumstances, not to the powers of nature. Indian women married to white men and living under different social and economic conditions are as fecund as white women.

As for body hair, the Indian's lack of which was taken by European savants as evidence of degeneracy and of the weakness of nature in America, Jefferson declares that with the Indians "it is disgraceful to be hairy on the body. They say it likens them to hogs." Therefore they "pluck the hair as fast as it appears." Traders married to Indian women, who have stopped this practice in their wives, declare "that nature is the same with them as with the whites." And even if hairlessness did prevail among Indians, this would be no proof of their lack of virility. Look at Negroes. They "have notoriously less hair than the whites; yet they are more ardent."

Examining more fully Buffon's judgments of the moral and mental faculties of the Indian, Jefferson writes: "But if cold and moisture be the agents of nature for diminishing the races of animals, how comes she all at once to suspend their operation as to the physical man of the new world, whom the Count acknowledges to be 'à peu près de même stature que l'homme de notre monde,' [about the same stature as men of our world] and to let loose their influence on his moral faculties? How has this 'combination of the elements and other physical causes, so contrary to the enlargement of ánimal nature in this new world, these obstacles to the development and formation of great germs,' been arrested and suspended, so as to permit the human body to acquire its just dimensions, and by what inconceivable process has their action been directed on his mind alone?" To form a complete and final estimate of the Indian's mental powers, we must have more data. Meanwhile full allowance must be made for the effects of the Indian's social and economic situation, when we shall "probably find that they are formed in mind as well as in body, on the same module with the 'Homo sapiens Europaeus' ".

As examples of Indian accomplishments Jefferson cites the oratorical abilities of Logan, famous Mingo chief. Here Jefferson got into hot water with contemporary critics because of the implied aspersions upon the white leader who was involved. Jefferson had heard of the incident at the home of Lord Dunmore in Williamsburg in 1774 and had jotted it down in his notebook.

In 1774 some Indians robbed a group of "land adventurers" on the Ohio River, and Captain Michael Cresap and a certain Daniel Greathouse led punitive expeditions of white men who retaliated by murdering many Indian men, women, and children, among them the family of Logan, renowned chief and friend of the whites. In a war of venegeance, Logan's Indians were defeated, and sued for peace. Logan himself disdained to attend the peace negotiations, but delivered his famous speech to Lord Dunmore by messenger:

"I appeal to any white man to say, if ever he entered

Logan's cabin hungry, and he gave him not meat; if ever he came cold and naked, and he clothed him not. During the course of the last long and bloody war Logan remained idle in his cabin, an advocate for peace. Such was my love for the whites, that my countrymen pointed as they passed, and said, 'Logan is the friend of white men.' I had even thought to have lived with you, but for the injuries of one man, Colonel Cresap, who, last spring, in cold blood, and unprovoked, murdered all the relations of Logan, not even sparing my women and children. There runs not a drop of my blood in the veins of any living creature. This called on me for revenge. I have sought it: I have killed many: I have fully glutted my vengeance: for my country I rejoice at the beams of peace. But do not harbor a thought that mine is the joy of fear. Logan never felt fear. He will not turn on his heel to save his life. Who is there to mourn for Logan?—Not one."

Jefferson always had a deep feeling for the American Indian, to which this story appealed, along with the sheer eloquence of the speech itself. In his later defense of his use of it he noted how often it was given to school boys as an exercise. But it was for its "apt proof" against Buffon's charges that the climate of America affected not only animal nature but also "the moral faculties of man" that he used it in his *Notes on Virginia.*

Jefferson's concluding section in his arguments on the animals and Indians of America is a nice combination of praise and censure of Monsieur Buffon. His purpose had been to suggest "a doubt, whether the bulk and faculties of animals depend on the side of the Atlantic on which their food happens to grow, or which furnishes the elements of which they are compounded? Whether nature has enlisted herself as a Cis or Trans-Atlantic partisan? I am induced to suspect there has been more eloquence than sound reasoning displayed in support of this theory; that it is one of those cases where the judgment has been seduced by a glowing pen; and whilst I render every tribute of honor and esteem to the celebrated zoologist, who has added, and is still adding, so many precious things to the treasures of science, I must doubt whether in this instance he has not cherished error also, by lending her a moment his vivid imagination and bewitching language."

Considering, next, European theories on the acclimatization of the white race in America, Jefferson attacks the Abbé Raynal, who had here applied the Buffonian theories of degeneracy. He quotes Raynal: "On droit etre étonné . . . que l'Amérique n'ait pas encore produit un bon poëte, un habile mathématicien, un de génie dans un seul art, ou seule science." ("One is astonished that America has not yet produced a good poet, an able mathematician, a single genius in any art or science.")

Jefferson replies that the situation will undoubtedly be different when the people of America have existed as long as the Greeks did "before they produced a Homer, the Romans a Virgil, the French a Racine and Voltaire, the English a Shakespeare and Milton. . . ." Moreover, he adds in a footnote, the world has not yet produced more than two poets universally acknowledged supreme—Homer and Virgil. Aside from these two, nations are in disagreement as to who is a supreme poet.

As to America's not having produced able mathematicians or men of genius in arts and science—Raynal's charges do not bear scrutiny. The name of George Washington, a genius in the art of war, will triumph over time and will in future ages "assume its just station among the most celebrated worthies of the world"—long after "that wretched philosophy shall be forgotten which would have arranged him among the degeneracies of nature"! In physics we have produced a Franklin, "than whom no one of the present age has made more important discoveries, nor has enriched philosophy with more, or more ingenious solutions of the phenomena of nature." Again, Jefferson had supposed David Rittenhouse "second to no astronomer living"; and in the matter of genius he must be the first "because he is self taught." Lauding Rittenhouse's orrery, he continues: "As an artist he has exhibited as great a proof of mechanical genius as the world has ever produced. He has not indeed made a world; but he has by imitation approached nearer its Maker than any man who has lived from the creation to this day!"

As in science and war, so also in government, oratory, painting, and plastic arts, it might be demonstrated that America, "though but a child of yesterday, has already given hopeful proofs of genius."

Comparing America with such countries as France and England, where genius may be considered to be properly cultivated, he makes the following calculation: "The United States contains three millions of inhabitants; France twenty millions; and the British islands ten. We produce a Washington, a Franklin, a Rittenhouse. France then should have half a dozen in each of these lines, and Great Britain half that number, equally eminent." Perhaps France has her full quota of genius, and Jefferson names Voltaire, Buffon, the Encyclopedists, and "the Abbé Raynal himself." As for Great Britain, the recent American Revolution has so cut off communication with her that Jefferson cannot be sure. But if he may judge of her present tendencies by the spirit with which she wages war, he must conclude that she is deficient both in science and civilization. Jefferson's animosity toward Great Britain so moves him here that he declares: "The sun of her glory is fast descending to the horizon. Her philosophy has crossed the channel, her freedom the Atlantic, and herself seems passing to that awful dissolution whose issue is not given human foresight to scan." The facts indicate that the United States has already produced her proportionate share of the world's men of genius and that the rate of increase and the range of her productions will be accelerated in the future.

Answering Barbé-Marbois's seventh query Jefferson gave a detailed meteorological study of Virginia's climate, comparing it with the climate of Europe. Jefferson's statistics give Virginia "considerably more" annual rainfall than corresponding latitudes in Europe. But from the information he has collected, he supposes "we have a much greater proportion of sunshine here than there." In fact, it may well turn out that "there are twice as many cloudy days in the middle parts of Europe, as in the United States of America." Jefferson's statistics also indicate that changes of temperature in America are "very sudden and great." But he appends a footnote containing statistics on this matter in Paris: in 1753 the mercury of Reaumur's thermometer stood at thirty and a half above zero and in 1776 it was sixteen below zero. "The extremities of heat and cold therefore at Paris, are greater than at Williamsburg, which is in the hottest part of Virginia."

As we have seen, Buffon based his criticism of nature in America largely upon the assumption that the atmosphere in America is damper than in Europe. In his original treatment of this problem in his *Notes,* Jefferson stated that "we are not furnished with observations sufficient to decide this question."

But while in France Jefferson was apprised of certain observations, which had convinced Franklin that Philadelphia was drier than both London and Paris. Franklin had devised a hygrometer to be made by Edward Nairne, London maker of scientific instruments. Jefferson immediately planned to have two or three hygrometers made, one to be sent to America and one for his own use in Paris. Jefferson seems to have received his instrument too late to make his proposed experiments before his departure from France in 1789.

Though unable to test it for himself, Jefferson was convinced by the work of Franklin, and from other sources and observations, that the American climate was superior to that of Europe. A particular peculiarity of America, he writes, is her cloudless skies. In Europe "the sun does not shine more than half the number of days in the year in which it does in America." In 1805 he informs his friend Count Volney that though America has greater and more frequent changes between heat and cold than has Europe, this is not harmful to her inhabitants because they are habituated to it just as Europeans are to lesser changes. And the American sky "is always clear," whereas that of Europe is "always cloudy." America may possibly have twice as much rain, but it falls "in half the time." Though he was in Paris for a number of years, he had seen but one completely cloudless day. Only two months after his return to Monticello, he was driven to remark to his daughter that for "twenty odd times" there was "not a speck of a cloud in the whole hemisphere!" Thinking no doubt of Buffon's assumption that America is cold, Jefferson points out that because of these greater periods of uninterrupted sunlight, in the same parallels of latitude we have a greater accumulation of heat in America than has Europe. For his friend Volney he draws the following conclusion: "Taking all these together, I prefer much the climate of the United States to that of Europe. I think it a more cheerful one."

Jefferson elaborates upon this cheerful sky of America and thereby discloses his awareness of a curious but commonly held eighteenth-century theory concerning the effect of England's climate upon her inhabitants, who were supposed to have been made morose and melancholic by it and more prone to suicide and murder than the people of other countries. In his *Esprit des lois* (1748) Montesquieu remarked that "the English are apt to commit suicide most unaccountably; they destroy themselves even in the bosom of happiness." In America, when Dr. Benjamin Rush sought to demonstrate the influence of physical causes upon the moral faculty, he pointed to November in England, when one might expect "the perpetration of the worst species of murder." This will help us to understand Jefferson's conviction that America had a cheerful climate. America's sunny sky, he writes Volney, "has eradicated from our constitutions all disposition to hang ourselves, which we might otherwise have inherited from our English ancestors."

Jefferson's views on climate are recapitulated in a long letter to Chastellux written from Paris, June 7, 1785. Chastellux had written to thank Jefferson for a copy of his *Notes* and to request permission to publish extracts from it in the *Journal of Physics*. Because this would mean inclusion of his attacks on Buffon and others, Jefferson sought to make his position clear. He points out that it is not Buffon, but Raynal, who has applied the theory of degeneracy to man in America, though even Buffon "goes, indeed, within one step of it." He appeals to Chastellux' own knowledge of America "to say, whether the lower class of people in America are less informed and less susceptible of information, than the lower class in Europe; and whether those in America, who have received such an education as that country can give, are less improved by it than Europeans of the same degree of education."

He defends the Indians against the historian Robertson, who "never was in America" and "relates nothing on his own knowledge," but is "a compiler only of the relations of others, and a mere translator of the opinions of Monsieur Buffon." De Pauw comes in for severe criticism. "Paw," as Jefferson calls him, who was the originator of this charge of the degeneracy of man in the New World, was "nothing but a compiler from the works of others; and of the most unlucky description; for he seems to have read the writings of travellers, only to collect and republish their lies. It is really remarkable, that in three volumes 12 mo, of small print, it is scarcely possible to find one truth, and yet, that the author should be able to produce authority for every fact he states, as he says he can." These sources are then critically analyzed. From that Jefferson proceeds to a defense of the innate mental and physical qualities of the American Indian. He has nothing to add to the material on animals in his *Notes,* but he is happy to add to the material on climate Franklin's refutation of the charge that the atmosphere of America is more humid than that of Europe.

As an extension of his counterattack upon the Buffonites, Jefferson distributed copies of his *Notes on Virginia* to people of position and prestige. From Paris he sent copies to friends in America and England and to friends and correspondents on the Continent. These were often accompanied with letters going further into mistaken European ideas about his homeland. Copies reached such varied figures as Humboldt and the Spanish Prince of Parma. The latter received his from Thomas Pinckney, American envoy in London, for other Americans sought circulation for this accurate and patriotic work on their country.

When an article on the United States was being prepared for the French *Encyclopédie,* the author submitted questions to Jefferson and the work was compiled, in part, from Jefferson's minute and careful replies. Jefferson, however, found much in it to complain of, as he explained to Van Hogendorp in August, 1786. The two first sections, largely derived from the Abbé Raynal, "are therefore wrong exactly in the same proportion the other sections are generally right." But even elsewhere there are errors. Jefferson recommended to Hogendorp, instead, a work soon to be published by Mazzei, "who has been many years a resident of Virginia, is well informed and possessed of a masculine understanding."

This work, *Recherches historiques et politiques sur les États-Unis, par un citoyen de Virginia,* in three volumes, appeared in Paris in 1788. It was published, as Professor Gilbert Chinard [3] points out, to confute errors about Amer-

ica, particularly "the purely materialistic or biological in-
terpretation of the characteristics of the American people."
Professor Chinard traces "the fine hand of Jefferson . . .
in many passages." It attacks Raynal, De Pauw, Buffon,
Montesquieu, and Mably. "It is not because of the climate,"
wrote Mazzei, "that the Americans constitute a people different from all others. The difference comes not from
physical but from moral circumstances."

Jefferson met Buffon (apparently in late 1785 or very
early 1786) and their relations seem to have been reason-
ably amicable. The following is Jefferson's account of the
meeting, as quoted by Daniel Webster:

"When I was in France, the Marquis de Chastellux carried me over to Buffon's residence in the country, and introduced me to him.

"It was Buffon's practice to remain in his study till
dinner time, and receive no visitors under any pretence;
but his house was open and his grounds, and a servant
showed them very civilly, and invited all strangers and
friends to remain to dine. We saw Buffon in the garden,
but carefully avoided him; but we dined with him, and he
proved himself then, as he always did, a man of extraordinary powers in conversation. He did not declaim; he
was singularly agreeable.

"I was introduced to him as Mr. Jefferson, who, in some
notes on Virginia, had combated some of his opinions. Instead of entering into an argument, he took down his last
work, presented it to me, and said, 'When Mr. Jefferson
shall have read this, he will be perfectly satisfied that I am
right.' " [4]

There are references in Jefferson's correspondence to
developments in his acquaintance with Buffon, to whom,
in the name of the American Philosophical Society he conveyed "un diplome de membre correspondant" (a diploma
as corresponding member).[5]

Anticipating these meetings, Jefferson, before embark-

ing for France, purchased one of the weapons he proposed
to arm himself with against Buffon. We have the details
from Webster. "Being about to embark from Philadelphia
for France," Webster quotes him, "I observed an uncom-
monly large panther skin at the door of a hatter's shop. I
bought it for half a Jo (sixteen dollars) on the spot, determining to carry it to France, to convince Monsieur Buffon
of his mistake in relation to this animal; which he had con-
founded with the cougar." Jefferson's panther skin was
convincing. As he informed Francis Hopkinson in December, 1786, Buffon did not know our panther, but "I gave
him the stripped skin of one I bought in Philadelphia, and
it presents him a new species, which will appear in his next
volumes."

In conversations with Buffon Jefferson found this savant
vague about the elk and deer of America. He "even thinks
that our deer never had horns more than a foot long" and
so has classed it with the roebuck! Jefferson, who has
examined the red deer of France, "at a distance of about
sixty yards," is convinced that they are the same creatures
as those of America. To convince Buffon of his mistake,
Jefferson writes to Archibald Cary (January 7, 1786) to
find "the largest pair of buck's horns" and a red and blue
skin, if possible with the bones of the head in the skin and
the horns on. Also he would like the bones of the legs left
in the skin, with the hooves on, "so that, having only made
an incision all along the belly and neck, to take the animal
out at, we could, by sewing up that incision, and stuffing
the skin, present the true size and form of the animal."
This would, he says, be "a most precious present." Cary is
further to try to borrow the elk horns owned by David
Ross. To increase the chances of getting a whole skin, some
two weeks later Jefferson writes to Archibald Stuart: [You]
"could not oblige me more than by sending me the horns,
skeleton, and skin of an elk."

In early January of 1786 Jefferson writes to Francis Hopkinson making two requests: One was to find a pamphlet on "the subjects of attraction and impulsion" written many years ago by Cadwallader Colden. Buffon, who admired the work, had owned one but it had gone astray, and Jefferson would like to replace it for him. The other request was for American grouse and pheasant, a male and female of each, prepared by "some apothecary's boy" and packed for shipment, by methods described in the *Encyclopédie* or Buffon's *Natural History*. Jefferson has noticed that the King's cabinet of natural history, of which Buffon was superintendent, lacked these specimens, and Jefferson missed no opportunity to secure better representation of the natural history of his country.

In June Hopkinson sends Jefferson a description of a strange new bird shot in New Jersey. It has long and very white feathers growing from the top of its head, and attached to the middle claw of each foot is "a perfect *small tooth'd Comb*"—with which he must have "com'd his elegant Plumage." Hopkinson possesses one of the feet and two of the feathers, and plans to send them over to Buffon, to the belief expressed by Hopkinson that the creature was probably already known to "so great a natural Historian as Mr. Buffon." [6] Jefferson replied "You must not presume too strongly, that your comb-footed bird is known to M. de Buffon." Whom Jefferson had found ignorant of the American panther, and who had to be informed "that our deer is not a Chevreuil." In the same letter Jefferson voices his disappointments over not getting specimens of the deer for Buffon. How can his friends in Virginia, where the deer abounds, have let him down? Would Hopkinson but get some elk horns, which Buffon has never seen, this would decide "whether it be an elk or a deer." On August 1, 1787, the parts of Hopkinson's strange bird arrive. But Jefferson notified Hopkinson that ". . . the comb, which you mention as annexed to the foot, has totally disappeared."

Jefferson finally got his horns, "a very good specimen,

four feet long." This delighted Jefferson who had been challenged by Buffon to produce a pair even one foot long. In a moment of patriotic enthusiasm Jefferson boasted to Buffon "that the reindeer [of Europe] (which Buffon believed to be the same as the American moose) could walk under the belly of our moose." Buffon "entirely scouted the idea" [7] and Jefferson sought to make good the boast. He turned to John Sullivan, President of New Hampshire, one of the scientific correspondents upon whom he relied for data on the moose, deer, elk, and caribou. Sullivan had failed in an earlier promise to send Jefferson certain specimens. Now Jefferson asked him to make good.

This time Sullivan really went into action. As Jefferson recounted it, "He had made the acquisition an object of a regular campaign, and that too of a winter one. The troops he employed sallied forth, as he writes me, in the month of March—much snow—a herd attacked—one killed—in the wilderness—a road cut twenty miles—to be drawn by hand from the frontiers to his house—bones to be cleaned, etc., etc., etc. In fine, he puts himself to an infinitude of trouble, more than I meant: he did it cheerfully, and I feel myself really under obligations to him."

Further details are supplied by Sullivan himself. The moose was transported by men on foot for twenty miles through the woods to a highway and thence to Durham, New Hampshire. The preservation proved a problem, the flesh being "in a state of putrefaction." Every Indian near "was at work to prepare the bones and cleanse them from the remaining flesh, and to preserve the skin with the hair on and with the hoofs on, and the bones of the legs and thighs in the skin without putrefaction, and the job was both expensive and difficult and such as was never attempted before in this quarter. . . ." It proved impossible to prepare the skull properly, so that the head bones would be left in the skin. However, the skin of the head is whole, he assures Jefferson, and may be drawn on at will. Also he

sends Jefferson the horns of a deer, an elk, and a caribou,
which may be substituted for the horns of the moose.
Moose horns are not good in the early spring. Sullivan then
listed the expenses, which he assumed correctly would
startle Jefferson:

	Pounds	S	D
Lawful money	61	17	2
Equal in Sterling to	46	7	10½

Sullivan's next problem was the shipping, for which
there was no simple solution in that period. A Captain
Samuel Pierce, of Portsmouth, agreed to take the box to
London without charge, from whence it could be sent to
Jefferson at relatively small shipping cost. Sullivan sent
Pierce minute instructions. The addressed side of the box
must be up, moisture must be avoided, and it must be kept
in a cool, airy place. He informs Jefferson of the sailing
dates but adverse winds delay the sailing, which gives Sullivan a chance to add a rare pair of roebuck horns to the
specimens. These, the largest he has ever known of, are
"free of charge." The expense account was worrying Sullivan. At last winds, ship, specimens and all were ready, and
Captain Pierce sailed away—leaving the box behind him!
New arrangements had to be made. Jefferson at one time
considered the box lost and gave the matter up as a waste
of money.

Then suddenly the box appeared. Jefferson gratefully
writes Sullivan, on October 5, 1787, that he received "a few
days ago the box containing the skin, bones, and horns of
the moose, and other animals, which your Excellency has
been so kind as to take so much trouble to obtain and
forward. They were all in good enough condition, except
that a good deal of the hair of the moose had fallen off.
However, there remained still enough to give a good idea
of the animal, and I am in hopes Monsieur de Buffon will
be able to have him stuffed, and placed on his legs in the
King's Cabinet. He was in the country when I sent the box

to the Cabinet, so that I have as yet no answer from him. I am persuaded he will find the moose to be a different animal from any he had described in his work. I am equally persuaded that our elk and deer are animals of a different species from any existing in Europe. Unluckily, the horns of them now received are remarkably small. However, I have taken measures to procure some from Virginia. The moose is really a valuable acquisition. . . ."

Jefferson does not feel that the skeletons of certain other animals Sullivan might send would be worth the expense or bother. "You have already gone to far more trouble than I intended," says Jefferson, "and I beg you to accept my sincere thanks." But, "Should a pair of large horns of the elk or deer fall into your way by accident, I would thank you to keep them till some vessel should be coming directly from your nearest port to Havre. So also of very large horns of the moose, for I understand they are sometimes enormously large indeed." Bigness remained important to Jefferson in his continued concern to confute the European theories of the degeneration of species in America.[8]

The day after Jefferson received his precious box he writes Monsieur Buffon:

I am happy to be able to present to you at this moment, the bones and skin of a moose, the horns of another individual of the same species, the horns of the caribou, the elk, the deer, the spiked horned buck, and the roebuck of America. They all come from New Hampshire and Massachusetts and were received by me yesterday. I give you their popular names, as it rests with yourself to decide their real names. The skin of the moose was dressed with the hair on, but a great deal of it has come off, and the rest is ready to drop off. The horns of the elk are remarkably small. I have certainly seen some of them which would have weighed five or six times as much. This is the animal which we call the elk in the southern parts of America, and of which I have given some description in the notes on Virginia, of which I had the honor of presenting you a copy. I really doubt whether the flat-horned elk exists in America; and I think this may be properly classed with the elk, the principal difference being in the horns. I have seen the daim, the cerf, the chevreuil of Europe. But the animal we call elk, and which may be distinguished as the round-horned elk, is very different from them. I have never seen the brand-hirtz or cerf d'Ardennes, nor the European elk. Could I get a sight of them, I think I should be able to say which of them the American elk resembles most, as I am tolerably well acquainted with that animal. I must observe also, that the horns of the deer, which accompany these spoils, are not the fifth or sixth part of the weight of some that I have seen. This individual has been of three years of age, according to our method of judging. I have taken measures, particularly, to be furnished with large horns of our elk and our deer, and therefore beg of you not to consider those now sent, as furnishing a specimen of their ordinary size. I really suspect you will find that the moose, the round-horned elk, and the American deer, are species not existing in Europe. The moose is, perhaps. of a new class. I wish these spoils, Sir, may have the merit of adding anything new to the treasures of nature, which have so fortunately come under your observation, and of which she seems to have given you the key: they will in that case be some gratification to you, which it will be pleasing to me to have procured. . . ."

In a letter to John Rutledge, who had seen the moose while passing through Paris, Jefferson says Buffon had known this animal by name only and had supposed it to be the same as the "Rennedeer of Lapland." Buffon "describes the Renne to be about three feet high, and truly, the moose you saw here was seven feet high, and there are some of them ten feet high. The experiment was expensive to me, having cost me hunting, curing, and transporting, sixty guineas."

The cost was apparently worth it, for, according to Webster, Jefferson said Sullivan's specimen had "convinced Mr. Buffon. He promised in his next volume to set these things right also, but he died directly afterwards."

Jefferson's arguments that the mammoth was not an elephant did not go down equally well with Buffon. Following Daubenton, Buffon considered it "beyond all doubt" that the mammoth was but an American form of the elephant.

A few brief additional points of interest. Before leaving America Jefferson had stopped at Yale, on his way to Boston, to see Yale's President, Ezra Stiles. About a month before he sailed from Boston he bethought himself of the possibility of getting information on the mammoth from Stiles, for his forthcoming discussions with Buffon.

"After I had the pleasure of seeing you in New Haven," he writes Stiles, June 10, 1784, "I received information that you were in possession of several facts relative to the huge bones of the Animal incognitum found in America, or of the Mammoth as the Russians call the same animal whose bones they also find in the Northern parts of their empire. Mons.ʳ de Buffon the celebrated Physiologist of the present age, who has advanced a theory in general very degrading to America, has in this particular also adopted an opinion which I think not founded in fact. It is that this animal was the same with the elephant of Asia and Africa. I think it certain that it was a different animal; having therefore on a particular occasion drawn his opinion into question I am still anxious of getting every additional information on the subject which may serve either to confirm or to correct the conclusion I had formed." Hence he requests Stiles to send him any facts he may know of.[9]

Stiles' letters show him to share Jefferson's opinion that this animal cannot be the same as the elephant. Stiles is apparently not too sure that some of these bones may not belong to an ancient race of giants, a belief still current in late eighteenth-century thought. Nature's infinite chain made such a link appear possible and the possibility received support from the traditions of former races of giants.

In a letter from Paris, July 17, 1785, Jefferson thanks Stiles for "information as to the great bones found on the Hudson river" which he believes belong to the same creature found on the Ohio. Hence they cannot have "be-

longed to any human figure." He remains convinced that
the animal itself "must have been much larger than an elephant." But Buffon held to his opinion that they were the
same.

When, during his Presidency, Jefferson sent some bones
of this huge creature to the National Institute of France,
Cuvier and others positively identified it as a mastodon.
Jefferson's scientific and patriotic interest in vertebrate
paleontology and his battle with Buffon went on. His
"Memoir on the Discovery of Certain Bones of a Quadruped of the Clawed Kind in the Western Parts of Virginia,"
read before the American Philosophical Society on March
10, 1797, and later published in its *Transactions,* quotes
and attacks Buffon for his statement "q'il y a dans la com-
binaison des éléments et des autres causes physiques,
quelque chose de contraire a l'aggrandisement de la nature
vivante *dans ce nouveau monde;* qu'il y a des obstacles au
développement et peut-être à la formation des grands
germes." (There is something in the combination of elements and other physical causes that hinders the growth of
living nature in the new world, that prevents the development and perhaps even the formation of large germs.)
Here, again, Jefferson berates Buffon for considering the
mammoth and the elephant identical, and cites what he
considers inconsistencies in Buffon on this point. He then
turns directly to the *Megalonyx,* which he has identified as
a huge lion, "of more than three times the volume of the
African." He reminds his readers that while in Paris he
delivered to Buffon "the skeleton of our palmated elk,
called original or moose, 7 feet high over the shoulders, he
is often considerably higher. I cannot find that the European elk is more than two thirds of that height: consequently not one third of the bulk of the American. He
acknowledges the palmated deer (daim) of America to be
larger and stronger than that of the Old World. He considers the round horned deer of these States and of Louisi-

ana as the roe, and admits they are of three times his size."

From all this evidence it certainly appears, says Jefferson, that Buffon is wrong: "Are we then from all this to draw a conclusion, the reverse of that of M. de Buffon. That nature, has formed the larger animals of America, like its lakes, its rivers, and mountains, on a greater and prouder scale than in the other hemisphere? Not at all, we are to conclude that she has formed some things large and some small, on both sides of the earth for reasons which she has not enabled us to penetrate; and that we ought not to shut our eyes upon one half of her facts, and build systems on the other half." Buffon had been in his grave some nine years by this time. But to Jefferson—and to many another American—his shadow lingered on.

About this time Jefferson engaged in a correspondence with the Spanish Prince of Parma, whom he assures that "we have very credible evidence" that the great *Megalonyx* "now exists in the neighborhood of the Mississippi, to which object our enquiries are now directed." And with this Jefferson is off on his favorite subject: "the enormous mass of two such animals as the Megalonyx and Mammoth, with a thousand other facts, will surely suffice to dissipate the dreams of Buffon, Robertson & De Paw who have imagined that the soil & climate of America did not admit of animals on so large a scale as the other parts of the earth."

Jefferson used two anecdotes about Franklin to take a dig at Raynal. He was aware that Raynal had retracted his theory of the degeneracy of Europeans in North America; but because of the damage Raynal had done, Jefferson bore him no good will.

The first of these anecdotes is the well-known Polly Baker story. One day at Passy, Franklin and Silas Deane were discussing the errors in Raynal's *Histoire des deux Indes* when in walked Raynal himself. As Jefferson recounts it: "After the usual salutations, Silas Deane said to

him, 'The Doctor and myself, Abbé, were just speaking of
the errors of fact into which you have been led in your
history.' 'Oh, no Sir,' said the Abbé, 'that is impossible. I
took the greatest care not to insert a single fact, for which I
had not the most unquestionable authority.' 'Why,' says
Deane, 'there is the story of Polly Baker, and the eloquent
apology you have put into her mouth, when brought before the court of Massachusetts to suffer punishment under
a law which you cite, for having had a bastard. I know
there never was such a law in Massachusetts.' 'Be assured,'
said the Abbé, 'you are mistaken, and that that is a true
story. I do not immediately recollect indeed the particular
information on which I quote it; but I am certain that I
had for it unquestionable authority.' Doctor Franklin, who
had been for some time shaking with unrestrained laughter
at the Abbé's confidence in his authority for that tale, said,
'I will tell you, Abbé, the origin of that story. When I was
a printer and editor of a newspaper, we were sometimes
slack of news, and to amuse our customers, I used to fill up
our vacant columns with anecdotes and fables, and fancies
of my own, and this of Polly Baker is a story of my making,
on one of these occasions.' The Abbé, without the least dis-
concert, exclaimed with a laugh, 'Oh, very well, Doctor, I
had rather relate your stories than other men's truths.' "

The second anecdote was about a dinner party at Passy,
where half the guests were American, the other half
French. The Abbé Raynal was among the latter. During
the dinner the Abbé, as Jefferson puts it, "got on his favorite theory of the degeneracy of animals, and even of man,
in America, and urged it with his usual eloquence. The
Doctor [Franklin] at length noticing the accidental stature
and position of his guests, at table, 'Come,' says he, 'M.
l'Abbé, let us try this question by the fact before us. We
are here one half Americans, and one half French, and it
happens that the Americans have placed themselves on one
side of the table, and our French Friends are on the other.

Let both parties rise, and we will see on which side nature has degenerated.' It happened that his American guests were Carmichael, Harmer, Humphreys, and others of the finest stature and form; while those of the other side were remarkably diminutive, and the Abbé himself particularly, was a mere shrimp. He parried the appeal, however, by a complimentary admission of exceptions, among which the Doctor himself was a conspicuous one."

Jefferson's countering of Buffon's theories about the American climate had little immediate effect. Buffon, however, paid him the compliment of writing: "I should have counselled you, sir, before publishing my Natural History, and then I should have been sure of the facts." [10]

Though Thomas Jefferson used science in the cause of patriotism, we never find him blindly distorting, obscuring, hiding, or denying objective facts. He served the interests of scientific truth as well as the interests of his country. Jefferson's love of America may be as *well* found in other parts of his biography, but it is nowhere any *better* seen than in the series of incidents we have just witnessed— from his sixteen-dollar panther skin to the ratty-looking moose's carcass which he so proudly presented to the great M. Georges Louis Leclerc, Comte de Buffon.

8

The New World vs. the Old

•

Echoes of the controversy over America's climate reverberated up and down the United States for years. It stimulated an avid interest in the flora and fauna of the land, in its aborigines, in its forests, in land clearance, meteorology and weather, population, longevity, and so forth. Discussions were taken as signs of patriotism and involved a clamorous following of ministers, college professors, scientists, physicians, moralists, Fourth of July orators, novelists, poets, historians, "philosophers," travelers and Northerners and Southerners, all imbued with a proper (or improper) sectional pride. They held forth in learned journals, books, popular magazines, newspapers, and in the discussions of the American Academy of Arts and Sciences and the American Philosophical Society.

The magazine *American Museum* entertained its readers with Governor Henry Ellis's "Account of the Heat of the Weather in Georgia"; a resume of Benjamin Rush's "Enquiry into the Influence of Physical Causes upon the Moral Faculty"; Dr. Hugh Williamson's "Attempt to Account for the Change of Climate, which Has Been Observed in the Middle Colonies of North America"; Benjamin Franklin's "Physical and Meteorological Observations, Conjectures, and Suppositions"; an announcement that one of the purposes of the newly formed Medical Society of Delaware is the study of the effects of seasons and climates on man; a letter by Samuel L. Mitchill on the climate of New York; a poser by an anonymous questioner: "If the blackness of Africans and East Indians within the torrid zone be the effect of climate—why are not the original natives of America, within the same latitude, equally black"; an article entitled "American Longevity"; etc.

Similar material appears in the *Transactions* of the American Philosophical Society and the *Memoirs* of the American Academy of Arts and Sciences. Volume four (1799) of the *Transactions* contains at least six papers on climate, "including a most important communication of Thomas Wright on 'Drying up the marshes of the maritime parts of North America.' " [1] And preceding issues had contained studies of the climate of West Florida; and of the changes in the climate of America; meteorological tables; reports on experiments on evaporation, and the hygrometer; and articles on longevity, the honey-bee (with oblique glances at climate, Raynal, and De Pauw), the severity and destructiveness of the winter of 1779–1780, etc.

The American Philosophical Society took considerable interest in the census of 1800.[2] It petitioned "The Honourable Senate and House of Representatives of the United States" to include not only a record of the total population but also "the effect of the soil and climate of the United States on the inhabitants thereof." The members of the Society "flattered themselves, that from these data truths will result very satisfactory to our citizens, that under the joint influence of soil, climate and occupation, the duration of human life in this portion of the earth will be found at least equal to what it is in any other, and that its population increases with a rapidity unequalled in all others."

Joining Jefferson in this discussion on climate, then and later, were such other American luminaries as Franklin, Hamilton, St. John de Crevecoeur, Timothy Dwight, Samuel Williams, the Peales, Charles Jared Ingersoll, Ira Allen, Jeremy Belknap, Jedidiah Morse, Benjamin Rush, William Barton, Hugh Williamson, John Bristed, Robert Fulton, Washington Irving, James Fenimore Cooper, Henry David Thoreau, and numerous others. Americans writing on this subject began their discussions by summarizing for their readers the distorted portrayal of their country made by European critics. Thus many Americans became acquainted, if only at second hand with the notions of the Europeans.

Raynal, De Pauw, Robertson, and Buffon were the chief targets. Any "blunders" Raynal might make, said one critic, could readily be accounted for by his "florid" imagination, which led him to write "in defiance of all truth." In one of his *Federalist* papers, Alexander Hamilton used De Pauw's detractions to rally patriotic sentiment around his ideas of nationalism, union, and the Constitution. Dr. Benjamin Smith Barton, arguing that the honey-bee was imported into America, remarks: "It has been so much the rage to speculate falsely on the subject of America, that I should not be surprised to find such a writer as De Pauw, assigning a weakness of their political union as the reason why honey-bees were not discovered in the new world. Raynal would, probably, reason thus likewise, had not this fine writer believed that there is something in the climate of America, that is unfavourable to the generation of good things. Ye philosophers of Europe! Come visit our countries."

On another occasion, Dr. Barton comments on how unlike the historian Gibbon is Dr. Robertson, "who with stronger and with better lights to guide him, has deformed his *History of America* with the most palpable falsehoods and errors, concerning the physical conditions of this continent, and of its inhabitants!"

As for Buffon, Americans never tired of demonstrating how far even so great a man might, upon occasion, begin with erroneous facts, employ erroneous reasoning, and arrive at erroneous conclusions. Timothy Dwight accused Buffon of employing "mystic language" when he spoke of "a deficiency of matter" in American nature. Dwight, a theologian, had little admiration for Buffon anyhow because his theories of the formation of the earth went counter to Genesis. Such errors about the United States were easily accountable; for the man who could discover the origin of the earth "in the impact of a comet against the surface of the sun, which struck off a quantity of melted glass, sufficient to form the world, can discover any thing, and make any thing, which he pleases." Other Americans found Buffon "extravagant," "cracked," full of "egregious errors" arising from "a deficiency of practical knowledge," guilty of "visionary wanderings," a good example of all "theorizing Frenchmen," just another of those "credulous philosophers" of Europe who listen to the tales of "ignorant and inaccurate travellers," a lover of paradox, riddle, and mystery, a would-be scientist as full of fables as Aesop.

Attacks against the theory of degeneracy sometimes took odd forms. The inhabitants of Vermont "stuffed the skin of an elk of gigantic dimensions and sent it to England as a specimen of what Vermont could produce, with an intimation that her men, also, were hard to beat." [3] Alexander Wilson, father of American ornithology, said of Buffon's theory of the degeneracy of animal life in the New World that it "would raise the question 'whether the *ka-te-dids* of America were not originally nightingales of the Old World.' " [4] In Dwight's view the theory, though "dignified with the name of philosophy, and made the subject of grave discussions of grave men, [it] ranks with the stories of Lilliput and Brobdingnag; and would be readily supposed to have had its origin in the Island of Laputa."

The American Indians figured conspicuously in the discussion. Buffon, with De Pauw and others echoing him, had described the Indians as "weak automatons" with "small and feeble" organs of generation, men of inferior physical strength, stupid and unfeeling creatures who lacked any love for their parents or children—evidence that nature had abused human kind in America "more than any other animal."

Few Americans at this period in our history entertained any Rousseauistic or primitivistic sentiments about the Indian or life close to nature. But these European notions offended the American's sense of truth and his national pride. In their defense they were surprisingly frank regarding the Indian's sexual capabilities. The militancy of Americans in defense of their country provoked the French traveler Volney to the angry comment that Americans were so "inspired with zeal for their own cause" that they "make it their favourite business to combat European writers. They act as if they were the advocates and avengers of their predecessors, the Indians."

We have seen Jefferson, in his *Notes on Virginia,* defending the Indian as of good stature and of normal physical energy and vivacity, sexual appetite and organs, hair growth, natural affection, bravery, and love of society. One critic thought "Jefferson emphasized his virtues and meliorated his weaknesses in a eulogy which has not been surpassed." [5] To Jefferson, "the proofs of genius given by the Indians of North America place him on a level with the whites in the same uncultivated state." He had "seen some thousands" of them himself, had "conversed much with them," and had "found in them a masculine, sound understanding" in a body physically fit and properly trained for the kind of life the Indian led.

One of the Indian's foremost defenders was Samuel Williams, author of a *History of Vermont.* "In no race of men," he writes, "has the human body appeared to be better formed, more nicely adjusted, or to be more perfectly proportioned in all its members and parts. No deficiency therefore arose from any impotency, or want of vigour, in any of the powers of nature. . . . No such animal was ever seen in America, as the Indian M. de Buffon described in Paris." Concerning the Indian's lesser sexual urge Williams reads Europe a moral lesson. The unnatural sexual desire created by European luxury has led European philosophers to view the Indian as unattracted to his female. Lucky for the Indian, that he is spared this excessive and artificial lust!

The Indian's physical inferiority was presumed to be proven by the fact that he could not grow hair upon his body. And this was held to be another demonstration of the impotency of nature in the New World. The body of the Indian consequently received close inspection. Jefferson asserted that Indians, male and female, could grow hair as well as the whites.[6]

John Davis, an Americanized English traveler in this country from 1798 to 1802, quotes Colonel John Butler, Agent of Indian Affairs, to the effect that several "Mohocks" have razors and "if the Indians were to practise shaving from their youth, many of them would have as strong beards as *Europeans.*" Major Guy Ward of Long Island, Davis adds, read "both Buffon's and Jefferson's philosophic chapter on beards" and was moved to see which was correct. As soon as the chin of a certain young Montauk Indian became "razorable," he taught him to shave and encouraged beard growing. This young native now has a "handsome beard; it is dark, bushy, and repulsive; and before he reaches the age of thirty (he is now only twenty-three) he may . . . appear with dignity at the Court of the Grand Turk."

Readers of certain popular magazines or of the works of

James Adair, Samuel Williams, and others, were given detailed explanations of how the Indians, who thought that to be hairy was to look like pigs, plucked their hair. According to Adair, (*History of the American Indians, 1775*), the Indians "deplume themselves" with a kind of tweezers formerly made of clam-shells but "now of middle-sized wire, in the shape of a gun-worm."

Discussions of the climate of America and its effect upon man naturally turned to problems of health, population, and longevity. The theory of the physical degeneration of man in the New World implied innate constitutional weaknesses. It was supported by the trend in medicine, from 1750 to 1850, which repudiated the contagion theory and was "in favor of . . . the classical concept of poisons emanating from decaying animal and vegetable materials, transmitted by impure airs and waters."[7] This seemed to support arguments that America's heavy forests, rank vegetation, improperly cultivated soil, excessive humidity, noxious vapors, and generally unsatisfactory climate must lower animal vitality.

In his *View of the Soil and Climate of the United States of America,* Volney enlarges on four maladies scandalously prevalent in the new world—coughs which far too frequently pass into consumption, catarrhs, and all complaints arising from obstructed perspiration; tooth decay, which mars personal beauty and leads to other ailments; "autumnal intermittents," or agues and fevers, which enfeeble the constitution and shorten life (Southern people, particularly, are as old at fifty as they would be at sixty-five or seventy in Europe); and yellow fever, which, asserts Volney, is not of foreign origin, as the physicians of the College of Philadelphia assert out of national vanity and a land jobber's desire not to discourage immigration. Volney attributes these maladies partly to irrational dress, a too sedentary life, the drinking of too hot tea, generally bad dietary habits (such as the excessive use of salt pork), and public and private nastiness which often exceeds anything he "ever saw in Turkey." Fundamentally, however, he sees them as "the direct offspring" of her "soil and climate."

In the answers to the charges of degeneracy nothing was more popular than the unanswerable argument of America's fecundity, her phenomenal population growth. It figured also in glowing prophecies of the future growth of America, her assumption of a proud place among the nations, and her material and cultural progress.[8]

While in France Jefferson had let his imagination go in the revisions he suggested in the article "États Unis" to be published in the *Encyclopédie méthodique*. He pointed out that when the population density of the United States (in a territory not yet extended by the Louisiana purchase and other steps in our westward expansion) reaches that of Great Britain, it will number one hundred million. Then, extending his horizons, he estimated that when the best parts of North and South America are similarly inhabited, there will be "twelve hundred millions" of people—"a number greater than the present population of the whole globe is supposed to amount to." In 1816, he predicted a population for the United States of twenty million in twenty years and of forty million in forty years.

Among European books that aroused American ire was Parkinson's *A Tour in America,* which Robert Fulton, then in England, attacked in British journals. Parkinson took the usual line that nature had given the United States a debilitating climate and an unproductive soil.

How is it, then, asks Fulton, that the United States has "such a most extraordinary increase in population?" Continuing the debate, over a quarter of a century later, Samuel Southland, in his "Anniversary Address" before the Columbian Institute of Washington, D.C., saw the United States as "a region, holding the seeds of more animal, mineral, vegetable, agricultural, manufacturing, and commercial wealth, than Russia, resting upon two continents. . . . The Valley of the Mississippi is capable of bearing upon its bosom more than thirty millions of prosperous freemen; the Atlantic seaboard, of sustaining an equal population. . . ."

A similarly proud rejoinder is William Barton's "Observations on the Probabilities of the Duration of Human Life, and the Progress of Population, in the United States of America," read (perhaps in parts) before the American Philosophical Society in 1791. Nowhere else in the world, he maintains, is the natural increase in population so rapid as in the United States. He excludes from consideration any increment due to immigration.

In addition to the statistics of the "prodigious" population increase, Barton provides detailed analytical data of the proportion of births to marriages, population under sixteen years of age, ratio of births to deaths, longevity, ratio of annual deaths to number of living inhabitants. This data supports his conclusion "that the probabilities of life, *in all its* stages, from its commencement to the utmost possible verge of its duration, are higher in these United States, than in such European countries, as are esteemed the most favourable to life. And, if this position be well founded, it follows—the bodily constitutions of the American people are proportionably *healthful*." And this because of the climate of America, whose winters "brace and invigorate the bodies of the people: and the genial warmth of our summers increases the generative principle of animal nature. . . ." Barton's sources include Condorcet, Clavigero, Ulloa, Buffon, and Jefferson.

Americans suspected that European theories of American climate were partly motivated by the desire of its politicians and businessmen to discourage emigration to the United States and thus retard the growth of its population and its power among the nations. Jeremy Belknap declared that certain persons across the Atlantic represented America as "a grave to Europeans" in order to "throw dis-

couragement on emigration to this country." To counter
this Americans who wrote upon immigration sometimes
cited the advantages of America's climate. Thus Franklin,
in his "Information to Those Who Would Remove to
America" (1782), spoke of "the salubrity of the air, the
healthiness of the climate."

Foreign critics, and travelers, were often particularly dis-
paraging toward American women. To prove that the
climate of Philadelphia was "not so congenial to the well-
being of the human constitution as that of England,"
Fearon, in her *Sketches of America,* declared the women of
that city to be as old at twenty-seven as the Londoner at
forty. She did not see a rosy cheek in all the town. Darus-
mont, in his *Views of Society and Manners in America,*
found American women to be beauties up to the age of
twenty-five, but subsequently, under the effects of the
American sun and early marriage, to go into a rapid decline. Peter Kalm, Swedish botanist, declared that some
American women cannot bear children after the age of
thirty, which he attributes to the extreme changeableness
of the American climate. In France, the Abbé Robin, em-
broidering upon the tales of De Pauw, declared that the
humid American climate rendered its men indolent, after
twenty, and aged its women prematurely.[9]

In reply Americans declared their women to be as good
as the best, praised their early maturity, vigor, health,
bloom, and natural beauty. They explained early marriages
as "the inclinations of nature . . . directed towards their
proper objects." They proudly tabulated statistics on their
longevity, their rapid increase in population, their high
birthrate, which indicated that the American climate promoted fecundity. Franklin, in a letter to Joseph Priestley,
insisted "there is nothing unhealthy in the air of woods;
for we Americans have everywhere our country habitations
in the midst of woods, and no people on earth enjoy better
health, or are more prolific."

As another proof of America's salubrious climate, attention was drawn to the longevity of Americans. Material on the subject filled the newspapers, popular magazines, and learned journals. Long-lived Indians are pointed to by Dr. Thomas Bond, in a statement before the American Philosophical Society, as evidence of American healthful climate (1782). In his communication to the same Society, in 1791, William Barton lists numerous cases of longevity, and calculates the chances of living beyond sixteen to be greater in America than in Europe. He names an impressive number of centennarians from Massachusetts, New York, and Connecticut, while the longevity records of Virginia, North Carolina, Georgia, South Carolina, Florida, and Spanish America as well, justify the belief that "their climates are favorable to a long duration of human life." With great pride he dwells on the centennarian of Chesterfield County, Virginia, who "began to cut teeth before his death"—at the age of a hundred and twenty-five. Barton's data and conclusions are offered as "an ample refutation of those writers, who, influenced by European prejudices, or considering the subject in a superficial manner, have asserted, that the Americans are not so long-lived as the Europeans."

The controversy lasted for years. In 1810, Jared Ingersoll, in his *Inchiquin, the Jesuit's Letters*,[10] after summarizing the views of Buffon, Raynal, Daubenton, and English travelers in America, remarked: "it is amazing how current they continue to this day, notwithstanding the proofs that have successively adduced themselves of their falsification and baseness." Fifteen years later, J. E. Worcester, speaking before the American Academy of Arts and Sciences upon "Longevity and the Expectation of Life in the United States," was still confuting the assertions of "European philosophers, 'that the principle of life is deteriorated in the climate of America.'"

Between 1727 to 1825, according to Worcester, 132 Americans lived to be 110 years or over, the oldest being

Flora Thompson, Negress, of Harba Island, Pennsylvania, who attained to 150 years. Forty-eight lived 120 years or more. Comparing this with English vital statistics, he concludes that the United States, "considering its age and population, can produce its full share of instances of remarkable longevity." Turning to South America, Worcester cites the case of Louisa Trexo, who was living in October, 1780, at the age of 175. Humboldt is his authority for the case of a Peruvian Indian who died at Lima, at the age of 147 years, after a marriage that lasted 90 years to a woman who lived to the ripe age of 117 herself. Up to the age of 130 Humboldt's Indian could walk some ten miles a day.

Another controversial point centered about the effects of America's extensive forests upon climate, air, and human health.[11] Belknap maintained that the tall, luxuriant growth of our forests not only indicates a rich soil but also "conduces to absorb noxious vapours." Franklin felicitated Joseph Priestley upon his theory that "the vegetable creation should restore the air which is spoiled by the animal part of it." His own observations in America confirmed this principle, he said. In 1780 he wrote to Francis Hopkinson that the "greatest discovery made in Europe for some time past is Dr. Ingenhousz's relating to the great use of trees in producing wholesome air."

An equally sore issue was the European supposition of America's excessive humidity, to account for which three explanations were given: One, that the Western World was indeed a new world, rather recently risen from the ocean floor; a second, that a post-Noachan flood had inundated the Western hemisphere; the third, which the proponents of the other two also held, that the vast, impenetrable American forests both generated moisture and hindered its evaporation by screening out the sun's rays.

Among the chief confuters of this theory was Franklin, who, with his hygrometer, which gave great satisfaction to

Jefferson, was proving the United States to be drier than Europe. Timothy Dwight stated flatly that the atmosphere of New England is not even as moist as that of Europe in the same latitudes. As for an inundation since Noah's flood, the theory "was formed by the Count [Buffon] himself; whose imagination found little difficulty in deluging worlds, or making them; while Mr. de Pauw found as little, in swallowing either the deluges, or the worlds." And as for the forests and vegetation of America (especially of New England) Dwight took pride in their extent, variety, rapid increase, duration, and grandeur, which "denote an energy, a power in the vegetable life, which nature has never exceeded in the same climate, in any other part of the globe."

As population increased, however, these primeval American forests began to disappear. And as the trees fell, discussions turned on the effects of land clearing upon climate and health. Practicality then gave the discussion another turn. In his *Travels,* Isaac Weld observes that Americans are astonished to hear of people taking delight in wooded scenery. "To them, the sight of a wheat field or a cabbage garden would convey pleasure far greater than that of the most romantic woodland views. They have an unconquerable aversion to trees; and whenever a settlement is made, they cut away all before them without mercy; not one is spared. . . ." The man who cuts down the largest number and has the largest clearing around his house "is looked upon as the most industrious citizen, and the one that is making the greatest improvements in the country." [12]

The man with the ax was esteemed as one who contributed wheat fields and cabbage patches to national wealth and was simultaneously improving the national health. It was argued that as forests were cut down, bogs eradicated, and civilization advanced, the climate of America was rendered milder and more healthful.

Ira Allen waxed lyrical over the man who cleared land

in Vermont as one who "sees the effect of his own powers, aided by the goodness of Providence; he sees that man can embellish the most rude spot, the stagnant air vanishes with the woods, the rank vegetation feels the purifying influence of the sun; he drains the swamp, putrid exhalations flit off on lazy wing, and fevers and agues accompany them."

Among others, Jefferson pointed out how land clearance affected the prevailing winds over a given area. It was thought that the clearing of the land, by increasing the power and range of the east and south winds, might well lead to a general melioration of America's climate and reduce the pernicious effects of the northwest winds.

On that point Americans were ready to credit European critics. Peter Kalm remarked how this extreme "inconsistency and changeableness of the weather," which varied as much as "five or six times a day," was said by many to be the reason why the life span in America was shorter than that in Europe. A translator of Chastellux declared the "rapid changes of the temperature of the Air in America . . . are apt to destroy the best European constitutions," and enlarged upon the dangers of the northwest wind, which swept across the seaboard after blowing over "such immense boundless tracts of lakes and forests. . . ." Dr. Hugh Williamson felt that clearing the land had increased reflection of the sun's rays and hence had checked the northwest winds.

It was held that simply through the clearing away of trees and the admission of sunlight to the face of the earth the supposedly intense cold of America had been noticeably reduced. In England David Hume, from a study of ancient sources, concluded that the climate of Europe too had become milder as its forests had been cut down. Using similar arguments Samuel Williams informed his readers that the rapid alteration of America's climate "is the subject of common observation and experience." Clearing and cultivation cause the earth's surface to become more warm and dry; the "whole temperature of the climate, becomes more equal, uniform and moderate." Land and roads become drier and harder; stagnant waters disappear; small streams dry up, "and the redundant waters are carried off"; snow decreases; winds take new directions; and weather and seasons alter. These conditions, always following cultivation, have already caused a "remarkable change of climate in those states, which have been long settled."

The interrelation of climate and genius was another subject of controversy. Jefferson, as we have seen, offered statistical proof that the United States had produced its quota of geniuses. In an article in the *American Museum* (1787) entitled "On American Genius," the author cites Jefferson's refutation and adds a new roster of celebrities to Jefferson's list, among them West, Copley, Trumbull, Brown, and Barlow.

The novelist Charles Brockden Brown joined the defenders, both in outright debate and in the American themes he used in his own novels. In the *Monthly Magazine* for December, 1800, Brown took issue with certain ideas expressed in *Poems, Chiefly Occasional,* by William Clifton. Brown particularly objected to the kind of thing expressed in Clifton's lines

> "In these cold shades, beneath these shifting skies,
> Where Fancy sickens, and where Genius dies;
> Where few and feeble are the Muses strains,
> And no fine frenzy riots in the veins."

A poet in America, said Brown, is not obliged to dwell "in deeper shades" than one in Great Britain, for it is "well known that we have more resplendent sunshine in one day than England enjoys in six." And he gave the damning evidence of the British poet Armstrong:

> "The baleful east
> Withers the tender spring, and sourly checks
> The fancy of the year. Our fathers talk—
> Of summers, balmy airs, and skies serene;

> Good heaven! for what unexpected crimes
> This dismal change! . . .
> Indulgent Nature! O dissolve this gloom! . . .
> And may once more the circling seasons rule
> The year; nor mix in every monstrous day."

Our relative literary barrenness, Brown thought, was due to insufficient encouragement of culture.

Early in 1812 Jared Ingersoll declared that the "natural genius of man is very similar in all climates." Dwight produced a lengthy survey of the literature and learning of the United States to disprove adverse British opinion. John Bristed, in a similar survey, granted that high achievements in scholarship and poetry must wait on posterity, but America had already outstripped the world in inventive genius.

Dr. Williamson, conceding that climate did affect man in many ways, held that this was to America's advantage: "If a distinction may be looked for, in the process of time, between the American and the native of the old continent; if the inhabitants of either continent are to excel those of the other in strength of body or of mind; if there is any part of the globe in which the human species may be expected to arrive at the greatest perfection, I cherish the pleasing hope, that the favoured place will be found in America." The "proper nursery of genius, learning, industry, and the liberal arts, is a temperate climate, in a country that is diversified by hills, enjoying a clear atmosphere. The reader will be pleased to consider," says Williamson, "whether there is any part of the old continent, in which these circumstances occur, in so extensive a degree, as they do in America, at least in North America."

As forests are cut down and marshes drained off, Williamson continues, "the American atmosphere will become more pure, for it will be less charged with vegetable exhalations." Such a "pure state of the atmosphere must have a considerable effect upon the temper and genius of the inhabitants." Add to the improvement in climate the blessings of civil liberty and America is certain to outstrip the world.

Had Americans not been too angered with De Pauw and Buffon over their criticisms, they would have realized that each of these authors had suggested the possibility that through his industry man in America might make his world quite habitable. In a reply to one of his French critics, De Pauw pointed out that "America has been colonized, huge forests razed, waters drained, and the air purified by the smoke of many fires, all of which has modified the climate considerably." And Buffon, in a passage following one of his most damning criticisms, declared: "Some centuries hence, when the lands are cultivated, the forests cut down, the courses of the rivers properly directed, and the marshes drained, this same country will become the most fertile, the most wholesome, and the richest in the whole world, as it is already in all the parts which have experienced the industry and skill of man."

Jefferson, as we have seen, was certain that the climate of America had begun to undergo a change. He found that winds from the east now reached farther inland than formerly, and thought these easterly winds might eventually reach the Mississippi River. He wrote to Chastellux, in 1782, that the main causes of the changes so far observed were "the progress of agriculture and population, through which the woods have been cleared." [13] Jefferson even speculated on the effects upon the climate of America which might result if a canal were cut through the Isthmus of Panama.

Chastellux, one of Jefferson's visitors at Monticello, applauded Jefferson's application to meteorological observation, which, "of all the branches of philosophy, is the most proper for the Americans to cultivate." Chastellux then advised Americans how to clear and settle their land so as to produce the finest climate. They were "to disperse the settlements as much as possible, and to leave some groves of trees standing between them." Thus would the inhabited territory be kept healthy, "and as there yet remain considerable marshes which they cannot drain, there is no risk of admitting the winds too easily, as they would serve to carry off the exhalations."

Perhaps the most curious advice given to Americans, on that score, came from Dr. Thomas Wright, "Licentiate of the College of Surgeons in Ireland, and Teacher of Anatomy." While serving as surgeon with the British forces during the Revolutionary War, he had noticed that his men suffered from "the intermittents" when near swampy lands, and that winds purified the air and restored health. This suggested the plan which he communicated to the American Philosophical Society, and which was read before that Society in 1794 [14] and later published in its *Transactions*:

"It is evidenced in the most legible characters of nature that the eastern coast of North America has been of very late Neptunian origin . . ." and has not yet been "fully relinquished by its antient oceanic possessor." To drain all the marshes would be too great a task. So Americans must resort to a method less gigantic: "Let it be supposed that the N.W. and S.E. are the asseclae or prevailing winds of North America; let the surveyor general make out a tract of say 100 or 200 miles in a right line to be cleared of trees; then every blast from these two opposite points will ventilate 200 miles of country, bearing along the fumes of all the marshes, while the great *visto* or avenue skirted with wood at both sides would furnish the most salubrious and consequently valuable situation for settlers." In extenuation of Dr. Wright, it might be recalled that Erasmus Darwin once suggested that the climate of a given place might be "made more equable by towing icebergs from the polar to the tropical regions." [15]

The controversy over America's climate took some odd

political turns. Dr. Thomas Bond, in his "Anniversay Oration" before the American Philosophical Society in 1782,
declared that if Britain had really known the excellent effects of America's climate upon the bodies and minds of
the colonists, she would never have tried to enslave them.
M. L. Davis, in a fiery patriotic "Oration" in "St. Paul's
Church, on the Fourth of July, 1800" castigated European
philosophers, "their Raynals and their Buffons," for holding our animals, plants, and men inferior. He counseled
these "Haughty and imperious Europeans" to stay on their
side of the Atlantic, and exhorted Americans "to cultivate
and cherish a national character." One feels that Buffon
and Raynal may have figured in the nationalistic tendencies which eventuated in the Monroe Doctrine!

What was generally considered the most satisfactory refutation of European criticisms was made by John Bristed
in his *Resources of the United States of America* (1818).
"The character of nations . . . is formed, not by *physical*,
but by *moral* causes and influences, as government, religion, and education. . . ." Reviewing the "theory of the
French philosophers," Bristed dwelt with obvious pleasure
on the anecdote of Franklin's dinner at Passy, where six
"stout, well-proportioned, tall, handsome" Americans put
in the shade the "ludicrous" Frenchmen, who were "all
little, lank, yellow, shrivelled personages, resembling Java
monkeys" and who "peeped up at their opposite neigh-
bours, and were silent—though not satisfied." The Americans "have compelled the meteor-flag of England, which
had waved in triumph on the ocean for a thousand years, to
lower its ancient ensign beneath the new-born standard of
her child." Surely *this* cannot be the work of men who have
degenerated in a pernicious climate! Nor can the steam-
boat be the production of a genius weakened by climate.

Bristed concludes: "At all events, it is *too late* now to
oppose any mere theory respecting the degeneracy of men
in America, to the irresistible argument of contrary facts,

seeing, that Americans have, for a series of years, displayed the utmost intelligence, enterprise, spirit, and perseverance in all the occupations of peace; and, likewise, exhibited the most consummate skill, intrepidity, and heroism in war, whether conflicting in the field or on the ocean. The truth is, that the great mass of the American people *surpasses* that of all other countries in shrewdness of intellect, in general intelligence, and in that versatile capacity which enables men to enter upon and prosecute successfully, new situations and untried employments. It would be difficult for any country to show that it has produced men of greater genius, in their respective departments, than Rittenhouse, Franklin, and West."

9

Politics, Religion, and Science

•

A survey of the intense political antagonism to Jefferson and his Republican Party can aid us in understanding the interrelation of Jefferson's scientific interests and political activities. Few leaders in the history of our country have suffered such acrimonious abuse from political opponents as he. "Households, families, communities, trades, and professions were split on political lines, in hot and abusive enmity, according as they held Federalist or antifederalist views. . . ." [1] Controversy began to simmer hotly during Jefferson's Vice-Presidency and it boiled over during the campaigns of 1800 and 1804. Jefferson's political theories and policies, religion, economics, morality, private life, public services, philosophy, scientific activities, love of gadgets and inventions all became targets.

A contemporary observer reported: "The history of the world cannot produce a parallel wherein the grossness of abuse and the malignity of temper have been carried to such an unbounded excess. The present Administrations have been attacked with a virulence which has nearly exceeded the ingenuity of grammarians to coin words adequate to its import. The whole vocabulary of the English language, expressive of the malignant passions, has within a few years been exhausted to defame the reputation of almost every Republican in the government." [2]

In the House of Representatives Matthew-Lyon spat in the face of Roger Griswald; and passersby in the streets witnessed a brawl between the editors Benjamin Franklin Bache and John Ward Fenno.[3] As early as 1792, while Secretary of State, Jefferson had declared that party animosities in Philadelphia "have raised a wall of separation between those who differ in political sentiments. They must love misery indeed who would rather at the sight of an honest man feel the torment of hatred and aversion than the benign spasms of benevolence and esteem." [4] Some six months after he had become Vice-President, he wrote that men "who have been intimate all their lives, cross the streets to avoid meeting, and turn their heads the other way, lest they should be obliged to touch their hats." [5] In 1798 he pictured Philadelphia as a place "where envy, hatred, malice, revenge, and all the worst passions of men, are marshalled, to make one another as miserable as possible." [6]

Bitter feeling against the supposed French influence in politics, religion, and philosophy brought on a riot in a New England church when a hat with a French cockade fell from the gallery upon the heads of those below. When the notorious Federalist Fisher Ames shuffled off his mortal coil in 1808, his funeral was taken over by members of his party, and his indignant brother, mother, and other members of his family refused to attend.[7] On the other hand, Jeffersonians in Essex County, Massachusetts, assailed the Federalists as sycophants of British monarchy and circulated tickets which bore the English coat of arms over Federalists' names; while over their own candidate flew the American eagle.[8]

New Yorkers, who were largely Federalist and Episcopalian, were "all but abjectly respectful of the mother-country, and members spoke of 'His Majesty's ship' in the harbours, while they deprecated American fruits and productions. . . . Many of the members were also given to railing at modern degeneracy: they sighed as they discussed the good old times and mourned over the ruins of ancient virtue." When a candidate for a degree at Columbia College, uttered antifederalist sentiments in his commencement oration, the provost withheld his diploma.[9]

Certain banks in New York City and Albany refused loans to followers of Jefferson. As late as 1812, when a woolen factory was opened in Trenton Falls, "it was expressly stated that no Democrat would be permitted to buy stock."[10] In Charleston, South Carolina, Henry William Desaussure warned his audience of the dire consequences if the immoral, irreligious, philosophizing, Constitution-hating, Washington-slandering, French-loving, slave-liberating, Banneker-loving, Paine-loving, bank-hating, navy-hating, cowardly, radical, and all-round dangerous Thomas Jefferson were placed in the highest seat of the land. The citizens of Massachusetts were advised by Claudius Herrick: ". . . should Jacobinism gain the ascendancy; let every man arm himself, not only to defend his property, his wife, and children, but to secure his life, from the dagger of his Jacobin neighbor."[11] The *Connecticut Courant* thus poetized a procession of Jefferson's followers:

> "And now across the Green
> A motley throng there pours,
> Drunkards and whores
> And rogues in scores.
> They all rejoice."[12]

Jefferson's friend, Benjamin Waterhouse, lost his position on the medical faculty of Harvard. In a letter written many years later, Waterhouse recounts the warning issued to the Harvard faculty at the time: "When Mr. Jefferson came into office, the late Judge Lowell . . . a very influential governor of this University, and a warm friend of mine, gave us, of the college to understand, that the church and all our other sacred institutions were in danger, particularly the University, that therefore it behooved us Professors to rally with the clergy, and together form *the front rank* in the Massachusetts army of federalism, in opposition to infidelity, Jacobinism, and Jeffersonism. . . . My associates, and the clergy very generally swallowed and relished this doctrine, while I remained silent." [13] His silence was not taken for consent and Waterhouse lost his job.

Federalists also persecuted refugee French scientists, "including the first Du Pont. John Adams had the greatest difficulty in restraining his administration from prosecuting Joseph Priestley, the discoverer of oxygen; and Thomas Cooper, a close friend of Priestley's and a college president was sentenced to six months in jail and a fine of $900." [14]

Touring the country during the Embargo, an English traveler in New England remarked that the terms "Federals" and "Anti-federals" were rapidly becoming obsolete. Current synonyms for the first were "traitors, tories, damned tories, and British tories"; and for the second "jacobins, French tories, republicans and democrats." [15]

Federalist speakers and writers referred to their opponents, individually or collectively, as atheists, infidels, drunkards, anarchists, libertines, rancorous Jacobins, scoffing deists, sniveling fanatics, reptiles of Democracy, idle profligates, desperadoes, yelpers of the Democratic kennels, tools of a baboon, frog-eating, blood-drinking Cannibals, gallican traitors, demons of sedition, malignant knaves,[16] slave-driving nabobs of Virginia, scum of the political pot,[17] opponents of religion and manners, sons of vice and ignorance.

William Cobbett quoted a saying that the current animosities had "shaken the gall bladder" of the country. Parson Weems thought it time to publish "The Philanthropist or a Good Twelve Cents Worth of Political Love Powder for the Fair Daughters and Patriotic Sons of Virginia."

In such an atmosphere it is little wonder that Jefferson's scientific and inventive interests were attacked by his opponents. Soon after his retirement from the Presidency, in referring to this political grist which had been ground from the raw materials of his science, Jefferson wrote: "Of all the charges brought against me by my political adversaries, that of possessing some science has probably done them the least credit. Our countrymen are too enlightened themselves, to believe that ignorance is the best qualification for their service." In later life he again spoke reservedly but with continued asperity of his political opponents who had deemed "even science itself as well as my affection for it as a fit object of ridicule and a disqualification for the affairs of government."

The word "philosopher" was applied to Thomas Jefferson as a term of derision by his enemies, and of honor by his supporters. "His enemies," said Jared Ingersoll, "will not allow him to be any thing but a philosopher: his friends extol him as a sage." In Jefferson's day the words "philosophy" and "philosopher" had a different implication from the one they have today. "Philosopher" might designate a man who loved and pursued all branches of learning. In a more specific sense "philosophy" denoted science, and to be a "philosopher" was to be a scientist.

But the word "philosophy"—and even "science"—had also gathered some rather derogatory connotations, particularly injurious to a man's political and religious standing. To call Jefferson a "philosopher" in the latter sense was to imply that he was dangerous, politically unreliable, and an enemy of religion. "Philosophy"—or science—could then signify an unwholesome prying into the secrets of nature for the purpose of discrediting the Bible, promoting atheism, encouraging a harmful nationalism, a deistic naturalism, materialism, the wildest ideas of the Enlightenment, chaotic and uncontrolled speculation, impracticality, confused and fuzzy thinking, tedious, trivial, and indiscriminate discussion, a modernism which would destroy the finest values of the past, Jacobinism (that is, rampant Gallican radicalism), political anarchy, blind and servile love of France (home of rationalism, the philosophes and all godlessness)—and any other evil that came to a Federalist's mind.

This was expressed, among many others, by the Reverend Clement C. Moore who declared: "Wretched, indeed, is our country, if she is to be enlightened by these philosophers; philosophers whose industry is equalled by nothing but their vanity; whose pursuits are impeded by no danger nor difficulty; by no law, human or divine; who think nothing too great for them to grasp, and nothing too minute to be observed: they dig into the bowels of the earth and climb the loftiest mountains; they traverse the ocean, and explore the regions of the air; they search the written records of antiquity, and the traditions of savages; they build up theories of shells and bones and straws." And to what end? To reduce man to a state of savagery, to extinguish the cheerful Christian light of hope, to "quench the thirst for immortality, and to degrade man "from the rank of angels." [18] The Reverend Eli Smith maintained that "to be a scholar, a philosopher and a gentleman, it is necessary to deny revelation, contemn the bible, profane the holy Sabbath, reproach the ministers of Christ, tread under foot the blood of the covenant, and do despite to the spirit of grace." And the Reverend John Mason attacked the "infidels, who admit nothing for which they cannot find adequate 'natural agents' " and excoriated Jefferson for his leadership in this kind of thing, Jefferson having questioned the Flood and other religious miracles.

Who wants a philosopher at the head of our government? cried Jefferson's opponents. Nobody, replied the New York Federalist, Gouverneur Morris, who desired none of "those philosophical gentlemen, those citizens of the world as they call themselves, in our public council." [19] Nobody, replied William Cobbett, vituperative publisher of *Porcupine's Gazette*, who ran a quotation in his magazine to the effect that "of all beings, a philosopher makes the worst politician," and asserted that "if one circumstance more than another could disqualify Mr. Jefferson from the Presidency, it would be the charge of his being a philosopher." Nor, according to Cobbett, was Jefferson truly a philosopher. He but wore "the *mask* of philosophy." To see how really impractical these philosophical politicians could be, one had but to look at John Locke, whose constitution for Carolina had proved "so full of *theoretic whimsies*, that it was soon thrown aside." Or at the Frenchman Condorcet, "a particular friend of our American philosopher," whose proposed constitution for France contained "more obscurities than were ever before piled up in any system of government," and had also been thrust aside.

Jefferson, whom Cobbett further accused of cowardice during the revolutionary war, has only "the *inferior* characteristics, and the *externals* of philosophy," which, as applied to politics, are "want of steadiness, a constitutional indecision and versatility, visionary, wild and speculative systems." Jefferson's eccentricity is seen in his sending a copy of Banneker's Almanac to Condorcet "as the highest proof of his admiration for the Negro's work." Jefferson's affectation of simplicity in dress and manners is but the "appearance of philosophy." How can voters possibly elect such a *"poor, timid, philosopher"* to the Presidency? Contrast him with Washington and "the spirited and truly patriotic HAMILTON." Who would want the "philosopher" who avoided the revolutionary battlegrounds and retired to write his *Notes on Virginia*! Jefferson's reputation "is not bottomed on *solid merit*"; his abilities "have been more directed to the acquirement of literary fame than to the substantial good of his country." His election will obviously debase the glorious name of America, prostrate her at the feet of France, subvert her excellent Constitution, and destroy her present prosperity!

Cobbett used Jefferson's friendship for the astronomer David Rittenhouse as an additional target. Rittenhouse, said Cobbett, "was a great philosopher, but the only proof we had of *his political* talents was his suffering himself to be wheedled into the *Presidency* of the *Democratic Society* of Philadelphia," for which act he was justly ashamed. How absurd to think that scientific research and statesmanship could ever prove compatible: "Let us suppose one of these exploring and profound philosophers elected President of the United States, and a foreign minister, on his first introduction into his cabinet, surprising him in the act of inspecting the *skin and the scarf skin* of a *black and white pig,* in order to discover the causes of difference which nature has created in their colour, or with the same view anatomizing the kidnies and glands of a Negro, to ascertain the *nature of his secretions*? Would not the minister's first observation be, that the philosopher would be better employed in his retirement at home, and his second, that such a President would furnish excellent materials for him to make use of."

Jefferson as philosopher-scientist was the butt of a satirical Fourth of July Oration of 1799 delivered by the New England Federalist lawyer David Daggett, entitled "Sun-Beams May Be Extracted from Cucumbers, But the Process Is Tedious." To orient his readers, Daggett opens with a survey of Jonathan Swift's academy at Lagoda in Laputa, where "projectors" (that is, experimenters and inventors) were trying to make a marble pin-cushion, prevent the growth of wool on sheep, abolish the use of words, and extract sunbeams from cucumbers, the last experiment having gone on for eight years and being expected to take eight years more.

Daggett then surveys the activities of modern "projectors." He cites a machine, not long since invented, called an *automaton,* designed to carry a load anywhere "without the aid of horses, oxen, or any other animal." It was perfect —except "that it would not go." Balloons became another butt. "A few years ago," says Daggett," the Learned insisted that it was grovelling to travel either by *land* or *water,* but that the truly *philosophical* mode was to go by air. Hence, in all parts of the world, speculatists were mounted in balloons, with the whole apparatus of living and dying, and were flying through the Heavens, to the utter astonishment and mortification of those poor illiterate wretches who were doomed to tug and sweat on the earth. To be sure this method of travelling was somewhat precarious—a flow of wind, regardless of the principles of this machine, might destroy it, or, by the giving way of one *philosophical* pin, *peg,* or *rope,* it might be let into the sea, or dashed against a rock, and thus its precious contents miserably perish." A busybody might ask, Dagget thinks, "if it was intended that men should fly through the air, why were they not made with feathers and wings. . . ?" Again, there is the submarine, in which modern man is "constantly *groping* among shark, sturgeon and seahorses." Despite all these "great, and learned, and ingenious men, . . . the stupid, foolish, plodding people of this and other countries, still keep their oxen and their horses. . . ."

"The plow, harrow, spade, hoe, sickle and scythe," also "have undergone a thorough change, on mathematical principles. . . ." Man no longer has to toil for his living on the farm, except for some "old fashioned" fellows in New England—and she "abounds with them"—who still resort to honest sweat. At the same time, modern physicians, dismissing past medicine as "quackery and nonsense," rely on *"reason, unerring reason"* and find a cure-all in electricity.

Similarly education, morals, and politics are all subverted by the doctrines imported from iniquitous France, where it is "declared and established, by law, that ancient habits, customs and manners, modes of thinking, reasoning and acting ought to be ridiculed, despised and rejected, for a totally new order of things has taken place."

"But it will be enquired," says Daggett, "where have these novel theories appeared? I answer—They have dawned upon New England—they have glowed in the southern states—they have burnt in France. We have seen a few projectors in Boats, Balloons and Automatons—A few philosophical farmers—A few attempts to propagate the breed of naked sheep—and we have at least one Philosopher in the United States, who has taken an accurate mensuration of the mammoth's bones—made surprising discoveries in the doctrine of vibrating pendulums, and astonished the world with the precise gauge and dimensions of all the aboriginals of America." Surely, concluded Daggett, no sensible men could go to the polls and vote for Philosopher Jefferson!

In "The Claims of Thomas Jefferson to the Presidency, Examined at the Bar of Christianity" (1800), its probable author, Asbury Dickens, also sees Jefferson disqualified for the presidency because of his science. "Science and government are two different paths. He that walks in one, becomes, at every step, less qualified to walk with steadfastness or vigour in the other. The most lamentable prelude, the worst preparation possible for a ruler of men, was a life passed like that of Newton.—Would to heaven that the parallel that some choose to suggest between that divine sage and the sage of Monticello, were complete"—that Thomas Jefferson had remained a philosopher and stayed out of politics!

From assailing his general concern for science, his opponents extended their attacks to specific scientific interests of his. The mammoth received a large share of their attention. Cobbett's magazine ran a piece "from the classical pen of Mr. [Joseph] Dennie," containing the line "Sooner shall mammoth pay his British debt?" which those in the know immediately recognized as another thrust at Jefferson, who had been maligned as having swindled his British creditors. Cobbett had previously printed extracts from a letter by a gentleman from Georgia, whose wonder over Jefferson's reasons for accepting the Vice-Presidency, were answered by Cobbett's revelations that Jefferson intended to put himself at the head of a French party. Jefferson, according to the gentleman from Georgia, should surely be able to see "that his *French faction* is but a *temporary monster*" which bears within itself the principles of its own destruction, like the "mammoth." "These monsters have both engaged a considerable share of that gentleman's attention."

New England Federalists attacked Jefferson as a "mammoth infidel," as well as "a drunkard, an anarchist, and a libertine." [20] His proposed new-fangled gunboat for the Navy was thus abused in verse by Fessenden:

> "Dog-fishes, dolphins, if they've wit,
> To our Sea-Mammoth will submit,
> No grampus dare to stand a scratch
> And even a shark would find his match!"

—which carried a double thrust. It hit at Jefferson himself, and it played ironically on the smallness of the gunboats, which was made much of by opponents to Jefferson's naval plans.

The satirists of the mammoth were presented with a new butt in the mammoth cheese, weighing 1,235 pounds, which Jefferson's admirers in Cheshire, Massachusetts, made and presented to him in 1801. The cheese was delivered by John Leland, a Baptist clergyman and staunch

Jeffersonian, after a journey overland and by sea. For his part in it Leland was castigated by the New England Congregational clergyman, Manasseh Cutler, as "the cheesemonger, a poor, ignorant, illiterate, clownish preacher." [21] According to the traveler John Davis, who was in Baltimore when Leland and his mammoth cheese debarked, all Baltimore was excited. Men, women, and children flocked to see the great cheese, whose circumference equaled the hindmost wheel of a wagon. On to Washington went the cheese aboard a wagon drawn by four richly caparisoned horses. It was accepted with sincere expressions of appreciation by Jefferson, who had it exhibited in his unfurnished East Room, which he forthwith humorously termed "the Mammoth Room." The Cheese was seen a year later in the President's House by a young damsel on her way to Virginia. Mrs. Madison showed it off along with other objects of interest to visitors.[22]

Joseph Dennie, Philadelphia reactionary, who at one time went on trial for his attacks on democracy, made it the subject of a derisive ballad, "Reflection of Mr. Jefferson," published in his magazine, *The Port Folio*, in March, 1802. Jefferson is made to say:

> "In this great cheese I see myself portray'd
> My life and fortune in this useless mass."

He, too, was once as pure as the milk "from which this monster came,/ 'Till turn'd, by philosophic rennet, sour," since when "I am become indeed a man of curds."

Dennie also used the cheese for a prose satire in his *Port Folio*, a mock address to the President by the inhabitants of Cheshire:

A GREAT NEW-YEAR'S GIFT.
The *greatest* Cheese in America,
FOR
The *greatest* Man in America
TO WIT

The Author of the History of the *greatest* Beast in America.

"GREAT SIR . . . We have a *great* attachment to the constitution, and we have, for several years past, had *great* apprehensions that the *great* features of it were not properly attended to: Our joy, of course, must have been *great,* on your election to the first *great* office in the nation, having had *great* evidence, from your *great* sentiments, that it would be your *greatest strife and glory to turn back the government to its virgin purity.* The trust is *great.* The task is *great.* But we feel a *great* consolation, that the *great* ruler of the *great* universe, who raises up *great* men to achieve *great* events, has raised up a *great* Jefferson, to defend the *great* principles of republicanism. . . . With this address, we send you a *great* Cheese, by the hands of the *greatest* men amongst us, as a *huge peppercorn* of the *great* esteem we bear our *chief* magistrate. . . . This *great* cheese, *great* sir, was not made by a *great* lord, for his *great* majesty, nor with a view to gain *great* offices or *great* titles, but by the *great* personal labour of the *greatest* farmers in our *great* state, without the assistance of a single slave, for an president of a *great* people. . . . May the *Almighty* God greatly preserve your life for a *long* time, as a *great* blessing to the United States, and to the world at *large.*"

Jefferson's interest in the Indian was another target of his adversaries. According to Jefferson the Indians of America probably went further back into antiquity than the inhabitants of Asia. Wrong, said the Reverend Moore! "Scripture says that the world was peopled from one pair, placed in Asia." [23] Jefferson had also defended the physical strength of the Indian from the charges of degeneracy made by Buffon. Cobbett ran a letter by Luther Martin in his *Gazette* (1797) berating Jefferson for "examining minutely every part of [the Indian's] frame" and declaring that though the hand of the Indian is smaller than that of the European, yet *"ses organes de la generation ne sont plus faibles ou plus petits"* (his organs of generation are not smaller or feebler).

Martin also attacked Jefferson hotly for his praise of the

Mingo Chief Logan, who was murdered at the hands of Cresap. All philosophers, thought Martin, "are pretty much the same." Give them a theory, and there is no telling to what ends they will go to prove it. Jefferson "had his hypothesis to establish, or, what is much the same thing, he had the hypothesis of Buffon to overthrow." Therefore, to praise the Indian he accepted without verification whatever story came to hand. Hence no one need be astonished to see this philosopher Jefferson sacrificing the good name of Michael Cresap to his theories. Why am I so concerned over this? asks Martin. Because "the daughter of Michael Cresap was the mother of my children." Stung by this, Jefferson spent much time securing all manner of testimony to disprove or corroborate what he had related in his *Notes on Virginia*. This material was published as an appendix to his original account.

Other attacks were directed at Jefferson's interest in inventions and machinery and their applications. His swivel chair became "Mr. Jefferson's whirligig"; he was said to have invented it "so as to look all ways at once." [24] His grist mill on the Rivana River was said to be located where there was no water to run it! His gunboats were caught in the storm of Fessenden's poetry:

> "Our Gun-Boats! themes of admiration
> To every seaman in the nation,
> The very essence, in reality,
> Of vast philosophisticality!"

His attempt to establish an accurate unit of measurement was jeered at as "the doctrine of vibrating pendulums." His proposed drydock was ridiculed. In his old age, his poverty was attributed to his "fantastic projects and theoretical experiments." [25]

Jefferson's efforts to encourage the raising of fine-wooled merinos were distorted by his opponents into "attempts to propagate the breed of naked sheep." Because, during the Embargo, he permitted the importation of "two parcels of

Merino sheep," "a very valuable machine which spins cotton, wool, and flax equally," and "two tierces" of cotton seed from the Mediterranean area, he was attacked as a law-breaker and a criminal, and his defense on the grounds of the internationalism of science was derided.

The opposition likewise subjected Jefferson's interest in natural history to all manner of jibes. He was accused of being a "feeder of prairie-dogs and bull-frogs," [26] of "weighing the rats and mice" of the New World to prove them larger than those of the Old, of being so "philosophical" as to examine the skin of a black-and-white pig in front of a foreign Ambassador. Dennie published a satire of Jefferson in the form of a supposed fragment of diary found along the banks of the Potomac:

> "*Monday 8 o'clock, 20th February, 1804*
> Left Sally [a reference to the charge of immorality so often leveled at Jefferson]—damn's bore, to rise early—but must seem industrious, though nothing to do. Met Madison at breakfast —don't much like him—talked of virtue and conscience— thought he looked hard at me—. . . .
> *10 o'clock.* Wrote half a page of my dissertation on cockroaches—servant came in to say people below wanted to see me on public business—cursed their impertinence—sent word I was out. . . .—returned to my cockroaches in a fret, and couldn't write. . . .
> Ordered my horse—never ride with a servant—looks proud— mob wouldn't like it—must gull the boobies. . . ." [27]

During the Embargo, which hurt New England trade, the youthful poet William Cullen Bryant, incensed like others in New England, penned the following rhymed diatribe against Jefferson:

> "Go, wretch, resign thy presidential chair,
> Disclose thy secret measures, foul or fair,
> Go, search with curious eyes for horned frogs,
> 'Mid the Wild wastes of Louisiana bogs;
> Or where the Ohio rolls his turbid stream
> Dig for huge bones, thy glory and thy theme."

Opposition newspapers made a great deal out of a supposed Salt Mountain in the territory included in the Louisiana Purchase. In the mass of documents which Jefferson collected and presented to Congress to provide information on the Louisiana territory were references to gigantic Indians and to a mountain of salt 180 miles long and forty-five miles wide about a thousand miles up the Missouri River. Corroborative testimony was reported from traders so respected that Jefferson considered these reports verified. It was declared that some had even taken four hundred weight of saltpeter from caves in that area and sold it profitably in New Orleans.

The existence of the salt mountain became a matter of public debate, with the Jeffersonians as believers and the anti-Jeffersonians as doubters. Some argued that salt found in such huge quantities underground should be found in huger quantities above ground; some that perhaps the whole mountain was not salt, that it just had salt mines in it. A correspondent to a paper friendly to Jefferson quoted Dr. Waterhouse of Harvard as saying recorded salt deposits elsewhere suggested the possibility of a great Salt Mountain. Other defenders pointed out that the traders who had seen the mountain knew more about it than the Federalists who had not. Samples of the mountain salt were reported as received at Washington, New York, Boston, and other cities.

To Federalists, the Salt Mountain was but another proof of the extent to which the credulity of "the greatest philosopher of the present age" could be stretched. All former tales of marvels to be found in the West, they said, were now become but "pepper-corns to this mountain;—which an ingenious southern researcher supposes to be no other than the basement of the *pillar of salt* into which *Lot's* wife was turned, as recorded in the bible." A burlesque report was printed of "a vast river of *golden eagles* ready coined, which, at a trifling expence in cutting canals and constructing locks, may easily be turned into the treasury of the United States." Even more remarkable was the discovery of "a 'DRY-DOCK,' which appears to have sprung up *almost spontaneously; very little labour having been required in the production of it.*'" But this was not all, continued the *Columbian Centinel & Massachusetts Federalist.* Near this Western dry dock had been found a bloody arena, "which for a vast distance around is thickly strewed with the bones of that wonderful animal, the mammoth." Unlike modern Jeffersonians, who would multiply these mammoths, continued this newspaper, the more intelligent savages of the region used to herd them together and watch them mangle and destroy each other and so become extinct, "to the regret of every true philosopher and politician."

Another Federalist paper dragged in the old accusation that Jefferson behaved like a "philosophical" coward when the British troops approached Monticello; it called the attention of its readers to the fact that this Salt Mountain was larger than Carter's Mountain, to which Jefferson had gone in retreat. The novelist Charles Brockden Brown assailed Jefferson's belief in the Salt Mountain as another proof of that "astonishing degree of credulity" which sustained his love for things French and his gullibility toward stories of marvels in Louisiana. Another critic found this to be a case of Jefferson's "philosophic fogs."

In this respect Jefferson may be blamed for making himself vulnerable. He had expressed belief in the probable existence of such creatures as huge lions, great mammoths, and gigantic sloths out in the northwestern wilds. His theory of the non-extinction of species led him to anticipate the discovery of these and other marvels. His good friend Samuel L. Mitchill testified that Jefferson certainly did believe in this Louisiana Salt Mountain and that he distributed specimens of salt said to have come from it. But Jefferson was not alone in this.

Among Jefferson's attackers were Washington Irving, whose Federalist inclinations and satirical gifts drew him into the political arena. His farcical *Salmagundi; or the Whim-Whams and Opinions of Launcelot Longstaff, & Others*, a series of twenty periodical pamphlets published in New York, 1807–1808, written with the collaboration of William Irving and James Kirke Paulding, contain many jibes at the expense of contemporary scientists and scientific societies. More pertinent here is a series of nine letters which a supposed Tripolitan prisoner named Mustapha Rub-a-Dub Keli Khan writes back home to his friend Asem Hacchem, Principal Slave-Driver to His Highness the Bashaw of Tripoli. Mustapha finds Congress to be "a blustering, windy assembly, where everything is carried by noise, tumult, and debate." He marvels at the inhuman verbal civil war carried on by the Americans, at the continuous discharge of "heavy artillery, consisting of large sheets, loaded with scoundrel! villain! liar! rascal! numskull! nincompoop! dunderhead! wise-acre! blockhead! jackass!" Even that "puissant bashaw" the President is "wofully" and "ignominiously pelted."

But this Grand American Bashaw is largely to blame because of his refusal to believe in the deluge and the story of Balaam's ass, his association with that "professed anteduluvian" Tom Paine, his insistence upon wearing red breeches (a color in great detestation with the Americans because of a dispute of some twenty years ago "with the Barbarians of the British Islands"), his attempts to run the government and handle foreign powers not through action but through proclamations, his penny-pinching economy, and his scientific propensities: . . . he amuses himself with impaling butterflies and pickling tadpoles." [28]

In Irving's *"Knickerbocker's History of New York"* Jefferson is caricatured in the figure of William Kieft.[29] He is shown as full of animus toward his enemies, ruled at home by petticoat government, a pedant especially devoted to

dead languages, a hypocrite who affects democratic manners and dress, a man of paper who governed by proclama-
tion instead of action, who made his office a laboratory for
political experiments, a shallow know-it-all. "Of metaphysics he knew enough to confound all hearers and himself into the bargain." He knew logic to such a degree that
he "seldom got into an argument without getting into a
perplexity." He had mastered "one half of the Chinese
alphabet: and was unanimously pronounced a 'universal
genius!' "

Even as a boy Kieft had made "very curious investigations" into the nature of windmills, "which was one of the
reasons why he afterwards came to be so ingenious a governor." This love of science he carried over into adulthood,
for he had "skirmished smartly on the frontiers of several
of the sciences, was fond of experimental philosophy, and
prided himself upon inventions of all kinds." His house
bore ample testimony to these interests and his ingenuity.
Here were to be found "patent smoke-jacks that required a
horse to work them; Dutch ovens that roasted meat without fire; carts that went before Horses; weather-cocks that
turned against the wind." In addition, the house was "beset
with paralytic cats and dogs," the subject of its owner's
indulgence in "experimental philosophy." The "yelling
and yelping of these latter unhappy victims of science,
while aiding the pursuit of knowledge, soon gained for the
place the name of 'Dog's Misery'. . . ." Such was the beautiful Monticello as sketched by the pen of satire!

Before turning to direct attacks upon Jefferson's religious opinions, it might be well to consider, briefly, contemporary feelings about the relation between religion and
science. For many and complicated reasons conservatives
had begun to feel, after the end of the Revolutionary War,
that religion stood in jeopardy from the growing religious
indifference, French scepticism, atheism, Deism, the En-

lightenment, scientific rationalism, and the new scientific discoveries.

William Scales, Fellow of the Royal Society of England, attacked Harvard as a "seminary of sophistry, falsehood and folly," which furthered infidelity by means of science. He objected to being fed John Locke and Isaac Newton, the latter of whom he found to be "a great fabricator of falsehoods, and a destroyer of the work of God." [30] William Ellery Channing described Harvard in the middle 1790's as pervaded by a spirit of "skepticism." In the early 1800's Dr. Lyman Beecher found Yale "in a most ungodly state." The church was "almost extinct," the students were "skeptical and rowdies were plenty." Many rooms contained wine and liquor. Intemperance, profanity, gambling and licentiousness were rampant. During the 1790's members of the classes addressed each other as Voltaire, Rousseau, D'Alembert, and so forth. [31]

Electricity was the exception. Attacks on Franklin for the impiety of inventing the lightning rod were short-lived. Franklin became famous and revered, and electricity became popular. John Winthrop defended Franklin in the Harvard Chapel. [32] Reverend Ezra Stiles, President of Yale, did experiments in electricity. Franklin's house, as he tells us, "was continually full, for some time, with people who came to see these new wonders." On the banks of the Schuykill River, the great philosopher himself entertained friends by astonishing them with such marvels as killing a turkey for dinner by "electrical shock" and roasting it "by the electrical jack, before a fire kindled by the electrified bottle. . . ." [33] Up and down the coast from Boston to Philadelphia went Franklin's friend the Reverend Ebenezer Kinnersley, in a series of popular, illustrated, scientific lectures on electricity. Kinnersley explained to listeners that lightning rods were neither presumptuous nor irreligious. [34] Nearer the turn of the century the great showman Falconi entertained audiences with "natural and philosophical" experiments, one of which was hailed as "Expulsion by Electricity." [35] At least in this field, science was in the driver's seat.

But such was not the case in other scientific fields. In a talk before the Philadelphia Society for Promoting Agriculture in 1811, entitled "Changes of Timber and Plants, Races of Animals Extinct," Richard Peters argued that nature "delights in, and actually effects, entire changes and successions in the vegetable productions of the earth." The clearing and cultivating of land in America, he said, "cannot fail to make material *changes* in the climate, the general state of the atmosphere, and the soil." From all this he concluded that there must "naturally and necessarily" be "corresponding mutations in the productions of the earth." Peters knew he was on controversial ground. "By some," he said, "I well know that this sentiment is reprobated as profane and *atheistical*." Peters' fears were not groundless, for he was "acetosely" criticized for his "impiety" and "unphilosophical absurdity."

Answering votaries of chemistry, the Reverend Samuel Miller in his *Brief Retrospect of the Eighteenth Century* (1803) acknowledged the significant accomplishments of chemistry. Its empire, he said, had been "wonderfully extended" and its useful applications to metals, medicines, fluids, gases, and the analysis of animal, vegetable, and mineral matter had surpassed the dreams of many. But he found cause for alarm in the fact that a "few extravagant and enthusiastic votaries of chemistry have undertaken, on chemical principles, to account for all the phenomena of *motion, life,* and mind; and on those very facts which clearly prove wise design, and the superintending care of an INFINITE INTELLIGENCE, have attempted to build a fabric of *atheistical* philosophy."

In Kentucky the naturalist Constantine Rafinesque's magazine, *Western Minerva,* was proscribed, under the influence of what he considered narrow religious prejudice.

He complained to Jefferson about it in 1821. "It has been condamned [*sic*]," he stated, "before its appearance (upon some proof sheets) by a new kind of Western Literary Inquisition and Censorship. . . . The principal motives stated in the verbal decree of this new Inquisition, were that the Journal was too learned, that it dared to inculcate political and moral Wisdom, to surmise that the Sun does not stand still and has an orbit and that the Earth therefore performs a spiral course through Space, to teach Agricultural truths, to employ mystification against ignorance and folly &c., &c. You will perhaps hardly believe that this could happen in the U. St. . . ." But Jefferson probably had little difficulty believing that this kind of thing could happen.[36] He no doubt recalled only too clearly attacks upon his own scientific speculations in his *Notes on Virginia*. In 1804 one attacker, referring to geology, had commented: "Whenever modern philosophers talk about mountains, something impious is likely to be near at hand."

There were those, however, who saw no necessary conflict between science and religion or who, sensing the rising opposition between them sought to reconcile the conflict. Dr. Benjamin Rush, anticipating the day when doctors would largely supplant religious missionaries since they could win more converts by curing diseases, was nevertheless careful to point out that medical knowledge and practice in no way went counter to religion. He was for utilizing science and religion together in curing patients. He wanted "the divine and the philosopher" to "embrace each other" in eradicating vice and perfecting the moral faculty. Samuel Mitchill, in his "Discourse on the Character and Services of Thomas Jefferson, More Especially as a Promoter of Natural and Physical Science" (1826) effected a simple reconciliation between religion and the problem of the extinction of species by declaring that if species do become extinct it is "because in the judgment of the ALL-WISE, it ought to be so; we ought to submit reverently to the decision."

Those who saw no conflict between religion and science maintained that God's mind and will could be discovered "in the fair volumes of Creation around us, and in the fairer volume of his written Word." Science and Revelation could walk peacefully together, hand in hand. It was partly through nature that one looked up to nature's God. The study of nature was therefore one of the best avenues to ultimate religious truth. Over the naturalist John Bartram's greenhouse hung the motto:

> "Slave to no sect, who takes no private road,
> But looks through nature, up to nature's God!"

Let no one point out that the attitudes, discoveries, and conclusions of science sometimes ran counter to certain cherished assertions in the Bible and religious modes of perceiving them and harmony might reign. Or again, as long as one did not, like Thomas Jefferson, run for an important political office, his opinions might not disturb the public peace. Most men did not run for such office and hence their views caused them and their friends little embarrassment. Most scientists preserved the reigning harmony by insisting that science was a buttress of religion. A formality in some cases, in general this appears to have been sincere. The fact, however, that they were so careful to show that their science worked in collaboration with religion and was not its foe is a sign of the smoldering conflict underneath.

In a speech delivered by Governor James Bowdoin of Massachusetts to the American Academy of Arts and Sciences in 1780, he stressed that contemplation of the works of nature in all their variety, beauty, and usefulness must "force upon us the idea of a SUPREME MIND." When we look at these works of the Supreme Mind, "they powerfully persuade us to exclaim, in the rapturous and sublime language of inspiration, 'Great and marvellous are thy works, LORD GOD. Almighty, in wisdom hast thou made them all.' "

Benjamin Rush, in his eulogy of David Rittenhouse, found "a natural connection between a knowledge of the works of nature and just ideas of the divine perfections" and spoke of "the beneficial influence of philosophy upon religion." Rush hinted at daring opinions: "It remains yet to be determined, whether all the moral as well as natural attributes of the Deity may not be discovered in the form, and economy of the material world." But he quickly re-assured any listeners who may have thought this deistical. Though Rittenhouse *may* have held this opinion, he has-tened to add, he was nevertheless a scientist whose religion was not wholly derived from the natural and material world—he believed in Revelations.

In 1775 Rittenhouse, himself, in his "Oration" before the American Philosophical Society, asserted that "nothing can better demonstrate the immediate presence of the deity in every part of space, whether vacant or occupied by matter, than astronomy does. It was from an astronomer St. Paul quoted that exalted expression, so often since re-peated, '*In God we live, and move, and have our being.*' "

James Bowdoin went even higher than St. Paul for his re-ligious authority. He declared that the Creator himself was "the first and supremely great Naturalist" when he made known to Adam "the nature and qualities of things, and the uses to which they might be applied, so far as man's well-being required." Besides, the Creator gave man suf-ficient faculties and intended he should gain "a further degree in natural knowledge." As we have seen, Jefferson's friend Charles Willson Peale considered his museum far more than a money-making exhibition. In a letter to Jef-ferson in 1802, after asserting the practical scientific values of his establishment, he informed the President that it is "fully demonstrated that viewing the wonderful structure of a great number of *beings best formed for their respective stations,* elevates the mind to an Admiration and Adoration of the Great Author!"

Similarly Benjamin Rush, writing to Jefferson in 1811 of having subscribed to a learned commentary upon the Bible, observed that the author points out that in beasts "God shows his wondrous skill and power: in the vast elephant, and still more in the *colossal* mammoth, or *megalonyx.* . . . This animal is an astonishing effect of God's power. He seems to have produced him merely to show what he could do. . . ."

As for mathematics, according to Dr. Thomas Bond's "Anniversary Oration" before the American Philosophical Society in 1782, it saves us from "idle *Speculation,* Scepticism, and rash Presumption"; through mathematics we are made to "acknowledge the Blessings of Heaven with a pious affection." The newer science of chemistry had similar defenders. Richard Peters' "On Gypsum," read before the Philadelphia Academy for the Promotion of Agriculture in 1807, found a direct relation between chemistry and religion. "It is not surprising," he declared, "that chymical pursuits should fascinate enquiring minds. They open the great, and often hidden springs of operation, by which the purposes of the creator are effected. So far are they from encouraging the wild and flagitious speculations of sceptics, that they teach us, with humble adoration and ardent gratitude, to '*Look through Nature up to Nature's God.'*"

Undoubtedly the latent religious distrust of the new science helps to explain the intensity of the conservative antagonism to Jefferson. The fear was genuine that with Jefferson at the head of the government orthodox religion in the United States would be in danger of attack. Most of the antagonism, however, must be attributed to political and economic interests which used this fear for their own ends. At best they believed the threat to religion, latent in science, particularly Jefferson's science, a danger also to the established social order. Though Federalists wanted it to appear otherwise, it was "republicanism and not religion that was at stake in the election of 1800." [37]

The fear of many New Englanders that with Jefferson in office religion and they would be in danger of persecution was so real that, following his election in 1800, "old ladies in Connecticut . . . hid their family Bibles because it was supposed that his very first official act, perhaps even before announcing his cabinet, would be to issue a ukase ordering all copies of the sacred volume to be seized and burned." [38] Rumors had spread that, as President, Jefferson would use public funds to bribe teachers, civil servants, military officers, and even pastors to ignore religion or even teach anti-religious doctrines, to pay lecturers to go up and down the land expounding texts from Tom Paine's *Age of Reason,* to erect buildings where these lecturers would hold Christ up to derision and exhort the people to throw off the yoke of priests, to endow colleges and commission professors to propagate deism and anarchy, and, through pensions and other inducements, to bribe Congress to pass laws subversive of religion.

Such rumors were behind the violence, never seen before or since in our country, that characterized the anti-Jefferson propaganda. The Reverend Stanley Griswold in "Truth Its Own Test, and God Its Only Judge" (1800) remarked upon the "savage ferocity with which *honest reputation* is mangled," the "opposition to *science* so boldly manifested," and the "vile arts of a few arch-Demagogues and their sub-deceivers to stigmatize *philosophy* and bring it into contempt under wrongful names." Abraham Bishop in an "Oration" delivered in Wallingford, Connecticut (1801), remarked that "all the sermons for two years past, aimed ostensibly at democratic infidels and infidel philosophy, were in fact aimed at Mr. Jefferson." Bishop could have extended his dates further back. When

Adams was elected President and Jefferson Vice-President in 1796, a public prayer by the Reverend Jedidiah Champion of Litchfield, Connecticut, an ardent Federalist, closed with the words, 'O Lord! wilt Thou bestow upon the Vice President a double portion of Thy grace, for *Thou knowest he needs it.*' " [39] Another divine, Dominie Rhinebeck, in New York, "refused to give the name of Thomas Jefferson to an infant presented at the font." Being a follower of Adams, the Dominie christened the child "John." [40] As late as 1830 the public library of Philadelphia refused shelf space for Jefferson's life and correspondence.[41] In the opinion of the Reverend Eli Smith the election of Jefferson meant that things had become so bad as to serve as prelude to the Second Coming of Christ and the arrival of a new Millenium.

In a sermon entitled "Serious Considerations on the Election of a President," the Reverend William Linn accuses Jefferson of contradicting the scriptures, of profaning the Sabbath with banquets, of believing in complete religious liberty, and of planning to eliminate religious instruction from the primary school curriculum. Jefferson's refusal to believe in the Flood, Linn declares, "is a clear proof of his disrespect for divine revelation." Jefferson's faith he finds "too weak to receive *a miracle.*"

It was Linn who assailed Jefferson's belief that the Indians did not come from Asia but were indigenous to America. Does Jefferson, he goes on to ask, believe Scriptural Chronology or does he follow those profane philosophers who hold that the earth may be as old as 14,000 years? Jefferson's theory that the Negro may be a different race from the white man is another profanation of the Bible. "Sir, we excuse you not!" he writes. "You have degraded the blacks from the rank which God hath given them in the scale of being! You have advanced the strongest argument for their state of slavery! You have insulted human nature! You have contemned the word of truth and the meaning of salvation!" In fact, you are excluded "from any department among Christians!" Look, says Linn, what Jefferson's sentiments are understood to mean in Europe—and quotes from London "Monthly Reviewers" that Jefferson's ideas about the Negro imply that the Negro is kin to the orang-outang! Jefferson had said that his neighbor may have twenty gods for all he cares! Any man who says this kind of thing has but one intention—to make us a nation of atheists. Thomas Jefferson should be disqualified for election.

In the indignant Reverend John Mason's opinion Jefferson had reduced "the holy volume to a level with the dreams of Voltaire!" To Asbury Dickens Jefferson's brand of religious belief was "the vague and barren doctrine of what is called natural religion," which stamped Jefferson "no Christian." It was but "insanity" to call him a Christian, for he considered Christ a phantom and religion a fable. Should such a man become President of the United States? From what he called his "inmost soul," Dickens issued his thunderous answer: "GOD FORBID!"

In his *Observations upon Certain Passages in Mr. Jefferson's Notes on Virginia, Which Appear to Have a Tendency to Subvert Religion, and Establish a False Philosophy,* Clement Clarke Moore feared that Jefferson was not looking through nature up to nature's God, but down at nature's Devil. He had only recently read Jefferson's *Notes,* and was startled that a book so full of infidelity could have circulated in a Christian country for twenty years without a reply.

After looking at the junction of the Potomac and Shenandoah rivers, Jefferson maintains that the earth must have been created in time, mountains first, then rivers. But, according to Buffon, gloats Moore, the earth was knocked blazing out of the sun 50,000 years ago by a comet. The philosophers can't agree! However, on one thing they find agreement easy: their mutual opposition to scripture. Buffon, called to account for his impiety, got off with a clumsy equivocation. Jefferson, too, has left a retreat open; he only says that it is the *first glance* at the scene which makes him think the way he does. In denying the Flood Jefferson again denies the Bible. How in the world can Jefferson possibly know how much water the atmosphere can contain? And how can he grant profane Jewish, Grecian, and Latin books equal authority with the Bible? Or deny the miracles? As for arguments about the antiquity of the Indians based on a study of their language—Dr. Barton of Philadelphia has shown up Jefferson as an ignoramus in linguistics. Jefferson's denial of Asiatic ancestors for the Indians indicates that to him the Garden of Eden is but "a pretty Eastern tale." A modern philosopher like Jefferson places man in the same genus with animals, and allows him to be only a higher species, ascended to by minute gradations from one creature to another, implying that the Negro is intermediate between ape to man, thus lowering him from his just sphere. Jefferson's writing, concludes Moore, is but a sweet-sounding concert of "philosophy and infidelity."

Fortunately Jefferson's followers rose to his standard so effectively and in such numbers that the day was saved for a broader democracy than the Federalists were prepared to offer, a greater humaneness in society, a greater tolerance in religion, a greater spirit of freedom for scientific inquiry.

10

Recognition at Home and Abroad

•

Despite this partisan vilification of Jefferson's political, religious, and scientific theories, interests, and activities, he enjoyed a high contemporary repute both as a statesman of broad culture and as a scientist, who applied "philosophy" for the good of his native country and the general human welfare. Many hailed Jefferson as a citizen of the world of ideas in the best and most inclusive sense of the word. Detractors railing at the incompetency of "philosophers" could not obscure the cold fact that Jefferson had reached heights of culture and international prestige, not only by his philosophical breadth but by his mastery of practical politics.

Some even said that the "stateman" was "frequently sunk in the politician." But they acknowledged him to be an enlightened gentleman endowed with some of the best intellectual and social attributes which a leader in the world's greatest republic should possess.

The author of The Declaration of Independence was considered to have drawn together and expressed in im-

mortal form some of the most ennobling theories and practical conclusions arrived at by the best minds of his day. He
was a man who loved culture. In earlier life he had termed
music "the favorite passion of my soul." A few months before his death he could write delightedly that "Nobody
slept the first night" after the installation of a new piano-
forte in his home. He had stood spellbound before the
architectural beauty of the *Maison Quarree* in Nimes. He
had turned such aesthetic responsiveness into the practical
construction of the convenient, functional, and beautiful
Monticello. He had assembled and put to creative use one
of the finest libraries of his day in America. ("I cannot live
without books," he said.) A principle in his educational
theory was that the benefits derived from education should
be spread abroad in the land and among all classes. In his
old age he sought to give practical application to these
theories in the creation of a university which would, he expected, help bring his native country into equality with the
culture of Europe, and his native Southland into equality
with the educational advances of Harvard and Yale.

This political leader could read Greek, Latin, Anglo-
Saxon, French, Italian, and Spanish; could speak French
well and Italian competently; could arrange a quatri-
lingual Bible with the Greek, Latin, French, and English
texts in parallel columns. Eighteen foreign authorities were
cited in his *Notes on Virginia;* and quotations were translated from four foreign languages. He left Washington in
1808 with a trunk full of Indian vocabularies which he expected to use as the basis for a linguistic and ethnological
study of the American native. He wrote a fifty-page treatise
entitled "An Essay Towards Facilitating Instruction in the
Anglo-Saxon and Modern Dialects of the English Language For the Use of the University of Virginia." His interest in poetry led to a thirty-seven-page essay, "Thoughts on
English Prosody," in which he disputed Dr. Samuel Johnson's "quantitative" theory as inadequate to explain con-

temporary versification and outlined an accentual prosody which anticipated present-day views. He could discuss politics, land clearing, meteorology, climate, and natural philosophy with the Marquis de Chastellux, then pick up his copy of James Macpherson's *Ossian* from its place beside the punch bowl there at Monticello to read passages from it.

He could make a brilliant showing as his country's ambassador at Paris during a period of tension and change, yet find time to look into the standardization of parts in the manufacture of muskets or the application of steam to a gristmill. He could pass on to Ezra Stiles of Yale information on recent European scientific developments, and send to Baron de Geisner "a pretty little popular tune which will amuse you for a day or so." He could grow twenty-three rice plants in pots scattered about his room while serving as Secretary of State, while preparing, for Congress, a "Plan for Establishing Uniformity in the Coinage, Weights, and Measures of the United States." His baggage on his trip to Philadelphia, to serve as Vice-President, could include a fossil collection on which he intended to report to the American Philosophical Society. As President he could fill an unoccupied wing of the presidential mansion with a veritable museum. He could build one of the beautiful homes of Virginia, yet make that, too, a veritable museum. On July 4, 1776, when the Declaration of Independence, written by him, was made public, he bought himself a thermometer and made four temperature readings.[1]

He could send copies of the *Encyclopédie* to Francis Hopkinson, Ben Franklin, and the College of Philadelphia —and stop to converse with an old French peasant woman over the condition of life she and her class, "the laboring poor," were forced to suffer under the yoke of European aristocracy. Known for the elegance of his kitchen and furnishings at Monticello, he could lie upon the straw-filled mattresses of French farm laborers, and eat at their tables, the better to apply knowledge to "the softening of their beds, or the throwing a morsel of meat into their kettle of vegetables." Birds might sometimes be mere ornithological specimens to him, yet he could write to his daughter Patsy what "enchantment" a French scene acquired when "every tree and bush was filled with nightingales in full song." To him the plow was an agricultural implement, yet he could write of a plowed field that in "point of beauty nothing can exceed that of the waving lines and rows winding along the face of the hills and valleys." This man who could talk science with a Barton, a Rittenhouse, a Rush, a Humboldt, or a Buffon, to whom a learned Polish Count wrote for American archaeological information and whom a Bavarian agricultural society honored with a membership, could refer to a French gardener as "among the most precious of my acquaintances."

There were those who detected Jefferson's scientific errors, who realized that his essay on the *Megalonyx*, was done without proper scientific care, who disputed with him on the matter of the non-extinction of species or the identification of the "mammoth." All recognized Benjamin Franklin as his superior in science and others as his superiors in special aspects of science. But few, whose opinions were worth attention, failed to accord him respect and admiration.

Jefferson never failed to acknowledge that he was not completely a scientist, but an "amateur," a man who loved it—and who might have attained greater accomplishments in it if public service had not claimed the major part of his time and energy. From the vantage point of the present, we can see what some of his contemporaries also realized, that his greatness consisted in his insistence upon freedom of the scientific mind, his emphasis upon objectivity and the accumulation of sufficient data before arriving at conclusions, his humane desire to see that scientific progress should lead to human happiness, his attempts to enlarge scientific knowledge and promote scientific research—even where this meant conclusions that confuted his own opinions or the general belief.

Once, stopping at Ford's tavern, which was located between Monticello and his other home, Poplar Forest, Jefferson found there a stranger, a clergyman, who engaged him in conversation without knowing who the man before him was. As Randall gives the incident in his *Life of Thomas Jefferson,* the clergyman "introduced the subject of certain mechanical operations which he had recently witnessed. Mr. Jefferson's inquiries and remarks, as he afterward declared, soon satisfied him that he was conversing with some eminent engineer. Agriculture next came up, and then he made up his mind that Mr. Jefferson was a planter. Finally, the topic of religion was broached, and the clergyman became suspicious that his companion was another clergyman, but he confessed that he could not discover to what particular persuasion he leaned! There was something in Mr. Jefferson's presence that did not invite the indulgence of personal curiosity, and no 'leading questions' were put to him." After Jefferson retired, the clergyman was amazed to discover from the landlord that this was none other than President Jefferson. Particular amazement arose from the fact that he found Jefferson's expressed religious sentiments so just.

According to an English traveler Mr. Jefferson was extensively considered in America the most learned man in the world. James Madison's statement that Jefferson "would be found to be the most learned man that had ever devoted so much time to public life" was perhaps nearer the truth, though it, too, requires some modification. It indicates, however, the respect Jefferson commanded in his day.[2] Dr. Benjamin Rush recalled the "whole of Mr. Jefferson's conversation on all subjects" as "instructing" and considered him "possessed" of "a genius of the first order.

It was universal in its objects. He was not less distinguished for his political, than his mathematical and philosophical knowledge." [3]

"His time and talents have been directed to the calm pursuits of natural philosophy," declared the *Monthly Magazine* in November, 1800, and continued: "He has enriched science by speculations in the topographical and zoological conditions of our country. Instead of reviling and traducing what mankind holds sacred, and preaching up new gods or new governments, he has been busy in the classification and analysis of the animate and inanimate worlds. . . ." Arguing against the charge frequently made against Jefferson that his "philosophic" or scientific interests militated against his practical handling of the affairs of government, Tench Coxe considered it no more disqualifying than another statesman's seeking distraction in a theater or a ballroom. He pointed to others who had combined affairs of state with an interest in science—Governor Bowdoin of Massachusetts, the incomparable Franklin, and Frederick the Great. Finishing his day, as administrator, with a review of his troops, Frederick might spend the remaining hours in a discussion of the work of the Italian scientist Spallanzani.

After personal contact with "philosopher" Jefferson, even opponents might leave with an altered opinion. Samuel L. Mitchill observed: "I have known one of his political adversaries . . . enter into his presence with a sentiment formed from the Opposition gazettes, as if he was going to see a fury or a monster, and return from the interview undeceived and disappointed, praising him as a well-bred and well-informed gentleman." And according to Senator Maclay of Pennsylvania, who had been present when Jefferson had appeared before a Senate committee in 1790 for questioning on foreign relations, he had a similar effect on hostile senators.[4]

As for the high regard of scientists for Jefferson the

scientist, we have the tribute by Benjamin Smith Barton in May, 1792, while Jefferson was Secretary of State. It appeared in a paper read before the American Philosophical Society, in which Barton renamed a plant *Jeffersonia*, formerly known as *Podophyllum diphyllum:*

From the account which I have given of this plant, I have little doubt that you will agree with me in considering it as a genus, distinct from the *Sanguinaria* and the *Podophyllum*, to both which, however, it must be confessed, it bears considerable relation. As I have not found it described by any authors, except Linnaeus and Clayton, neither of whom had seen the flowers, and as it is, certainly, a new family, I take the liberty of making it known to the botanist by the name of

JEFFERSONIA,

in honour of Thomas Jefferson, Esq. Secretary of State to the United-States.

I beg leave to observe to you, in this place, that in imposing upon this genus the name of Mr. Jefferson, I have had no reference to his political character, or to his reputation for general science, and for literature. My business was with his knowledge of natural history. In the various departments of this science, but especially in botany and in zoology, the information of this gentleman is equalled by that of few persons in the United-States.

Of the genus which I have been describing, we, as yet, know but one species, which I call

JEFFERSONIA BINATA.

Jeffersonia, it is interesting to notice, was later planted before the house at Monticello.[5] Barton also dedicated his *New Views of the Origin of the Tribes and Nations of America* to Jefferson.

As high a regard for Jefferson, the scientist and man of culture, was held abroad. The Duke de la Rochefoucauld-Liancourt in his *Travels through the United States of North America* reported that Jefferson possessed "a stock of information not inferior to that of any other man." [6] Chastellux wrote of him that he was "at once a musician, skilled in drawing; a geometrician, an astronomer, a na-

tural philosopher, legislator, and statesman." The Italian
Count Luigi Catiglioni, in his defense of America against
the degeneracy theories of Buffon and Raynal, pointed to
Washington, Franklin, John Adams, Thomas Jefferson,
David Rittenhouse, Benjamin Rush, the Bartrams, Manas-
seh Cutler, Jeremy Belknap, Francis Hopkinson, Joel
Barlow, and Benjamin West,[7] as evidence of America's
capacity to produce men of genius." The naturalist
Raffinesque listed Jefferson among the scientists entitled to
the name of philosopher.

At Jefferson's death his eulogists included the great
French scientist Cuvier, who praised his "enlightened love
for the sciences and . . . broad knowledge of scientific
subjects to which he has made notable contributions." [8]
His moldboard had brought him a gold medal from the
Agricultural Society of Paris, an organization of interna-
tional note. The naturalist Desmarest renamed Jefferson's
"Great-Claw" *Megalonyx jeffersoni* in his honor.[9] A de-
scription of his moldboard which he had sent to Sir John
Sinclair was published in the Edinburgh *Encyclopédie*.
Count Rumford and other British scientists turned to Jef-
ferson for facilitating the interchange of scientific knowl-
edge between Great Britain and America.[10] In Spain
Jefferson carried on scientific correspondence with the
Prince of Parma. His *Notes on Virginia* was translated into
German.

Asked in 1817 by a writer compiling material for a biography to furnish a list of the societies he belonged to,
Jefferson replied that they were "many and would be too
long to enumerate and would savor too much of vanity and
pedantry." He preferred to have himself merely recorded
as "a member of many literary societies in Europe and
America."

Ignoring this modest preference, we should note, first of
all, that he belonged to the American Philosophical Society, along with Presidents Washington, Adams, and

Madison. But Jefferson's membership was in no sense honorary. He was one of the society's most active members.

During seventeen of his forty-seven years of membership (from January, 1797, to November, 1814) he served as its third president, succeeding the eminent scientists Franklin and Rittenhouse. At other times he served as vice-president and as chairman and member of committees and advisory groups. He secured many learned papers for its sessions and provided it with many specimens of natural history and other objects of interest. These included his description of his plow, his analysis of the *Megalonyx,* certain of his Indian vocabularies, and documents on the Lewis and Clark Expedition. His meteorological observations were conveyed to the Society in 1779 by the Reverend James Madison, President of William and Mary. Wherever he happened to be he communicated to his fellow members scientific developments that he considered important. And he consulted them on the values of inventions submitted to him for patents.

The high regard of fellow scientists in the society was shown in his election to its highest offices. In turn he regarded his election as its president as "the most flattering incident" in his life. And, in 1800, he wrote of it to Robert Patterson as a mark of esteem which he valued as "among the most precious testimonies" of his life. The honor was indeed great. To "preside over this association," wrote Samuel Mitchill, "is, perhaps, as high an honor as can be conferred upon a scientific man in our country." [11]

The prestige of this office was used by Jefferson's political followers as campaign material. It was pointed out that Jefferson had succeeded "the great and virtuous Rittenhouse, who was the immediate successor of our immortal Franklin"—a kind of scientific apostolic succession that appears to have been politically effective.

Other American societies of which he was a member were the American Academy of Arts and Sciences (in which, despite later heated political opposition in New England, Jefferson was early recognized "as a leading literary and scientific light" [12]), the New York Historical Society, the American Antiquarian Society, the Society of Artists of the United States, the Virginia Society for the Promotion of Useful Knowledge,[13] the South Carolina Agricultural Society, the Agricultural Society of the Valley, the Albemarle Agricultural Society, and the Linnaean Society of Philadelphia.

His memberships in foreign societies were many. Randall, one of his first biographers, saw in Jefferson's possession "a large collection of diplomas, in almost every language of Europe, conferring degrees, honorary memberships, etc. on him. . . ." Among them were the Board of Agriculture of London, the Royal Institute of Sciences, Literature, and Fine Arts (Amsterdam), the Agronomic Society of Bavaria, the Agricultural Society of Paris, the Linnaean Society of Paris, and the Institut de France. The list of foreign associates proposed to this latter group at the time of Jefferson's election included Count Rumford, James Rennell, Immanuel Kant, Johann Gottfried von Herder, Dugald Stuart, Christoph Ebeling, Arthur Young, and David Ramsay. Jefferson received the highest vote in the secret balloting.[14]

This honor was pointed to with pride by Nicholas Biddle, in his "Eulogium on Thomas Jefferson" in 1827, "Jefferson is the only citizen of our country on whom it has been bestowed. . . . The eight foreign associates [of the Institut] being Jefferson of the United States, Rennel and Wilkins of England, Ouvaroff of Russia, Sestini of Italy, Heeren of Gottingen, Creuser of Heidelberg, and William Humboldt of Berlin."

Through Jefferson's hands there passed an extraordinary miscellany both of gifts and of requests for information. The gifts included shells, specimens of horns, an ivory broom, odd assortments of bones, rattlesnake rattles, the skin of a Rocky Mountain sheep, "a clipping" from a New York paper describing an animal found on the Ohio ("it is novel and will give you a subject of specula- tion," [15] writes the sender), worms, Hessian flies (these ar- rived while he was President), [16] dead birds, drawings and models of inventions (inventors sometimes sought his ad- vice before seeking patents), a bathometer, coins of Rome and Denmark, [17] Indian curiosities, specimens of Indian vocabularies, a statue salvaged from ruined fortifications in the western country, a plow from overseas and one from Jethro Wood, American inventor of cast-iron plows, sent as a "respectful tribute" to Jefferson for his work on the moldboard, and in hope of receiving Jefferson's approval of the plow, or his suggestions for improvements.

Inquirers sought information about the maple-sugar tree, and about the history of the cedar tree and the Lom- bardy poplar in America. Julien Niemcewicz requested seed of the seneca root (sorry to bother the President with this, but seneca root is useful in medicine and Jefferson might thus help to save some child's life). He received rutabaga seeds from an English traveler, also seeds of the breadfruit tree, a Chinese mulberry plant, moss picked at hot springs near the Washita River and sent to President Jefferson for him to examine the animalculae in it (which Jefferson sent on to Benjamin Smith Barton, for he had no microscope for such work in Washington.) [18] William Short wrote from Philadelphia to announce that he had just received a micrometer and telescope which he knew Jefferson would be interested in seeing.[19] Thomas Skidman invited Jefferson to enter into a correspondence on optics.

From the West came drawings and seed of the cotton tree, from New York a bottle of salad oil made from benne seed obtained from Mr. Milledge of Georgia ("the first per- haps that was ever made in the United States," says the sender), from Mr. Thouin, superintendent of the National Garden in Paris, a package containing seven hundred different kinds of seed ("of every country except the United States"), from Malta, seed of the wintermelon, from Natchez seed of the capsicum, from Tallahassee "twelve seeds of the indigenous orange of Florida," from Pike County, Missouri, a specimen of wild hemp, from South Carolina specimens of grapevine leaves for Jefferson to identify. The sender of this letter, Mr. Samuel Maverick, tells Jefferson his only excuse for bothering him with these two leaves is "the Emence [sic] Importance to this Country in the Introduction of a New and Valuable Article of Commerce, as well as a most delicious and agreeable fruit, the Introduction of which may perhaps ameliorate the awful effects of spiritual [sic] Liquor."

The pamphlets, books, speeches, transactions, drawings, and so forth, sent to Jefferson, were countless. They included Du Pont's observations on taxes, a treatise on slavery, a prospectus of a work which, its author proposed, should embrace the history of civilized man, political, moral, etc., etc., a map and book of travels, Adelung's view of the languages of the earth, a Cherokee Grammar, a translation of Buttman's Greek grammar, the Rudiments of English Grammar, Ticknor's syllabus of lectures on Spanish literature, a volume of poetry, editions of the Greek classics, an oration by Edward Everett, Colonel Taylor's New Views of the Constitution, a volume of American jurisprudence, a Fourth of July oration, an explanation of the Apocalypse, pamphlets on religion (sometimes from clergymen hopeful of converting Jefferson to orthodoxy), Peale's "Essay to Promote Domestic Happiness" (which Jefferson had all his grandchildren read), Humboldt's political essay on New Spain.

Items more in the field of science included a volume of Dr. Rush's introductory lectures, an address on medicine, a pamphlet on the cause, seat, and cure of disease, Odet's elementary lessons in chemistry, Thomas Cooper's introductory lecture to a course in chemistry, the Abbé Rochon's pamphlets and his book describing his application of the double refraction of the Iceland Spath to the measure of small angles, a work on General Geography (whose author was informed by Jefferson, with citations from authorities, that the potato is *not* native to North America), an astronomical work by Humboldt, a pamphlet on Mexican astronomy, still another pamphlet on astronomy (which, Jefferson comments, is over his head), two volumes from Cabanis on the moral faculty, Flourens' work, and a treatise on phlogiston. There were also the proceedings of the Agricultural Society of Paris (Jefferson is surprised that the French do not practice rotation of crops), a treatise on the culture of sugar cane and cotton in France, "Mr. Bowditch's very learned mathematical papers," Rogers' mathematical principles of natural philosophy, Beck's pamphlet on the climate of the West, a comparison of the climates of different states deduced from the observation of trees, a pamphlet on torpedoes, Robert Fulton's drawing of his "self-moving bélier hydraulique" (which, Jefferson assures him, will receive early attention), Kosciusko's treatise on flying artillery.

Others, still, were Michaux's account of his travels and a pamphlet on American trees, the *Flora Carolinaeensis* from Dr. John Shecut of Charleston, "the Flora Carolina of Walter, a very learned and good work," Bernard McMahon's *American Gardener's Calendar* (which Jefferson feels "from the rapid view he has taken of it & the original matter it appears to contain he has no doubt it will be found an useful aid to the friends of an art, too important to health & comfort & yet too much neglected in this country"), Henry Muhlenberg's catalogue of North American plants, and Humboldt's *Distributio Geographica Plantarum* (with Jefferson expressing gratitude for a work which sheds so much new and valuable light on botanical science").[20]

Almost as heavy was the stream of visitors to Monticello,

particularly after Jefferson's retirement from the Presidency. These included gate-crashers, as they would be called today, "impertinent gazers" (as biographer Randall called them), job-seekers, people who had heard and came to take advantage of Jefferson's lavish hospitality, people whom nightfall had overtaken on the road, close friends, the sons of close friends, well-wishers, admirers of all kinds, people of sincere intellectual interests who wished to see in person this mammoth of Monticello, people who sincerely respected his statesmanship and sought counsel and advice, scientists who wished to exchange information and discuss matters "philosophic," people who loved stimulating conversation and good books and knew they would find them there. In his eulogy at the joint commemoration of the deaths of Adams and Jefferson, Daniel Webster, who had himself been a guest at Monticello, dwelt on Jefferson's "kindness and hospitality, the charm of his conversation, the ease of his manners, the extent of his acquirements, and especially the full store of revolutionary incidents, which he possessed, and which he knew when and how to dispense, rendered his abode in a high degree attractive to his admiring countrymen, while his high public and scientific character drew towards him every intelligent and educated traveller from abroad." [21]

One of Jefferson's grandchildren wrote: "I have known a New England judge bring a letter of introduction to my grandfather, and stay three weeks. The learned Abbé Correa [of Portugal], always a welcome guest, passed some weeks of each year with us during the whole time of his stay in the country. We had persons from abroad, from all the States of the Union, from every part of the State, men, women, and children. In short, almost every day for at least eight months of the year, brought its contingent of guests. People of wealth, fashion, men in office, professional men, military and civil, lawyers, doctors, Protestant clergymen, Catholic priests, members of Congress, foreign ministers, missionaries, Indian agents, tourists, travellers, artists, strangers, friends. . . . and very varied, amusing and agreeable was the society afforded by this influx of guests. I have listened to very remarkable conversations carried on round the table, the fireside, or in the summer drawing-room. . . . There were few eminent men of our country, except perhaps some political adversaries, who did not visit him in his retirement, to say nothing of distinguished for-eigners." Entertainment was rather informal. Guests oc-cupied their time largely as they pleased. "M. Correa passed his time in the fields and the woods; some gentle-men preferred the library; others the drawing-room; others the quiet of their own chambers; or they strolled down the mountainside and under the shade of the trees. The ladies in like manner, consulted their ease and inclinations, and whiled away the time as best they might." [22]

Some visitors proved offensively rude. And the costs were a contributory reason for Jefferson's poverty in his old age. Mrs. Randolph (Jefferson's daughter Martha) said that at one time she had been required to furnish beds for fifty guests. The house servants, including children, once num-bered thirty-seven.[23] The visitors, testified his overseer, Bacon, "almost ate [Jefferson] out of house and home." Be-sides Jefferson's own ten stalls for his horses, his twenty-six extra ones were also often filled and additional horses had to be kept elewhere. "I have often," says Bacon, "sent a wagon-load of hay up to the stable, and the next morning there would not be enough left to make a hen's-nest." One fine beef lasted two days. Mrs. Randolph had to borrow extra beds. Bacon thought that there must not be a tavern anywhere that did such a flourishing business.[24]

A favorite topic of conversation was science. Dr. Benja-min Smith Barton, author of *Elements of Botany*, first ele-mentary book on this subject written by an American (1803), was informed that "some 'Weymouth Pines,' do grow as far south as the neighborhood of Monticello" and

that "Gladitsia grows very abundantly native about Monticello." With such visitors as his close friend Francis Walker
Gilmer and the Portuguese statesman, scholar, and botanist, the Abbé Correa da Serra, Jefferson drove to his smaller home, Poplar Forest. Together they made observations
of the native flora, gathered geological specimens, determined the elevation of the Peaks of Otter, etc. With
Chastellux he discussed deer, the change of climate in
America, the measures of English verse. A fireside discussion with the Duke of Saxo-Weimar had natural history for
its theme. With the Duke de la Rochefeucauld-Laincourt
the theme was agriculture. Visitors looked at geological
exhibits; George Ticknor was shown the "os frontis" of a
mammoth; the Baron de Montlezun inspected specimens
from Indian lore and natural history; Lieutenant Hall received information on looming and learned that the meridian of Monticello passed directly through a small cleft in a
distant mountain. Visitors' horses may have depleted Jefferson's supply of hay, but there were glorious compensa-
tions.[25]

As we have seen in the case of Niemcewicz and the
Seneca root and Maverick and the grape leaves, correspondents used Jefferson's scientific interests as an excuse
for making all sorts of claims on his time and help. Charles
Willson Peale wrote of Jefferson's "love of useful arts and
Science" which he used as a pretext to interest Jefferson in
attempts to make sea water drinkable. A request for succory
seed was predicated on Jefferson's pleasure "in giving aid
to its more extensive cultivation." Inventors of agricultural
machinery submitted their models to him before applying
for patents.[26]

In other cases the correspondence was purely in tribute
to Jefferson's scientific interests, and without a personal
motivation. Fontaine Maury sent Jefferson some Talevera
wheat lately gotten, through his brother, from the farm of
Sir Watkins Williams Wynne of Wynnstay in Wales, be-

cause of Jefferson's reputation as "a zealous promoter" of agriculture. When Nicholas King accidentally ran across some seeds "carefully folded up in a small bag of Chinese paper, & deposited among tea of the last importation," he immediately thought of sending them to President Jefferson, "than whom no person has been more zealous to enrich the United States by the introduction of new and useful vegetables." [27]

In England and France he was known for his interest in promoting agriculture and the introduction of new and useful agricultural implements and machinery. Benjamin Waterhouse found him an indispensable ally in the introduction of vaccination to America. The American Philosophical Society turned to him for a study of that great wheat pest the Hessian fly, for fossils and for other matters of scientific interest from the Western parts of America. The Spanish Prince of Parma was indebted to him for help in securing specimens for his cabinet of natural history. John Elmslie, Jr., wrote to Jefferson from Cape Town, Cape of Good Hope, communicating geological, mineralogical, and other scientific information about South Africa. "The desire which you have shown to the World for the extension of science," he wrote, "leads me to believe that communications of this sort will not be altogether unacceptable."

In large part Jefferson's literary and scientific reputation was due to his *Notes on Virginia*. The discussions it aroused placed Jefferson's name to the forefront in virtually all learned circles. There had been descriptions of certain parts of America before this,[28] but never so complete and excellent a study, done with the feeling of a literary artist, the perspective of a philosopher, and the comprehensiveness and exactness of a scientist.

Notes on Virginia was first privately printed by Jefferson in Paris, 1785 (two hundred copies, dated 1782). When a French bookseller was about to publish a hack-job, French translation, Jefferson secured a competent translator to make sure that a proper version should reach French readers. This appeared in 1787. There followed an English reprint of his original edition, in London, in 1788. A German translation, *Beschreibung von Virginie,* appeared in Leipzig, in 1789. The first American edition was published in Philadelphia in 1788—advertised in December, 1787, by the Richmond *Virginia Independent Chronicle* as "a handsome octavo volume, with elegant type and good paper . . . neatly bound and lettered," to be sold to subscribers "at the very moderate price of one dollar." Non-subscribers would have to pay "seven shillings and six pence Virginia currency." Philadelphia also saw a second edition in 1788. Many other American editions followed: Philadelphia, 1792, 1794, 1801, 1812, 1815, 1825; Baltimore, 1800 (two editions); New York, 1801, 1804; Newark, 1801; Boston, 1801, 1829, 1832; Trenton, 1803, 1812; Richmond, 1853.

In his survey of the *Notes,* from which most of the preceding information has been taken, Austin H. Clark points out that Jefferson's work was the precursor of somewhat similar reports later issued by state and Federal governments. "Measured by its influence, it was the most important scientific work published in America up to this time. It laid the foundation for Jefferson's high contemporary reputation as a universal scholar, and for his enduring fame as a pioneer American scientific man." [29]

The Reverend James Madison of Williamsburg, on December 28, 1786, wrote to Jefferson: "Your Book is read here, by every one who can get a View of it, with ye greatest Avidity." Three years later the same correspondent expressed the hope that Jefferson's book would "tend to excite the Spirit of philosophical Observation," which, he thought, should gratify Jefferson. Charles Thomson considered the book "a most excellent natural history not merely of Virginia but of North America and possibly equal if not superior to that of any country yet published." [30] With but slight modification, many Americans would have accepted Thomson's estimate as correct. Jefferson's opponent, the Reverend Clement Clarke Moore, expressed irritation because he had heard of the *Notes on Virginia* all his life; and another political enemy, Fessenden, imputed the praise of the book to political motives.

Riding on a stage coach from Philadelphia to New York, in 1801, on his way to his mammoth bone excavation, Charles Willson Peale got into an argument with an English fellow traveler over Jefferson's work. The Englishman had "wetted his whistle" with alcohol and his "pipes" were loud and grating upon the ears of Peale, who decided that he "ought not to be allowed to slobber his venom to poison the minds of some of our company." Peale felt that he satisfactorily put "John Bull" in his place concerning the merits of Jefferson's *Notes*.[31]

Contemporaries used the book as a source when they sought exact data about their country or wished to give their utterances an air of authority. Jedidiah Morse's *American Geography,* a very well-known book in its day, acknowledged Jefferson's book as the principal source of his chapter on Virginia, and the author advised readers who wanted further information to seek it there. Williams, in his *History of Vermont,* used Jefferson's meteorological data and information on the number of Indians in America, and their languages. Numbers of papers read before the American Philosophical Society and articles appearing in its "Transactions" cited the *Notes* as references. George Turner's learned "Memoir" on fossil remains occupied itself largely with the ideas of Gmelin, Daubenton, Buffon, and Jefferson. Thomas Pinckney sent a copy of the *Notes* to the Prince of Parma as testimony to Jefferson's scientific abilities. In 1818 Bristed used the *Notes* as evidence that America had produced "several respectable State and local histories." The list could go on and on.

Americans might disagree about Jefferson in other respects, but there was general agreement on the value of his defense of America against the detractions of Buffon and his followers. Tench Coxe hailed Jefferson for having "rescued our unknown country from the misrepresentations of Buffon"; the *American Museum* published an article headed "On American Genius—Hypothesis of Raynal and Buffon Refuted by Mr. Jefferson"; M. L. Davis's Fourth of July oration, in 1800, praised the Great Thomas Jefferson for his victory over Buffon. The President of William and Mary College was of the opinion that Jefferson's "confutation of a certain opinion so derogatory to America" was "complete." John Adams similarly applauded Jefferson's exposure of the mistakes "of Buffon, so unphilosophically borrowed from the despicable dreams of De Pau."

For the last word we may quote Samuel L. Mitchill, who uttered it in his eulogy on Jefferson after his death. "Mr. Jefferson, in stepping forward as he did in favour of American power, may be almost said to have proclaimed emancipation a second time." Such sentiments would have pleased the author of the Declaration of Independence.

•

References

•

Throughout this book, an effort has been made to distinguish between that meaning of the word *science* which signifies *sci-entia* or "all knowledge," and that meaning which signifies systematized and formulated knowledge related to the facts of the physical world and the laws which regulate their operation. Clear-cut distinctions are not always possible, for in Jefferson's day and particularly in Jefferson's own use of it the word *science* often carried with it both meanings at the same time. A somewhat similar difficulty occurs at times in the case of the words *philosophy* and *philosopher*. For a discussion of these terms, see Chapter 9.

CHAPTER 1

1. Edward Dumbauld, *Thomas Jefferson, American Tourist*. Norman, Oklahoma: University of Oklahoma Press, 1946, pp. 182–183. Besides being a readable and thorough study of Jefferson's travels, this book contains a great deal of interesting information on Jefferson's personality and character and on the conditions and matters of interest in the places he visited. Good bibliography.

2. Sarah N. Randolph, *The Domestic Life of Thomas Jefferson*. New York: Harper & Brothers, 1871, pp. 245, 249, 262–263. Contains intimate details of Jefferson's personality, love of his family, and private life in general, largely reflected through his letters.

3. Margaret Bayard Smith, *The First Forty Years of Washington Society*. New York: Charles Scribner's Sons, 1906, pp. 393–395. Valuable for its interesting first-hand information.

4. *Ibid.*, p. 385. Bernard Mayo, "A Peppercorn for Mr. Jefferson," *The Virginia Quarterly Review*, Vol. XIX (Spring, 1943), pp. 222–235. See p. 233. A readable article which focuses attention upon the lighter, more sociable, more charming side of Jefferson's nature, an aspect of the man not usually sufficiently emphasized.

5. Smith, *op. cit.*, p. 393. See also John Bakeless, *Lewis and Clark: Partners in Discovery*. New York: William Morrow & Company, Inc., 1947, pp. 354–355. For other collections made for Jefferson by Lewis and Clark, see pp. 162–163, 184–185.

6. For some of this paragraph, see William Dunlap, *Diary of William Dunlap, 1766–1839* (New York: printed for the New York Historical Society, 1930. Three volumes; Vol. II, p. 388); "Dr. Mitchill's Letters from Washington: 1801–1813," *Harper's New Monthly Magazine,* Vol. LVIII (April, 1879), pp. 740–755 (see pp. 740, 744); Charles Francis Adams (ed.), *Memoirs of John Quincy Adams, Comprising Portions of His Diary from 1795 to 1848* (Philadelphia: J. B. Lippincott Company, 1874–1877. Twelve volumes; Vol. I, p. 317).

7. Certain details in this paragraph will be found in Esther Singleton, *The Story of the White House* (New York: The McClure Company, 1907. Two volumes; Vol. I, pp. 42–43); "Dr. Mitchill's Letters from Washington: 1801–1813," p. 744; Mayo, *op. cit.*, pp. 229, 230; Adams, *op. cit.*, Vol. I, pp. 330, 317, 457–458, 472.

8. See Mayo, *op. cit.*, p. 230, and Charles C. Sellers, *Charles Willson Peale*. Philadelphia: The American Philosophical Society, 1947. Two volumes; Vol. II, p. 184. Sellers' work is valuable for a student of Jefferson since Jefferson and Peale were such close friends.

9. Adams, *op. cit.*, Vol. I, pp. 472–473.

10. Besides those references cited elsewhere in this book, such as those in Note 11 below and Note 21, Chap. III, the following items will be found useful for Jefferson's agricultural interests: Hugh H. Bennett, *Thomas Jefferson: Soil Conservationist* (Washington, D.C.: U.S. Government Printing Office. U.S. Department of Agriculture, Soil Conservation Service, Miscellaneous Publication No. 548. April, 1944); Charles A. Browne, "Thomas Jefferson and the Scientific Trends of His Time," *Chronica Botanica,* Vol. VIII (Summer, 1944), pp. 363–426 (see particularly pp. 398–412); Arthur H. Cole, "Agricultural Crazes," *American Economic Review,* Vol. XVI (December, 1926), pp. 622–639; Everett E. Edwards, compiler and editor, *Jefferson and Agriculture: A Sourcebook* . . . (Washington, D.C.: U.S. Department of Agriculture, Bureau of Agricultural Economics, Agricultural History Series No. 7, 1943); Lewis Cecil Gray, assisted by Esther Katherine Thompson, *History of Agriculture in the Southern United States to 1860* (Washington, D.C.: The Carnegie Institution of Washington, 1933. Two volumes; see Vol. II); A. R. Hall, *Early Erosion-Control Practices in Virginia* (Washington, D.C.: U.S. Government Printing Office. U.S. Department of Agriculture, Miscellaneous Publication No. 256. July, 1938); August C. Miller, Jr., "Jefferson as an Agriculturist," *Agricultural History,* Vol. XVI (April, 1942), pp. 65–78; C. B. Sherman, "Thomas Jefferson: Far-Sighted Farmer," *Better Crops with Plant Food: The Pocket Book of Agriculture,* Vol. XXVIII (November, 1944), pp. 18–21, 44–45; Rodney H. True, "Early Days of the Albemarle Agricultural Society," American Historical Association *Annual Report,* Vol. I (1918), pp. 241–259; Harry B. Weiss, "Thomas Jefferson and Economic Entomology," *Journal of Economic Entomology,* Vol. XXXVII (December, 1944), pp. 836–841; M. L. Wilson, "Thomas Jefferson—Farmer," *Proceedings of the American Philosophical Society,* Vol. LXXXVII (July, 1943), pp. 216–222. Hereafter, this last publication will be referred to simply as *Proceedings.*

11. Edwin M. Betts (ed.), *Thomas Jefferson's Garden Book, 1766–1824, with Relevant Extracts from His Other Writings.* Philadelphia: The American Philosophical Society, 1944, p. 255. Contains a great part of the essential information, thoroughly annotated, on Jefferson's interest in seeds, plants, gardening, and farming, along with such related

matters as weather, agricultural machinery, interwoven
highlights of Jefferson's biography, brief notes on certain
of Jefferson's friends and correspondents, and numerous
other matters. Makes easily available firsthand documents
otherwise difficult to obtain. The numerous references to
Professor Betts's work by the present writer are sufficiently
indicative of the usefulness of the book for certain aspects
of Jefferson's scientific activities.

12. Smith, *op. cit.*, p. 385.
13. Henry S. Randall, *The Life of Thomas Jefferson*. New
    York: Derby and Jackson, 1858. Three volumes; Vol. III,
    p. 336. The old standard biography. Now rapidly being
    superseded by the work of such recent students of Jeffer-
    son as Malone and Kimball (see later references). Also,
    George Ticknor, *Life, Letters, and Journals of George
    Ticknor* (Boston: James R. Osgood and Company, 1877.
    Two volumes; Vol. I, p. 34) and "The Sage of Monticello,"
    Niles' Weekly Register, Vol. XI (January 4, 1817), pp. 317–
    318. A very readable account of Jefferson's life at Monti-
    cello, including an interesting insight into his personality
    and reflections of his various interests pertinent to our pres-
    ent study, is to be found in Paul Wilstach, *Jefferson and
    Monticello*. Garden City, New York: Doubleday, Doran &
    Company, Inc., 1931. 3d Ed., Rev.
14. Betts, *op. cit.*, p. 104.
15. The preceding items which Jefferson paid to see are also
    from Betts, pp. 16, 69, 106.
16. Randall, *op. cit.*, Vol. II, opposite p. 456.
17. John Bigelow, "Jefferson's Financial Diary," *Harper's New
    Monthly Magazine,* Vol. LXX (March, 1885), pp. 534–542.
    See p. 541. See also William E. Curtis, *The True Thomas
    Jefferson*. Philadelphia and London: J. B. Lippincott Com-
    pany, 1901 (2d ed.), pp. 317–318.
18. Betts, *op. cit.*, p. ix.
19. Randall, *op. cit.*, Vol. I, p. 474.
20. Hamilton W. Pierson, *Jefferson at Monticello: The Private
    Life of Thomas Jefferson from Entirely New Materials*.
    New York: Charles Scribner's Sons, 1862, pp. 86–87. Inti-
    mate details of Jefferson as recounted by his faithful over-
    seer.
21. Randall, *op. cit.*, Vol. III, p. 341.
22. For certain facts in these last two paragraphs see Betts, *op.
    cit.*, pp. 4, 5, 12, 33–34, 67, 226.

23. Randall, *op. cit.,* Vol. I, opposite p. 44.

24. Betts, *op. cit.,* p. 265.

25. *Ibid.,* pp. 151, 160, 165, 190, 216, 272.

26. Randall, *op. cit.,* Vol. II. p. 407.

27. Edward Dumbauld, *op. cit.,* p. 14. Particularly good for Jefferson's life in France is Marie Kimball's *Jefferson: The Scene of Europe, 1784 to 1789.* New York: Coward-Mc-Cann, 1950.

28. "The Letters of Thomas Jefferson to William Short," *William and Mary College Quarterly,* 2d Series, Vol. XI (October, 1931), pp. 336–342. See pp. 338–339.

29. Dumas Malone, *Jefferson the Virginian.* Boston: Little, Brown and Company, 1948, p. 161. Volume I of a forthcoming four-volume work entitled *Jefferson and His Time.* This book reflects the finest qualities of historical perspective, penetrating and sympathetic biographical insight and feeling, sound judgment, and careful and comprehensive scholarship. Professor Malone's complete four-volume work will undoubtedly long remain a standard study of Thomas Jefferson. Very readable and valuable studies of the earlier part of Jefferson's private life and public career are to be found in Marie Kimball's *Jefferson: The Road to Glory, 1743 to 1776* (New York: Coward-McCann, Inc., 1943) and *Jefferson: War and Peace, 1776 to 1784* (New York: Coward-McCann, Inc., 1947), and in Claude G. Bowers' *The Young Jefferson, 1743–1789* (Boston: Houghton Mifflin Company, 1945).

30. The books from France are from Dumbauld, *op. cit.,* pp. 160–161. The books pertinent to chemistry are from C. A. Browne, "Thomas Jefferson's Relation to Chemistry," *Journal of Chemical Education,* Vol. XX (December, 1943), p. 574.

31. George T. Surface, "Investigations into the Character of Jefferson as a Scientist," *Journal of American History,* Vol. IV (1910), pp. 214–220. See p. 216. Jefferson turned not only to the moderns but also to classical writers for scientific knowledge. He particularly emphasized the value of the classics for moralists, lawyers, physicians, statesmen, and students of language and literature. He pointed out that for these and other groups the classics contain "stores of real science" which are of direct practical utility in such fields as mathematics, astronomy, and natural history. The physician might, he wrote in 1819, find in ancient sources

"as good a code of his art as has been given us to this day."
Jefferson condemned Plato on numerous occasions for
what he called the "whimsies" of his "foggy brain." Among
his other objections to this ancient, he cited his lack of a
sufficient knowledge of physics. Jefferson himself found the
classics personally useful in such fields as geography, astronomy, agriculture, and natural history. Useful for Jefferson's interest in the classics and for backgrounds are
Daniel J. Boorstin, *The Lost World of Thomas Jefferson*
(New York: Henry Holt and Company, Inc., 1948), Gilbert
Chinard, "Thomas Jefferson as a Classical Scholar," *The
American Scholar,* Vol. I (March, 1932), pp. 133–143, Gilbert Chinard, *The Literary Bible of Thomas Jefferson*
(Baltimore: The Johns Hopkins Press, 1928), Howard
Mumford Jones, *The Theory of American Literature* (Ith-
aca, New York: Cornell University Press, 1948), Adrienne
Koch, *The Philosophy of Thomas Jefferson* (New York:
Columbia University Press, 1943), Karl Lehmann, *Thomas
Jefferson: American Humanist* (New York: The Macmil-
lan Company, 1947), Louis B. Wright, "Thomas Jefferson
and the Classics," *Proceedings,* Vol. LXXXVII (July, 1943),
pp. 223–233. Several of these citations have useful references and bibliographies.

CHAPTER 2

1. G. Adolph Koch, *Republican Religion: The American Revolution and the Cult of Reason.* New York: Henry Holt and
   Company, Inc., 1944, p. 270. A readable and penetrating
   account of the spread and decline of religious radicalism.
   Contains valuable quotations from original sources.
2. As in so many cases, Jefferson uses *science* in both its general and its more specialized meaning.
3. Most of the above is from Betts, *Garden Book.* See particularly pp. 155, 217, 223–224, 227, 233, 237, 247, 287, 292, 362,
   380, 392, 416, 543–544, 548.
4. Roy J. Honeywell, *The Educational Work of Thomas Jefferson.* Cambridge, Massachusetts: Harvard University
   Press, 1931, p. 146. Excellent on Jefferson's ideas and plans
   in education.
5. Randolph, *The Domestic Life of Thomas Jefferson,* pp.
   394–395.

6. Most of this discussion is taken from the very thorough study by Robert A. Halsey, *How the President Thomas Jefferson and Dr. Benjamin Waterhouse Established Vaccination as a Public Health Procedure.* New York: published by the Author, 1936. Issued under the auspices of the New York Academy of Medicine. For the sake of students and admirers of Jefferson, this valuable article should be made more widely available.

7. See Browne, "Thomas Jefferson and the Scientific Trends of His Time," p. 386. A very readable and sound article.

8. Curtis, *True Thomas Jefferson,* p. 375. Interesting general discussion.

9. From Betts, *op. cit.,* p. 378.

10. From Honeywell, *op. cit.,* p. 116.

11. From Betts, *op. cit.,* p. 572.

12. Honeywell, *op. cit.,* p. 125.

13. *Ibid.,* p. 106. For the content of each of these schools see Honeywell's tabulation on p. 111.

14. From Edwin G. Conklin, "The American Philosophical Society and International Relations," *Proceedings,* Vol. XCI (February, 1947), pp. 1–9. See pp. 1–2. Useful survey of this problem.

15. From I. Bernard Cohen, "Benjamin Franklin and Aeronautics," *Journal of the Franklin Institute,* Vol. CCXXXII (August, 1941), pp. 101–128. See p. 112. Contains interesting illustrations from old prints.

16. Samuel A. Mitchell, "Astronomy during the Early Years of the American Philosophical Society," *Proceedings,* Vol. LXXXVI (September, 1942), pp. 13–21. See p. 15. Mitchell here quotes from Vol. I of the *Transactions* of the Society.

17. Gilbert Chinard, "Jefferson and the American Philosophical Society," *Proceedings,* Vol. LXXXVII (July, 1943), pp. 263–276. See pp. 265–266. Also Chinard, "The American Philosophical Society and the World of Science," *ibid.,* pp. 1–11. See p. 3. Readable and valuable articles.

18. Randolph, *op. cit.,* p. 150.

19. Betts, *op. cit.,* p. 109.

20. Some of these are from Betts. See his index for details.

21. "The Letters of Thomas Jefferson to William Short," *William and Mary College Quarterly,* 2d Series, Vol. XI (October, 1931), pp. 336–342. See p. 339.

22. Most of these are in Betts, *op. cit.,* pp. 122, 160, 289, 376, 401, 559. An account of Jefferson's interest in the live mate-

rial—seeds, roots, cuttings, plants—brought back by Lewis and Clark will be found in Rodney H. True, "Some Neglected Botanical Results of the Lewis and Clark Expedition," *Proceedings,* Vol. LXVII (1928), pp. 1–19.

23. For discussions of this aspect of Jefferson's thinking, see Edwin T. Martin, "Thomas Jefferson's Interest in Science and the Useful Arts," *The Emory University Quarterly,* Vol. II (June, 1946), pp. 65–73; *Thomas Jefferson and the Idea of Progress,* unpublished dissertation in the library of the University of Wisconsin; *Summaries of Doctoral Dissertations,* Madison, Wisconsin: University of Wisconsin Press, 1942. An excellent critical analysis of Jefferson's general philosophy will be found in Adrienne Koch, *The Philosophy of Thomas Jefferson.* New York: Columbia University Press, 1943. Readable and well-done studies on progress are J. B. Bury, *The Idea of Progress: An Inquiry into Its Origin and Growth* (New York: The Macmillan Company, 1932) and Arthur Alphonse Ekirch, *The Idea of Progress in America, 1815–1860* (New York: Columbia University Press, 1944).

CHAPTER 3

1. Dumbauld, *Thomas Jefferson,* p. 72.
2. George E. Hastings, *The Life and Works of Francis Hopkinson.* Chicago: The University of Chicago Press, 1926, p. 336. A good study of Hopkinson and also useful for Jefferson's correspondence with Hopkinson.
3. Lewis Leary, "Phaeton in Philadelphia: Jean Pierre Blanchard and the First Balloon Ascension in America, 1793," *The Pennsylvania Magazine of History and Biography,* Vol. LXVII (January, 1943), pp. 49–60. See pp. 54–55. This excellent and enjoyable account also deals with the political implications of this flight.
4. This and the previous information on Rush are from *The Autobiography of Benjamin Rush: His Travels through Life Together with His Commonplace Book for 1789–1813,* edited by George W. Corner, published for the American Philosophical Society by the Princeton University Press, 1948, p. 304. A valuable book for a student of this period.
5. Much information used in this account is from Carroll Frey's *First Air Voyage in America . . . Together with a Facsimile Reprinting of the Journal of My Forty-Fifth As-*

cension & the First in America by Jean Pierre Blanchard. Philadelphia: published by the Penn Mutual Life Insurance Company, 1943. Blanchard's journal is interesting reading. Other good accounts of the early days of aeronautics are to be found in: I. Bernard Cohen, "Benjamin Franklin and Aeronautics," *Journal of the Franklin Institute,* Vol. CCXXII (August, 1941), pp. 101–128; B. Joy Jeffries, "First Aerial Voyage across the English Channel. Diary of Dr. John Jeffries, the Aeronaut," *Magazine of History,* Vol. XIII (January, 1885), pp. 66–88 (this first trip across the Channel is good reading); Jeremiah Milbank, Jr., *The First Century of Flight in America,* Princeton, New Jersey: Princeton University Press, 1943 (very useful for the United States); Francis T. Miller, *The World in Air: The Story of Flying in Pictures,* New York and London: G. P. Putnam's Sons, 1930, Vol. I (a wealth of interesting information in this two-volume work); Charles C. Turner, *The Romance of Aeronautics: An Interesting Account of the Growth & Achievements of All Kinds of Aerial Craft,* London: Seeley, Service and Company Limited, 1912 (contains much miscellaneous and detailed material); A. Wolf, *A History of Science, Technology, and Philosophy in the Eighteenth Century,* New York: The Macmillan Company, 1939.

6. Marie Kimball, "Thomas Jefferson's French Furniture," *Antiques,* Vol. XV (February, 1929), pp. 123–128. See pp. 126–128. This and the following articles by Mrs. Kimball cited in the notes below are very useful for Jefferson's taste in furniture. They are generally well illustrated and contain valuable information.

7. John B. McMaster, *A History of the People of the United States, from the Revolution to the Civil War.* New York: D. Appleton and Company, Inc., 1907. Seven Volumes; Vol. II, p. 605.

8. For these last two cases see Margaret B. Smith, *The First Forty Years of Washington Society,* pp. 387, 392.

9. *Ibid.,* p. 384.

10. Marie Kimball, "The Furnishing of Monticello," *Antiques,* Vol. XII (November, 1927), pp. 380–385. See p. 383. *Ibid.* (December, 1927), pp. 482–486. See p. 484.

11. *Ibid.,* pp. 483–484. Mrs. Kimball points out that this chair bore a striking resemblance to the ceremonial chair used by Jefferson when Vice-President. Further, Jefferson is "credited with the introduction of the swivel chair to Amer-

ica—the one in which he is said to have written the Declaration of Independence."

12. Kimball, "Thomas Jefferson's French Furniture," p. 126. See p. 125, Fig. 3, for a picture of this clock.

13. For a discussion of this, see H. M. Kallen, "The Arts and Thomas Jefferson," *Ethics,* Vol. LIII (July, 1943), pp. 269–283. See p. 273. Among other useful discussions of Jefferson's general interest in the arts are: Eleanor D. Berman, *Thomas Jefferson among the Arts: An Essay in Early American Esthetics.* New York: Philosophical Library, Inc., 1947; Fiske Kimball, "Jefferson and the Arts," *Proceedings,* Vol. LXXXVII (July, 1943), pp. 238–245; Marie Kimball, "Thomas Jefferson, Patron of the Arts," *Antiques,* Vol. XLIII (April, 1943), pp. 164–167. No attempt is made here to cite works pertaining solely to Jefferson's specialized interests, such as music, painting, statuary, and architecture.

14. For a full account of Franklin's work on them, see Carl Van Doren, *Benjamin Franklin.* New York: Garden City Publishing Company, Inc., 1941, pp. 297–299.

15. Hastings, *op. cit.,* p. 363.

16. The quotation and some of the facts are from Betts, *Garden Book,* pp. 158, 171. Some details are also from Curtis, *True Thomas Jefferson,* pp. 372–373.

17. For an excellent, very detailed discussion of this, see C. Doris Hellman, "Jefferson's Efforts towards the Decimalization of the United States Weights and Measures," *Isis,* Vol. XVI (November, 1931), pp. 266–314. Jefferson's general interest in and contributions to mathematics are discussed in David Eugene Smith, *The Poetry of Mathematics and Other Essays.* New York: *Scripta Mathematica,* 1934. See the chapter entitled "Thomas Jefferson and Mathematics."

18. Some details of the foregoing account of the polygraph are from Sellers, *Charles Willson Peale,* Vol. II, pp. 159–161, 182–183, 189. Pictures of many of Jefferson's various inventions are to be found in such readily available places as *The National Geographic Magazine,* Vol. LV (April, 1929), pp. 481–503; *Popular Science Monthly, Vol.* CXLVIII (January, 1946), pp. 104–113; *The Saturday Evening Post,* Vol. CCXVIII (April 13, 1946), pp. 22–23; *Holiday,* Vol. III (April, 1948), pp. 48–49.

19. Margaret A. Whiting, "The Father of Gadgets," *Stone and Webster Journal,* Vol. XLIX (May, 1932), pp. 302–315. See p. 306.

20. True, "Early Days of the Albemarle Agricultural Society," p. 246. A good account of this agricultural society, in the formation and aims of which Jefferson had a hand.

21. Useful information on backgrounds, together with accounts of Jefferson's work on and estimates of his contribution to the plow, will be found in Holland Thompson, *The Age of Invention: A Chronicle of Mechanical Conquest* (New Haven: Yale University Press, 1921); M. L. Wilson, "Jefferson and His Moldboard Plow," *Land*, Vol. III (Summer, 1943), pp. 59–64; and M. L. Wilson, "Survey of Scientific Agriculture," *Proceedings*, Vol. LXXXVI (September, 1942), pp. 52–62. See also *ante*, Chap. I, Note 10; many of these references are also useful for Jefferson's work on the plow.

22. For Jefferson's agricultural library see Betts, *op. cit.*, Appendix VII: "Books and Pamphlets on Agriculture, Gardening, and Botany in the Library of Thomas Jefferson." See also Browne, "Thomas Jefferson and the Scientific Trends of His Time," pp. 399 *ff*. Some details concerning the plow in the pages which follow are from Betts.

CHAPTER 4

1. See Frederic A. Lucas, "Thomas Jefferson—Palaeontologist," *Natural History*, Vol. XXVI (May, 1926), pp. 328–330. See p. 330. Also Roland W. Brown, "Jefferson's Contribution to Paleontology," *Journal of the Washington Academy of Science*, Vol. XXXIII (September 15, 1943), pp. 257–259. See p. 258.

2. Joseph Leidy, "A Memoir on the Extinct Sloth Tribe of North America," *Smithsonian Contributions to Knowledge*, Vol. VII (1855), 66 pp., 16 plates. See p. 5.

3. *Proceedings* of the American Philosophical Society, Vol. LXXX (September, 1942), pp. 130–188. The article is by Professor George Gaylord Simpson, Professor of Vertebrate Paleontology, Columbia University, and Chairman of the Department of Geology and Paleontology, American Museum of Natural History.

4. The best book upon this subject is that of Professor Arthur O. Lovejoy, *The Great Chain of Being: A Study of the History of an Idea*. Cambridge, Massachusetts: Harvard University Press, 1936. Any student of this period should read

this entire discussion, particularly those chapters pertinent to the eighteenth and nineteenth centuries. Since Jefferson did not discuss the later temporalizing tendencies in the great-chain-of-being concept, in this chapter these have been omitted. All has, of course, been simplified in the manner that Jefferson appears to have thought of it.

5. For these data see Malone, *Jefferson the Virginian,* pp. 174–175.

6. From Chinard, "Jefferson and the American Philosophical Society," pp. 269–270.

7. For some of these see George Gaylord Simpson, "The Beginnings of Vertebrate Paleontology in North America," *Proceedings,* Vol. LXXXVI (September, 1942), pp. 130–188. See p. 156. The best single article on this subject; contains illustrations, maps, and bibliography. Professor Simpson's work has already been referred to earlier in the body of the present chapter.

8. *Loc. cit.* Professor Simpson points out that the collection actually contained "fossil bison, muskoxen, and deer" and that there were remains of the mastodon and true mammoth (as the term is used by modern scientists).

9. *Ibid.,* pp. 156–157.

10. Though Jefferson appears not to have been always consistent, especially if we may judge by his language, throughout his life he was inclined toward a nominalistic conception of species, classes, genera, etc. Such categories, he thought, are not in nature. They are merely useful, man-made distinctions. Nature produces individuals; man groups these into classes and species for the purpose of convenience. Jefferson wrote to Dr. John Manners in 1814: "Nature has, in truth, produced units only through all her works. Classes, orders, genera, species, are not of her work. Her creation is of individuals." Since such an infinitude of individuals is "far beyond the capacity of our memory, we are obliged, in aid of that, to distribute them into small groups"—and so on. But in doing this, "we fix arbitrarily" on those characteristics upon which we base our system. This being the case, it is interesting to notice Jefferson's attitude toward the fact that Cuvier had denominated the American "mammoth" as a *mastodon:* ". . . these discriminations being arbitrary," he wrote to Wistar in 1812, "according to the circumstances by which you chuse to characterise generically or specifically, all are free to adopt or reject them." For a

discussion of nominalistic tendencies in eighteenth-century science, see Lovejoy, *op. cit.*, pp. 228 *ff*.

11. It had other names at various times. Useful information on the rise of the natural-history museum in America will be found in such studies as Laura M. Bragg, "The Birth of the Museum Idea in America," *Charleston Museum Quarterly*, Vol. I (1923), pp. 3–12; George Brown Goode, "The Genesis of the United States National Museum," *Annual Report of the Board of Regents of the Smithsonian Institution, . . . for the Year Ending June 30, 1897. Report of the U.S. National Museum*, Part II. Washington, D.C.: Government Printing Office, 1901, and "Museum-History and Museums of History," *ibid.*; George Gaylord Simpson, "The First Natural History Museum in America," *Science*, Vol. XCVI (September 18, 1942), pp. 261–263. See also other bibliographical references in the present chapter.

12. See Harold S. Colton, "Peale's Museum," *Popular Science Monthly*, Vol. LXXV (September, 1909), pp. 221–238. See pp. 222–224, 234. Also Simpson, *op. cit.*, p. 158.

13. The standard work on Peale is that by Charles C. Sellers, *Charles Willson Peale*, already referred to in Chap. III, n. 18. Sellers' book is very readable and beautifully illustrated.

14. From Colton, *op. cit.*, p. 224.

15. See Sellers, *op. cit.*, pp. 233, 235; Colton, *op. cit.*, p. 225.

16. See Colton, *op. cit.*, pp. 230, 235; Sellers, *op. cit.*, pp. 233, 241, 242. For a full discussion see Sellers, Chap. VII.

17. Sellers, *op. cit.*, pp. 126, 130–131.

18. Colton, *op. cit.*, p. 228.

19. Simpson, *op. cit.*, p. 158.

20. For the Lewis and Clark collections see Sellers, *op. cit.*, Vol. II, pp. 239–241.

21. Chinard, "Jefferson and the American Philosophical Society," pp. 269–270.

22. Henry F. Osborn, "Thomas Jefferson as a Paleontologist," *Science* (N.S.), Vol. LXXXII (December 6, 1935), pp. 533–538. See p. 537.

CHAPTER 5

1. Alexander McAdie, "A Colonial Weather Service," *Popular Science Monthly*, Vol. XLV (July, 1894), pp. 331–337. Old but still useful article. An early recognition of Jefferson's contributions to problems in meteorology in America.

2. Lt. Col. Edgar Erskine Hume, "The foundation of American Meteorology by the United States Army Medical Department," *Bulletin of the History of Medicine,* Vol. VIII (February, 1940), pp. 202–238. See pp. 202–204. Useful general article on this subject.

3. *Ibid.,* pp. 204–208.

4. McAdie, *op. cit.,* pp. 333–334.

5. William J. Humphreys, "A Review of Papers on Meteorology and Climatology Published by the American Philosophical Society Prior to the Twentieth Century," *Proceedings,* Vol. LXXXVI (September, 1942), pp. 29–33. See p. 30.

6. See Betts, *Garden Book,* pp. ix, 441.

7. *Ibid.,* p. 77.

8. In Paul Leicester Ford (ed.), *The Writings of Thomas Jefferson.* New York: G. P. Putnam's Sons, 1892–1899. Ten volumes; Vol. V, pp. 159–160.

9. "Letters of Jefferson to William Short," Vol. XI, p. 389.

10. From Betts, *op. cit.,* p. 255.

11. Randall, *Life,* Vol. II, p. 20.

12. C. F. Volney, *A View of the Soil and Climate of the United States of America with Supplementary Remarks upon Florida; on the French Colonies on the Mississippi and Ohio, and in Canada; and on the Aboriginal Tribes of America.* Translated with Occasional Remarks by C. B. Brown. With Maps and Plates. Philadelphia: J. Conrad and Company, 1804, pp. 262–263, 291–292.

CHAPTER 6

1. Benjamin Bissell, *The American Indian in English Literature of the Eighteenth Century.* New Haven: Yale University Press, 1925, pp. 44–45. Contains useful material.

2. Lois Whitney, *Primitivism and the Idea of Progress in English Popular Literature of the Eighteenth Century.* Baltimore: The Johns Hopkins Press, 1934, pp. 51–53. An excellent study of these two ideas.

3. Irving Babbitt, *Rousseau and Romanticism.* Boston and New York: Houghton Mifflin Company, 1919, pp. 277–278. A readable, heated attack upon Rousseau and his school. See p. 278 for Chateaubriand's temporary disillusionment.

4. Dr. Benjamin Rush of Philadelphia became so disgusted with this romantic exaggeration that he wrote "An Account of the Vices Peculiar to the Indians of North America," in which he depicted the Indian's uncleanness (lack of constancy in marital relations), nastiness, drunkenness, gluttony, treachery, cruelty, idleness, theft, gaming, and degradation of women, and concluded that the Indian's supposed virtues are "rather the *qualities of necessity,* than the offspring of feeling, or principle." In short, according to Rush, civilization is far superior to current primitivistic idealizations of the state of nature and the noble savages who inhabit the utopian wilds. For a good account of the depiction of the Indian in American fiction, see especially Albert Keiser, *The Indian in American Literature.* New York: Oxford University Press, 1933.

5. Henry W. Church, "Corneille de Pauw, and the Controversy over His *Récherches Philosophiques sur les Américains,"* *Publications of the Modern Language Association of America,* Vol. LI (March, 1936), pp. 178–207. See pp. 191–192. The basic article on this subject.

6. Gilbert Chinard, "The American Philosophical Society and the World of Science," *Proceedings,* Vol. LXXXVII (July, 1943), pp. 1–11. See pp. 2–3. See also Edwin G. Conklin, "The American Philosophical Society and International Relations," *ibid.,* Vol. XCI (February, 1947), pp. 1–9. See pp. 7–8. Chinard's article has exhaustive lists of foreign members. Conklin offers a very useful account of the international outlook of scientists during this period.

7. William F. Falls, "Buffon, Franklin, and Two Academies," *Romanic Review,* Vol. XXIX (February, 1938), pp. 45–46.

8. Carl Van Doren, *Benjamin Franklin,* p. 163. See also Franklin's *Autobiography.*

9. Falls, *op. cit.,* pp. 42–45.

10. Harcourt Brown, "Buffon and the Royal Society of London," in M. F. Ashley Montagu (ed.), *Studies and Essays in the History of Science and Learning Offered in Homage to George Sarton on the Occasion of His Sixtieth Birthday, 31 August 1944.* New York: Henry Schuman, [n.d.], p. 145.

11. Simpson, "The Beginnings of Vertebrate Paleontology in North America," p. 145.

12. Church, *op. cit.*

13. Chinard, "Jefferson and the American Philosophical Society," p. 266.

14. Bury, *The Idea of Progress,* pp. 168–169.
15. Faÿ, *The Revolutionary Spirit in France and America.* See the entire analysis, pp. 8 *ff.*
16. Chinard, *loc. cit.*

It should be obvious, of course, that there were other and sometimes highly contrary opinions of the United States current in Europe. Besides those works already cited in this chapter which might be useful for a discussion of foreign opinion of our country during this period, one will find helpful brief studies in Michael Kraus's "America and the Utopian Ideal in the Eighteenth Century" (*Mississippi Valley Historical Review,* Vol. XXII [1936], pp. 487–504) and Merle Curti's "The Reputation of America Overseas (1776–1860)" (*American Quarterly,* Vol. I [1949], pp. 58–82) which provides a useful brief bibliography of the different phases of his study.

CHAPTER 7

1. Malone, *Jefferson the Virginian,* p. 375. Malone's chapter (No. XXVI) on the *Notes* is good. So is that (No. XI) of Marie Kimball in *Jefferson: War and Peace, 1776 to 1784.* See also the very helpful article of Ruth Henline, "A Study of *Notes On the State of Virginia* as an Evidence of Jefferson's Reaction against the Theories of the French Naturalists," *The Virginia Magazine of History and Biography,* Vol. LV (July, 1947), pp. 233–246.
2. Malone, *op. cit.,* p. 376.
3. Gilbert Chinard, "Eighteenth Century Theories on America as a Human Habitat," *Proceedings,* Vol. XCI (February, 1947), pp. 27–57. An exhaustive article on this subject, touching upon virtually every aspect of this curious phase of eighteenth-century thought about our country.
4. Fletcher Webster (ed.), *The Private Correspondence of Daniel Webster.* Boston: Little, Brown & Company, 1857. Two volumes; Vol. I, pp. 371–372.
5. Falls, "Buffon, Franklin, and Two Academies," pp. 41–42.
6. In Hastings, *Life and Works of Francis Hopkinson,* p. 349.
7. Webster, *op. cit.,* p. 372.
8. There is a brief discussion of the Jefferson-Sullivan affair in Kimball, *op. cit.,* pp. 283–285. The quotations from Sullivan are taken from the readable article by Anna C. Jones,

"Antlers for Jefferson," *New England Quarterly,* Vol. XII (June, 1939), pp. 333–348.

9. Quoted in Lucas, "Thomas Jefferson—Palaeontologist," p. 328.

10. Quoted in Harlow Shapley, "Notes on Thomas Jefferson as a Natural Philosopher," *Proceedings,* Vol. LXXXVII (July, 1943), pp. 234–237. See p. 235.

CHAPTER 8

1. Chinard, "Eighteenth Century Theories of America as a Human Habitat," p. 46.

2. Chinard, "The American Philosophical Society and the World of Science," pp. 7–9.

3. Taken from Jones, "Antlers for Jefferson," p. 333, who quotes from Miss Hemenway's *Gazeteer of Vermont,* Vol. II (1871), p. 858.

4. William E. Lingelbach, "The Library of the American Philosophical Society," *William and Mary College Quarterly,* 3d Series, Vol. III (January, 1946), pp. 48–69. See p. 59. Useful for Franklin and Jefferson during the period we are considering.

5. George T. Surface, "Investigations into the Character of Jefferson as a Scientist," *Journal of American History,* Vol. IV (1910), pp. 214–220. See p. 218.

6. Church, "Corneille de Pauw and the Controversy over His *Récherches Philosophiques sur les Américains,*" p. 190.

7. Richard H. Shryock, "The Health of the American People: A Historical Survey," *Proceedings,* Vol. XC (September, 1946), pp. 251–258. See p. 256. Several pages concern the period we are dealing with.

8. See Rutherford E. Delmage, "The American Idea of Progress, 1750–1800," *Proceedings,* Vol. XCI (October, 1947), pp. 307–314. See p. 6. Contains useful quotations. Pertinent material will also be found in Chinard, "Eighteenth Century Theories of America as a Human Habitat."

9. Faÿ, *The Revolutionary Spirit in France and America,* p. 177.

10. Jane L. Mesick, *The English Traveller in America, 1785–1835.* New York: Columbia University Press, 1922. See pp. 270–277. Still a good study of this subject.

11. For a very thorough study of this whole matter (with illustrations), see Gilbert Chinard, "The American Philosophical Society and the Early History of Forestry in America," *Proceedings,* Vol. LXXXIX (July, 1945), pp. 444–488.

12. Quoted in Chinard, *ibid., p. 482.*

13. From Chinard, "Eighteenth Century Theories of America as a Human Habitat," p. 34.

14. For biographical and historical details used here, see Chinard, "The American Philosophical Society and the Early History of Forestry in America," p. 455.

15. Carl Grabo, *A Newton Among Poets: Shelley's Use of Science in Prometheus Unbound.* Chapel Hill: University of North Carolina Press, 1930, pp. 37–38. Chapters III and IV are on Erasmus Darwin.

CHAPTER 9

1. Charles Warren, *Jacobin and Junto, or Early American Politics as Viewed in the Diary of Dr. Nathaniel Ames, 1758–1822.* Cambridge, Massachusetts: Harvard University Press, 1931. To catch the true state of political feeling during this period, the reader will find this valuable. See particularly Chaps. VI, VII, and VIII. See also this author's *Odd Byways in American History* (Cambridge, Massachusetts: Harvard University Press, 1942), Chap. VII: "How Jefferson's Death Was Reported in the Campaign of 1800."

2. *Ibid.,* p. 157.

3. Harold M. Ellis, *Joseph Dennie and His Circle: A Study in American Literature from 1792 to 1812.* Bulletin of the University of Texas, No. 40, Studies in English No. 3. Austin, Texas: University of Texas, 1915, p. 122. Quite useful for this period.

4. Dumbauld, *Thomas Jefferson, American Tourist,* p. 177.

5. *Ibid.,* pp. 183–184.

6. Randall, *Life,* Vol. II, p. 405.

7. For these last two instances see Warren, *op. cit.,* pp. 85–86, 222.

8. William A. Robinson, *Jeffersonian Democracy in New England.* New Haven: Yale University Press, 1916, Chap. II. A fine study of this problem. Based largely on contemporary newspapers. Valuable bibliography. Reflects economic, political, social, and religious opposition. Also

especially good for reflecting the intense conflicts of this period are Claude G. Bowers' *Jefferson and Hamilton: The Struggle for Democracy in America* (Boston: Houghton Mifflin Company, 1925) and *Jefferson in Power: The Death Struggle of the Federalists* (Boston: Houghton Mifflin Company, 1936; see particularly Chaps. XII, XIV, and XX).

9. Brooks, *The World of Washington Irving*, pp. 31–32.
10. Dixon R. Fox, *The Decline of Aristocracy in the Politics of New York*. New York: Columbia University, Longmans, Green & Co., Agents, 1919, p. 56. Useful for Jefferson's reputation in this state.
11. Quoted in Robinson, *op. cit.*, p. 97.
12. *Ibid.*, p. 66.
13. From Halsey, *How the President, Thomas Jefferson, and Dr. Benjamin Waterhouse Established Vaccination as a Public Health Procedure*.
14. Eliot Janeway, review of Dirk J. Struik's *Yankee Science in the Making* (Boston: Little, Brown & Company, 1948), *Saturday Review of Literature*, September 18, 1948. See p. 13.
15. From Robinson, *op. cit.*, pp. 95–96.
16. From Warren.
17. [Thomas G. Fessenden], *Democracy Unveiled; or, Tyranny Stripped of the Garb of Patriotism*. By Christopher Caustic. Boston: David Carlisle, 1805.
18. Koch, *Republican Religion*, p. 274. This book is indispensable for religious conflicts of this period.
19. Quoted in Struik, *Yankee Science in the Making*, pp. 152–153.
20. See Mayo, "A Peppercorn for Mr. Jefferson," p. 225, and Warren, *Jacobin and Junto*, p. 155. Besides Mayo's article, see also the illustrations of Jefferson's sense of humor in Wilstach, *Jefferson and Monticello*, pp. 165–178. There is a rich depiction of Jefferson and the social milieu of Washington in its early days in Bowers, *Jefferson in Power*, Chap. I.
21. Robinson, *op. cit.*, pp. 145–146.
22. McMaster, *History of the People of the United States*, Vol. II, p. 605; Mayo, *loc. cit.*
23. From Koch, *op. cit.*, p. 273. For Jefferson's ethnological opinions, including his allied interest in Indian languages and archaeology, see particularly Alexander F. Chamberlain, "Thomas Jefferson's Ethnological Opinions and Activities," *American Anthropologist*, New Series, Vol. IX

(July, 1907), pp. 499–509; Gilbert Chinard, "Jefferson and the American Philosophical Society," *Proceedings,* Vol. LXXXVII (July, 1943), pp. 263–276; Franklin Edgerton, "Notes on Early American Work in Linguistics," *ibid.,* pp. 25–34; Thomas A. Kirby, "Jefferson's Letters to Pickering," in Thomas A. Kirby and Henry Bosley Woolf (eds.), *Philologica: The Malone Anniversary Studies* (Baltimore: The Johns Hopkins Press, 1949); Karl Lehmann, *Thomas Jefferson: American Humanist* (New York: The Macmillan Company, 1947); Karl Lehmann-Hartleben, "Thomas Jefferson, Archaeologist," *American Journal of Archaeology,* Vol. XLVII (April-June, 1943), pp. 161–163; H. C. Montgomery, "Thomas Jefferson as a Philologist," *American Journal of Philology,* Vol. LXV (October, 1944), pp. 367–371; Clark Wissler, "The American Indian and the American Philosophical Society," *Proceedings,* Vol. LXXXVI (September, 1942), pp. 189–204.

24. Whiting, "Father of Gadgets," p. 307.
25. Randall, *op. cit.,* Vol. III, p. 330.
26. Perrin, *The Life and Works of Thomas Green Fessenden, 1771–1837,* p. 113.
27. From Ellis, *op. cit.,* p. 182.
28. *Ibid.,* p. 191.
29. For proof that Kieft is in many ways Thomas Jefferson, see the critical introduction to *Diedrich Knickerbocker's A History of New York* by Stanley T. Williams and Tremaine McDowell (eds.). New York: Harcourt, Brace and Company, Inc., 1927. The present discussion and quotations from Irving are from Henry A. Pochmann, *Washington Irving: Representative Selections, with Introduction, Bibliography, and Notes.* New York: American Book Company, 1934. Enlightening notes and quotations from Williams and McDowell are to be found in Pochmann, pp. 379–383.
30. From Harry H. Clark, "The Influence of Science on American Ideas, from 1775 to 1809," *Transactions* of the Wisconsin Academy of Sciences, Arts and Letters, Vol. XXXV (1944), pp. 305–349. See p. 309. A very useful article.
31. Frank G. Beardsley, *Religious Progress through Religious Revivals.* New York: American Tract Society, 1943, p. 181.
32. Bernard Faÿ, *Franklin, the Apostle of Modern Times.* Boston: Little, Brown & Company, 1929, pp. 226–227.

33. Van Doren, *Benjamin Franklin,* pp. 156, 158–159, 163.
34. *Ibid.,* p. 171.
35. George C. D. Odell, *Annals of the New York Stage.* New York: Columbia University Press, 1927–1949. Fifteen volumes; Vol. I, p. 398. A monumental study.
36. Edwin M. Betts, "The Correspondence between Constantine Samuel Rafinesque and Thomas Jefferson," *Proceedings,* Vol. LXXXVII (May, 1944), pp. 368–380. See p. 372.
37. Koch, *op. cit.,* p. 275.
38. Recounted in Max J. Herzberg, "Thomas Jefferson as a Man of Letters," *South Atlantic Quarterly,* Vol. XIII (October, 1914), pp. 310–327. See p. 323.
39. Koch, *op. cit.,* p. 272.
40. Fox, *loc. cit.*
41. Howard M. Jones, *America and French Culture, 1750–1848.* Chapel Hill, North Carolina: University of North Carolina Press, 1927, pp. 395–396. A thorough study, packed full of information on this subject.

CHAPTER 10

1. Betts, *Garden Book,* p. 69.
2. Randall, *Life,* Vol. III, pp. 674, 550.
3. Rush, *Autobiography* (edited by Corner), pp. 228, 151.
4. Henry Adams, *History of the United States of America during the First Administration of Thomas Jefferson.* New York: Charles Scribner's Sons, 1921. Two volumes; Vol. I, p. 186.
5. This quotation and information are from Betts, *op. cit.,* pp. 172–173. Plate XI (opposite p. 172) contains Barton's drawing of *Jeffersonia diphylla,* which, along with his paper, appeared in the *Transactions* of the American Philosophical Society in 1793.
6. From Randall, *op. cit.,* Vol. II, p. 306.
7. Pace, "The American Philosophical Society and Italy," p. 396.
8. From Chinard, "Jefferson and the American Philosophical Society," p. 275. This is a statement of Cuvier's tribute as it is found in the "Éloge de Thomas Jefferson" by Charles Lemesle.
9. Brown, "Jefferson's Contributions to Paleontology," p. 258.
10. *Loc. cit.*

11. Most of the details concerning Jefferson's relations with the American Philosophical Society are from Chinard's very useful article cited above.

12. Malone, *Jefferson the Virginian,* p. 422.

13. See Austin H. Clark, "Thomas Jefferson and Science," Washington Academy of Sciences *Journal,* Vol. XXXIII (July 15, 1943), pp. 193–203. See pp. 201–202. Readable and good general survey.

14. Chinard, "The American Philosophical Society and the World of Science," p. 9.

15. *Collections of the Massachusetts Historical Society,* 7th Series, Vol. I. Boston: published by the Society, 1900, p. 23.

16. For the flies and worms see Betts, *op. cit.,* pp. 286, 320.

17. For these last two, see Chinard, "Jefferson and the American Philosophical Society," p. 271.

18. Beginning with the request for seneca root, see Betts, *op. cit.,* pp. 236, 256, 275, 301, 307, 309, 351, 383–384, 434, 512, 595–596, 597. For Jethro Wood's plow (*ante*), see p. 561.

19. For Short, see *Collections of the Massachusetts Historical Society,* Vol. I, p. 190.

20. These last three items are from Betts, *op. cit.,* pp. 313, 531, 572–573.

21. See "Character of Jefferson," *The North American Review,* Vol. XL (January, 1835), pp. 170–232. See p. 229.

22. Randall, *op. cit.,* Vol. III, pp. 330–331.

23. *Ibid.,* p. 332.

24. Pierson, *Jefferson at Monticello,* pp. 124–125.

25. For most of this see Richard B. Davis, *Francis Walker Gilmer: Life and Learning in Jefferson's Virginia. . . .* (Richmond, Virginia: The Dietz Press, 1939, pp. 89, 90. Useful for Jefferson; Gilmer and Jefferson were good friends); Betts, *op. cit.,* pp. 96, 241 *ff.;* Randall, *op. cit.,* p. 522; Margaret R. Hitchcock, "The Mastodon of Thomas Jefferson," *Journal* of the Washington Academy of Sciences, Vol. XXI (March 4, 1931), pp. 80–86 (see p. 83); Frederick N. Luther, "Jefferson as a Naturalist," *Magazine of American History,* Vol. XIII (April, 1885), pp. 379–390 (see p. 389); Shapley, "Notes on Thomas Jefferson as a Natural Philosopher," p. 235; Randolph, *The Domestic Life of Thomas Jefferson,* p. 367. Additional insight into Jefferson's relations with his scientific visitors and his promotion of science through more personal means may be found in two articles by Richard Beale Davis, "Forgotten

Scientists in Old Virginia," *The Virginia Magazine of History and Biography*, Vol. XLVI (April, 1938), pp. 97–111, and "Forgotten Scientists in Georgia and South Carolina," *The Georgia Historical Quarterly*, Vol. XXVII (September, 1943), pp. 271–284.

26. For these last several items see Betts, *op. cit.*, pp. 275, 325, 380, 585, 597–598.
27. Whiting, "Father of Gadgets," p. 306.
28. For an account of these see Kimball, *Jefferson: War and Peace*, Chap. XI.
29. Austin H. Clark, *op. cit.*, pp. 197–198. See also the exact account in Kimball, *op. cit.*, pp. 295 ff., from which the dates of the first private printing and of the first French edition are taken.
30. From Malone, *op. cit.*, p. 388.
31. Sellers, *Charles Willson Peale*, Vol. II, pp. 127–129.

Index